Free Money For Your Retirement

by

Matthew Lesko

and

Mary Ann Martello

Researchers
Zsuzsa Beres; Giovina Taraschi
Melanie Coltan; Nancy Gibson
Mary Courtney Ore; Amy Hollingsworth
Allison Mays; Caroline Pharmer
Cindy Owens; Marcelle McCarthy
Bradley Sowash; Emily Subler;
Marty Brinkman, Laura Difore, Jennifer Maier

Production
Beth Meserve

Marketing
Kim McCoy

Support
Mercedes Sundeen

Cover
Ray Holland

Clip art used in this publication © Dynamic Graphics, Inc.; Totem Graphics; One Mile Up; Tech Pool; Image Club Graphics, Inc.; and Corel Corp.

FIRST EDITION

Library of Congress Cataloging-in-Publication date
    Lesko, Matthew
    Martello, Mary Ann

Free Money For Your Retirement

ISBN # 1-878346-60-1

Most books by Matthew Lesko are available at special quantity discounts for bulk purchases for sales promotions, premiums, fund-raising or educational use. Special books or book excerpts also can be created to fit specific needs.

For details, write Information USA, Special Markets, Attention: Kim McCoy, P.O. Box E, Kensington, MD 20895; or 1-800-797-7811, Marketing; {www.lesko.com}.

Table of Contents

Table of Contents

Information USA, Inc.

Table of Contents

Table of Contents

Information USA, Inc.

Table of Contents

Table of Contents

Information USA, Inc.

Table of Contents

Table of Contents

Table of Contents

Table of Contents

Table of Contents

You Don't Have To Be Wealthy To Retire Rich

That's true, if you know how to use the system.

Nearly half of all Americans (46%)[1] have less than $10,000 saved for their retirement. But this economic fact of life does not have to stop you from having your dream retirement. While you were working, you may not have been putting as much money as you wanted into retirement programs, but you certainly were putting more money than you ever dreamed of into tax supported programs that can now help finance a successful retirement.

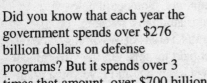

Did you know that each year the government spends over $276 billion dollars on defense programs? But it spends over 3 times that amount, over $700 billion, on programs for retirees.[2] And it's not just Social Security and Medicare.

No matter what your needs, or even your dreams are for retirement, there are hundreds of little-known government programs you have been paying into all these years that are now waiting for you to cash in on. Just think...

★ **If You Want To Travel...**
There are dozens of programs that give out money to citizens of all ages to travel not only around the United States but

also around the world. Quit dreaming about a Winnebago and go first class on Uncle Sam.

★ **If You Need The Best Health Care...**
There's money to pay for extra health insurance, prescription drugs, dentures and even long term care. You can even get the best doctors in the world to treat you for free. Don't think about getting on a bus to buy cheaper drugs in Canada or Mexico — the best bargains are right here in the USA, and they're FREE.

★ **If You Need Extra Spending Money...**
Would you ever believe there are programs that give out an extra $5,000 a year in spending money, or $1,000 to pay for insurance, or $200 towards new eyeglasses, or $7,000 to fix up your home or even $2,000 to buy a computer?

★ **If You Want To Volunteer...**
Retirement can be the best time to truly experience the joys of giving back to the community. You could help neighborhood kids, be a tour guide in a museum, or go horseback riding in the Grand Tetons of Wyoming to count wildlife. You can even get paid for this. Or, the government will help you start your own nonprofit and give you a grant to help you change the world the way you want it to change, and not the politician's way.

★ **If You Want To Be Your Own Boss...**
People would never retire if their boss was kind, understanding, flexible and valued their opinions. When you work for yourself, you have the best boss in the world. As your own boss, you are in control of everything... your schedule, your associates, your growth, your whole life. And if you choose a fun business, you can work in that environment forever. The best part is there are government programs that will help you choose the right business to

start, help you get the money you need, and help you with free marketing, free management and even free tax expertise to keep you growing.

★ **If You Want To Learn…**
You can get money to take courses in gardening or James Joyce. Uncle Sam will pay you to study anything from computers to violin making. You can go to college on your rich uncle's money either full time or part time. You can get a GED, a degree or a PhD. Life isn't about learning to live, it's about living to learn. And now you don't have to pay for it!

What You Don't Know
Can Hurt You

Most of us believe we are getting smarter as we're getting older. But getting smarter is not knowing the answers to questions, it's knowing that we don't know the answers to questions, and neither do the experts. The more of the world we see, the more we realize that many aspects of it are constantly changing, and what we learned last year may not work for us next year. I believe that the biggest challenge in our information overload society is not in getting the right answers — it's in asking the right questions.

Every year the government spends tax dollars on fun and useful programs that you now have time to take advantage of. These are programs you never heard of — programs where the government hands out billions a year to people just like you. But, unfortunately, they don't spend a nickel advertising the fact that these programs exist. Taxpayers have to find them themselves, and most don't know what to ask. But don't worry, I've done all the work for you. This book is loaded with money to finance your dream retirement. With this book, you'll know how to ask for:

- $1,000/Year To Pay For Extra Health Insurance
- FREE Courses In Computers Or Pottery
- $25,000 To Start A Business At Home
- The Government To Pay Your Mortgage
- $7,000 To Fix Up Your Home
- $1,300 Worth Of Free Dental Care
- A 50% Cut In Your Rent
- $250,000 To Work On Your Invention
- Money To Buy A Trailer or Trailer Home Park
- $500 For Turning In Annoying Telephone Solicitors
- $700 Discount On Your Utility Bills
- $15,000 To Attend A Cowboy Festival In Australia
- $25 A Day To Be A Moose Crossing Guard In Yosemite
- $150,000 To Buy A Country Inn
- Money To Get A Degree Or A PhD
- $10,000 To Buy A Talking Computer
- $3,000 To Help Kids In Your Neighborhood

How To Use This Book

First read the following chapters carefully:

- Money To Pay Your Bills
- Money For Drugs And Health Care
- Extra Money To Put In Your Pocket

These chapters are the most general in nature and can provide you with the money and help you need for a wide variety of the situations that will come up during your retirement years. Be sure to grab a pencil or some post-it notes to make life easier when you want to return to these items later. And be sure to keep your friends and family in mind as you go through these chapters. All the items listed may  not pertain directly to you in your present situation, but keep in mind how they might be helpful for a friend or how you may be able to use them later if your current situation changes. For example:

1) <u>Maybe you know someone who is worrying about the cost of supplemental insurance.</u>
   Turn to page 28 and read "3 Million Seniors & Disabled Don't Apply For Their Free $1,000 For Health Care." You'll see that an extra $1,000 would be helpful to most anyone.

2) <u>Do you want to know how to make your home more livable for your aging body</u>?
   Turn to page 40 and read "Money To Buy A Van, A Talking Computer or Rubber Door Grips." People will come out to your home and give you a free assessment of what you need and tell you about money programs to pay for it.

3) <u>Maybe your mother lives in another town and is having trouble paying for legal services.</u>
   Turn to page 48 and read "Free Consultants Help Find Medical & Living Help For Seniors." They will help you find someone near your mother who will do the work for free.

4) <u>Learn how to get back at annoying telephone solicitors and make $500 in the process</u>.
Turn to page 63 and read "Make $500 Turning In Annoying Telephone Solicitors."

5) <u>If prescription drugs are costing you a fortune and you want to learn how to get them free.</u>
Turn to page 31 and read "Make $40,000 And Get Free Prescription Drugs."

6) <u>Learn how to get a $7,000 grant to fix up your home</u>.
Turn to page 83 and read "Free Money To Fix Up Your Home" and page 86, "Money for Seniors And Those With A Disability To Buy or Fix Up A Home," or any of the other housing sources described in the book.

Start Having Fun With Your Life

If you don't start having fun now, when are you going to do it? If you're glad to get rid of your job, now you can find something to do that's really fun — something that you always wanted to do.

Become A Writer, Artist, Singer, Dancer, Or Travel Around The World

Don't you have a book idea you always wanted to work on? Or maybe you've been dabbling in paints, acrylics or clay and now you want to get serious. There's money out there for these artistic endeavors and they may be worth applying for.

Where to Start:
If you fancy yourself a writer, start on page 173, "Money To Write A Book." This chapter shows you the main sources for writers, both public and private. Remember when dealing with

the private sources not to send money to anyone to review or publish your book. If you are new to the system, look at the education chapters first and take some beginning writing classes. Or contact some of the writer's associations listed on page 179.

Artists should start on page 186, "Attention Artists! Over $180,000 Available From State Government." You can also ask these offices for additional sources that may be helpful to you. They should be aware of other organizations in your state that might provide money or even training. If the person on the telephone is not aware of what you are talking about, be sure to ask to talk with someone else who may be more knowledgeable. It may be the only way to get what you need.

Start Your Own Business

There's government money and help for you to start a small business out of your home, buy a golf course, or even buy the business from your old boss. Hundreds of programs are listed in the chapter called "Money For A Big Or Small Business," page 290. It may be a little overwhelming at first, but don't worry. Most people who want to start a business have no idea what they want to do. And most people that have their own business still have no idea what to do — they just know how to fake it and look good.

Where To Start:

The best place to start if you're thinking about a business is on page 290, "The Best Starting Places For Starting A Business." These offices are located in almost every county and their consultants will sit down and help you think through almost any business idea that may be rattling around in your brain. They will even set you up with special legal, technical or marketing expertise, if you require it.

But don't stop here. No one person or even one office can know everything. Our world has turned into something too big and confusing for any one person to know it all. So, if they don't give you the answer you need, keep trying the other sources listed. A good next step is your state Economic Development Office listed on page 370 under "State Money And Help For Your Business."

From here you should carefully read all the other business items to see how you can fit into what the government program is trying to accomplish. For example, page 381, "Unconventional Loan Programs To Start A Business When You Have No Money," might be the next place for you. Contact those offices in your state and see how they may be able to assist you. Remember, if they say they can't help you today, be sure to ask them for suggestions as to who might be able to help.

From here, you must keep on going. Keep your mind churning. If you can't get all you need today, try to figure out how you can at least start your business as a more modest venture than you initially envisioned. If it's a product or service you want to sell, go to page 278, "Free Local Help: The Best Place To Start To Sell To The Government." Remember, the government is the largest consumer of everything from pasta to web design, and the offices listed will help you find who in the government buys your product. They will also help you with all the paperwork to get your product sold. All you need is a product or service, a business card and a phone, and you're in business.

Go Back To School

Living in the 21st Century is not about "learning to live;" it is about "living to learn." Our fast changing society makes it impossible for anyone to learn one set of skills and then sit back and apply those skills to the end of life. The world keeps changing the rules. All of us have to continually keep acquiring new skills and information in order to just be a participant in our society. Today, even thirty year olds find themselves out of date. So fifty and sixty year olds can certainly find a lot of new things to learn.

Your learning doesn't have to involve becoming a computer genius. There are very few of us who have the talent to do that. But it can be a simple course in Spanish, pottery, or Internet access. Or, you can go back and get a GED, finish a degree or become a PhD. At 50 or 60, you can even become a doctor or lawyer and have the government pay for it. And who cares how old you are. If you make it to 60, you can live for another 30 years. More and more retirees are showing up on campus. A few years ago I was taking some courses at the University of Maryland, and there were retirees in my class taking the course for free when I had to pay full price. Older part-time students are the fastest growing segment of campus populations.

Doctors and gerontologists all seem to agree that the best way to live a long and healthy life is to stay active and intellectually involved. And what better way to do it than to keep learning!

Where To Start:
If it's a GED you need, or just some informal adult learning, turn to page 163, "How To Get A GED and More Adult Education." You can also look into your local county cooperative extension service for adult classes on things like investments, credit repair, gardening, or how to choose long-term care.

For college courses, turn to page 130, "350 Colleges You Can Go To For Free." This item lists colleges and universities around the country where you can go to school for free or next to nothing if you're over 55 or 60. It's a great deal! You can also go all the way to a PhD or a professional degree depending upon the university.

Be sure to check into all the other education money sources. There are separate money opportunities if you want to become a health professional, a teacher, study law enforcement or even study marine biology. The sources are all listed. Make sure you carefully go through them all.

But don't stop here. No one book has all the sources of money for education, not even this one. What we concentrate on here are government sources of money. There are still a lot of other private sources of money. Go to your local public library and talk to a reference librarian. They can show you many books that catalog college scholarships and other grants to higher education.

Remember, it's like the state lotteries, "You Have To Play To Win." And, by the way, did you realize that state lotteries are nothing more than another government program asking for your money? So quit playing the lotteries where you only have a 1 in 1,000,000 chance of winning. Instead, apply for any one of the hundreds of other government programs that are listed in this book and get up to a 65% chance of getting the money.

Training For A New Job

Each year the government gives money to over 9 million people to train them for a new or better job, and yet, you can never find any of these programs by looking in your Yellow Pages. These programs are handled by dozens of different agencies. They are at the federal, state and local level. There are even some nonprofit organizations that are getting government money to run these programs.

Where To Start
Go to page 129 and review "One Stop to Money and Help To Train For a New Job." These centers offer the best place to get an overview of the opportunities that may be available in your state. And be sure to investigate those programs that are

geared especially for seniors: page 104, "Free Training To Get A New Job" and page 102, "Job Training Programs Just For Seniors." And if you are a women who has recently changed her marital status, you should look at page 100, "Separated, Divorced and Widowed Women Get Free Help From 1200 Offices."

It is very important to review all the sources listed under training. You never know when you or even a friend or relative may need the help described here. And you don't have to stop here. There will always be more programs available than we can put into the book. New programs are being added every day. New organizations are always being formed to handle special training programs. To find additional programs, contact your state information operator listed on page 447 and ask for the State Office of Aging and the State Office of Labor. Both these offices should be able to point you to additional programs.

Work On Your Invention

Whatever you do, don't call one of those invention companies you hear advertised asking you for money to help with your invention. What these companies will charge you hundreds or even thousands of dollars for, you can get for FREE or next to nothing by contacting the organizations on page 231, "Money For Your Invention."

For additional sources of money to finance your invention, turn to page 235, "State Sources For Inventors." You should also contact page 290, "The Best Starting Places For Starting A Business," because their consultants can point you to state grants and even venture capital sources that assist inventors.

This Book Is Out Of Date!

I'm sorry to say this, but once we publish a book, it is out of date. But don't despair! The whole world is that way. By the time anybody publishes anything, it's out of date. Your Yellow Pages phone book sitting in your home is out of date. The brand new book you picked up at the bookstore discussing the latest treatments for cancer is out of date, because it won't contain the latest treatment announced in yesterday's newspaper. And even today's newspapers have trouble keeping current with the latest developments in some Washington scandal. That's why you can turn on the TV and watch the 24-hour scandal channel.

Life in the new millennium means learning how to live in a world with out-of-date information. In our swiftly moving society, everything seems to be changing every day. The only thing that will remain constant in our life is change. But learning how to deal with change is easy… if you're ready  for it. If you try to contact a source listed in this book and instead you get a Domino's Pizza delivery service, then someone has moved. But most likely the organization is still there. It's just at a different location.

Or maybe you contact a listed source looking for a specific program only to find that the office you called has never heard of the program and thinks you're crazy. Well, that may be true for some of our readers, but you must also remember that programs come and go the same way people who work on programs come and go. A program run by one bureaucrat this year may be replaced by another program, run by another bureaucrat, the following year. But they can both be out of the same office.

Your job in the new millennium, if you choose to accept it, is to realize that because a particular office doesn't have the exact program you are looking for, it may have a similar program under a different name or may know of another organization that may also be of help. **YOU HAVE TO ASK!**

I feel our changing world makes books like this one more valuable than ever. Most books tell you that they will provide you with answers. This book doesn't tell you the answers; it tells you the sources that have the latest answers. The answers are changing all the time, but sources that keep track of the latest answers change less frequently. The person studying the latest cures for cancer is less likely to change as quickly as a report professing to contain the latest cures.

You Won't Get Everything, But It's Important To Try

There will be two types of people who read this book. Those who hope to make only one telephone call and get a $100,000 grant within the next few weeks, and those who are aware that for most of us, it's going to take effort to get what you need and it still might not be everything you want. The important thing is that you try.

Help is out there, and it's available for all income levels. Sure, you might not be able to get an unlimited supply of free medications because you make over $40,000 a year, but you can still be eligible for free cancer surgery from the National

Institutes of Health, even if you are a millionaire. That's what ABC News reporter Sam Donaldson did.

Sure, you may not be able to qualify for a free or low-cost automobile, but you may be able to get free transportation for

your mom or grandma who needs a ride back and forth to the doctor. Or sure, you may not be able to get all the money you need to quit your job today and go back to school full-time maintaining your current style of life. But you can start going back to school part-time, or simplify your lifestyle and put together enough grants and loans and part time jobs to complete the education you need to do the kind of work you always dreamed of doing.

Try, try and try again! There are always exceptions. You only need one. If you don't ask, nothing will happen. Even though programs say they have certain requirements that you don't meet, ask how you can be an exception. All rules are not set in stone. Many bureaucrats in charge of the money or help have the power to bend the rules. And if they won't or can't, ask them who can. If you really need help, money, or information, don't worry about what people think about you or your tactics. Because most of these programs are from government sources or nonprofits, you have a right to them as much as anyone else.

Sure, nothing works all the time. But nothing works at all unless you try.

We Exaggerate!

The media made me do it! It's always nice to blame someone else for my faults, and the media seems to be the country's favorite whipping boy at the moment, so I might as well use them too. Like most people in our society who are trying to communicate to others, I use the media. And the media is bombarding the public with so much news, information and entertainment that it is becoming increasingly difficult to get anyone's attention.

Titles and headlines are used to try and cut through the noise and get your attention. It can be a 10 second teaser for your local

 news that will state something like "Mysteries of Life Solved, Highlights At 11." Or the photo on the front page of the newspaper at the checkout stand showing a baby with 8 heads! Nobody says they read those newspapers but one tabloid sells about 2.5 million copies a week and claims a readership of over 15 million.

Headlines are also used to entice you into the door to give something a try. Like a book title that says "Thinner Thighs In 30 Days." Would you still be interested in the book if it used a non-exaggerated title like "Here's A Book That Shows You How You May, Or May Not, Trim Your Thighs After A Long Period Of Hard Exercising And Hard Dieting." Not destined for the best seller list, is it?

Most people are smart enough to know that titles and headlines are often exaggerated, and I apologize to readers who are offended by such hyperbole. But I also think that it is important to use exaggerations and hyperbole in order to be as inclusive as possible in our work. If we are limiting in our titles, you may not investigate how to take advantage of certain programs. If our title says that this program does not apply to you so don't bother, you may not get the help you need.

A Lot Of Money Goes Unused

It does sound ridiculous, but it's true. Each year millions of Americans are eligible for extra money from the government and they never apply for it. If rich people hire high priced attorneys to make sure they take advantage of every tax benefit the government has to offer, why shouldn't the rest of us do all we can to take advantage of all the benefits that are offered to us? In case you're not aware, this is a rhetorical question.

During our research for this book I've uncovered studies that have shown:

* Over 6 million children who are living in families that are eligible for financial assistance don't receive it.[3]
* Over 4.7 million children are eligible for the government new Children's Health Insurance Program and are not enrolled. Almost every state now has a Children's Health Insurance Program (CHIPS) which extends medical coverage to many children.[4]
* 3 Million Seniors & Disabled Don't Apply for Their Free $1,000 For Health Care for their Medicare Premiums. Each year over 3 million eligible seniors and people with disabilities fail to apply for a little-known health care benefit.[5]

And I believe that this is just the tip of the iceberg. I feel quite certain that there must be millions of people who are unaware that even with incomes up to $40,000, they are eligible for free prescription drugs for themselves or their children, as well as free mammograms and cancer treatments. A benefit that can greatly enhance the quality of a someone's life must be a lot more important than a tax break for a vacation rental property! My guess is that all the people with vacation rental property know all the tax breaks that are available to them, but all the women eligible for free mammograms are not likely to know of the benefits to which they are entitled.

Matthew Lesko

[1] *Miles To Go: A Status Report On Americans' Plans For Retirement, Public Agenda and Fidelity Investment,* {www.publicagenda.org}
[2] Congressional Budget Office, CBO's Current Budget Projections, {www.cbo.gov}
[3] *Keeping Women and Children Last*, Ruth Sidel, Penguin Books, New York, p. 89
[4] *Help for Children Who Need Health Insurance, Food and Nutrition Service*, U.S. Department Of Agriculture; {www.fns.usda.gov/fns/MENU/WHATSNEW/CHIP/chipfns.htm#Background}
[5] *Shortchanged: Billions Withheld From Medicare Beneficiaries*, Families USA Publications, Washington, DC (www.familiesusa.org/SHTCHGPR.HTM)

MONEY TO PAY YOUR HEATING BILL

Storm windows, insulation, and even weatherstripping can help reduce your fuel bill. Families can receive assistance to weatherize their homes and apartments at no charge if you meet  certain income guidelines. States allocate dollars to nonprofit agencies for purchasing and installing energy-related repairs, with the average grant being $2,000 per year. The elderly and families with children get first dibs.

Contact your State Energy Office or the Weatherization Assistance Programs Branch, EE44, U.S. Department of Energy, 1000 Independence Ave., SW, Washington, DC 20585; 202-586-4074; {www.eren.doe.gov/buildings/state_and_ community/}.

50% Discount
On a New Heating System

The California Energy Commission offers residences and small businesses up to 50% of the cost of a new heating or air conditioning system if it meets their standards for "emerging renewable technologies," like solar heating, but more. Their program is called Emerging Renewables Buy-Down Program.

To learn more, contact California Energy Commission, Energy Call Center, 1516 North St., MS-25, Sacramento, CA 95814; 800-555-7794; {http://energy.ca.gov/greengrid/index.html}. Contact your state information operator listed in the Appendix and ask for your state utility commission to see if your state offers similar programs.

Free Help Fighting a High Electric Bill Or Stopping A TURN-OFF

The state utility commissions can help you fight high gas or electric bills. Some will even come out and make sure that your meter is not overcharging you.

They don't have money to pay for your bills, but they can negotiate payment arrangements with the company for you

Check For A $100 Heating Bill Tax Credit

The state of Michigan offers a home heating bill tax credit (that means you pay less in taxes) for people who are low income, or receiving public assistance or unemployment benefits.

Call your state department of taxation to learn about tax credits available to you. Michigan Department of Treasury, Lansing, MI 48956; 800-487-7000; {www.treas.state.mi.us/formspub/forms/indtax/MCR717.pdf}.

or suggest nonprofit organizations that may have emergency funds to help. For example, Maryland suggests the Fuel Fund for Central Maryland or the Maryland Energy Assistance program. The office can also force the utility not to cut off your service because of medical emergencies or cold weather. Contact your state information operator listed in the Appendix and ask for your state utility commission for further assistance.

$200 To Pay Your Phone Bill

The Salvation Army's Universal Telephone Assistance Program provides up to $200 to continue or restore telephone services. While the service is available to persons with limited income, expenses compared to income are evaluated on a case by case basis to ensure telephone access is available for emergencies, medical appointments and other needs.

For information or to apply, consult your telephone directory for the local Salvation Army office or contact Salvation Army National Headquarters, 615 Slaters Lane, P.O. Box 269, Alexandria, VA 22313; 703-684-5500; Fax: 703-684-3478; {www.salvationarmy.org}.

GET AN $84 REDUCTION ON YOUR TELEPHONE BILL

Link-Up and *Lifeline* are two government programs that offers up to $84 a year in discounts on your monthly bill and a 50% reduction for your hook-up service, or $30 whichever is less. These programs have income requirements that vary from state to state.

Ask your phone company about them, or contact your state information operator listed in the Appendix and ask for your state utility commission, or contact Federal Communications Commission, 1919 M Street, NW, Washington, DC 20554; 888-CALL-FCC; {www.fcc.gov}.

$800 FOOD MONEY

You don't get the cash, but you do get it in the form of Food Stamps. The Food Stamp Program was designed to help low income families buy the food they need to stay healthy and productive.

The amount of Food Stamps you get each month is determined by the number of people in your family and by the household income. The average benefit is about $71 dollars a month, but a 4-person household could get up to $408 a month. There are obviously income requirements you must meet.

To apply for the Program, look in the blue pages of your telephone book under "Food Stamps," "Social Services," or "Public Assistance." You can also find more information by contacting U.S. Department of Agriculture, Food and Nutrition Service, 3101 Park Ctr. Dr., Park Office Center Bldg., Alexandria, VA 22302; 703-305-2276; {www.fns. usda.gov/fsp}.

$4,800
Extra Money To Live On

Struggling to pay bills because you or your child are disabled? Supplemental Security Income (SSI) provides funds to individuals who are 65 or older, or blind, or have a disability, and who don't own much or have a lot of income.

SSI isn't just for adults. Monthly checks can go to disabled and blind children. There are income requirements you must meet and you or your child's disability will be screened. But it could mean an extra $400 a month and that could help a great deal!

For more information, contact Social Security Administration, Office of Public Inquiries, 6401 Security Blvd., Room 4-C-5 Annex, Baltimore, MD 21235; 800-772-1213; {www.ssa.gov}.

$402 A Week
When You're Out Of Work

In Massachusetts, you can receive up to $402 a week for 30 weeks, and in special circumstances, they will extend the benefits another 18 weeks.

Mass lay-offs, base closings, trade agreements, and high unemployment in your state all affect your ability to find and keep a job. If you are out of work, take advantage of unemployment insurance. This is the government's first line of defense against the ripple effects of unemployment.

$500 For Seniors and Disabled

The state of Pennsylvania offers up to $500 for seniors and people with disabilities who pay property taxes or rent. If you live in Pennsylvania, contact Department of Aging, 555 Walnut St., 5th Floor, Harrisburg, PA 17101; 717-783-1549. If you live elsewhere, contact your state information operator listed in the Appendix and ask for your state Office on Aging, or your state Department of Revenue.

All states are required to provide benefits up to 26 weeks and some extend them further. If your state has very high unemployment, you may be eligible for 13 additional weeks of compensation. If you lost your job because of an increase in imports, you may qualify to have your benefits extended up to an extra 52 weeks if you are in a job-retraining program.

Your weekly benefit amount depends upon your past wages within certain minimum and maximum limits that vary from state to state. Many states also will add additional funds depending upon the number of dependents. If you are denied benefits, learn about the appeal process, as your chances of winning are good. For more information, contact your state information operator listed in the Appendix and ask for your state Unemployment Insurance office.

$700 Discount On Your Utility Bills

The legislature in Massachusetts passed a law giving discounts up to $700 on heating bills for families making up to $30,000, along with up to 40% discount on electric bills, $108 off telephone bills, and $100 off oil bills. It's in the Massachusetts Budget for FY 99 (Line Item 4403-2110). Also:

☼ **Mason County** in the state of Washington offers a utility bill discount of $13 a month for seniors making less than $18,000, and disabled people at 125% of the poverty level. Contact Public Utility District #3, 307 W. Cota St., Shelton, WA 98584; 800-424-5555; {www.olywa.net/maspud3/bill.htm}.

☼ **Phoenix, Arizona** offers discounts on utility bills, discounts on phone bills and even help paying utility deposits and heating repairs for low income residents through the Arizona Public Service Energy Support Program, P.O. Box 6123-086Z, Phoenix, AZ 85008; 800-582-5706; {www.azstarnet.com/azinfo/ag997.htm}.

☼ **Ameritech in Illinois** gives a 100% discount on connection charges and $5.25 off the monthly bill to low income residents. To sign up, call Ameritech at 800-244-4444; {www.ameritech.com/media/releases/releases-1630.html}.

☼ **Ohio** offers reduced or free phone hook up service and possibly $8 a month off your phone bill for low income residents. Contact Public Utilities Commission, 180 E. Broad St., Columbus, OH 43215; 800-686-7826; {www.puc.state.oh.us}.

☼ **Pennsylvania Bell Atlantic** offers free telephone hook up and $9 monthly discount to low income residents through Lifeline and Universal Telephone Assistance Programs. To sign up, call 800-272-1006.

Contact your state information operator listed in the Appendix and ask for your state utilities office to find out about special discounts on your gas, electric, cable or telephone in your state.

Volunteers Get a
50% Discount On Food

It's called the Self-Help and Resource Exchange (SHARE), and it distributes food at 50% discounts to 5,415 community-based organizations, which in turn, give it to individuals. The only catch is that you have to volunteer your time in the community for at least 2 hours a month. You can coach little league or help fix up a playground.

To find a SHARE affiliate near you, contact SHARE, 6950 Friars Road, San Diego, CA 92108; 888-742-7372; Fax: 618-686-5185; {www.worldshare.org}.

GOVERNMENT SUPPORTED AGENCIES OFFER FREE MONEY AND HELP WHEN YOU DON'T KNOW WHERE TO TURN

If you need emergency money to pay a bill, or for housing, training, health care, or just additional support, these organizations can be of service and they are likely to have an office near you. Although these are private organizations, they do receive a portion of their funds from your favorite Uncle Sam.

1) Community Action Agencies

Nearly 1,000 agencies around the country received funds from the U.S. Government's Community Services Block Grants to offer education, counseling, employment, training, food packages, vouchers, weatherization and utility assistance, life skills, affordable housing, transportation, furnishings, recreation, emergency services, information and referral services. To locate an agency serving your area, contact: National Association Of Community Action Agencies, 1100 17th St., NW, Washington, DC 20036; 202-265-7546; Fax: 202-265-8850; {www.nacaa.org}.

2) Catholic Charities

Over 14,000 local organizations offer a variety of services for many different communities including: child care, elderly services, emergency financial services, emergency shelter, food pantries, housing assistance, job training, out-of-home care, parenting education, youth services, rental assistance, utility assistance, and health care. For an office near you, contact Catholic Charities USA, 1731 King Street #200, Alexandria, VA 22314; 703-549-1390; Fax: 703-549-1656; {www. catholiccharitiesusa.org}.

3) Salvation Army

Families in need can receive a wide range of services including: utility assistance, transitional housing, emergency food, furnishings, Section 8 tenant counseling, counseling, rent or mortgage assistance, and even clothing. Most services are for

---

50% Discount On Telephone Service

Under the Federal Communication Commission's Link-Up America and Lifeline programs, low income households seeking telephone service are given a 50% discount on local connection charges, and may be able to pay installment payments on the remaining charge. These programs are available in most states.

To sign up for this service, contact the customer service representative at your local telephone company.

---

households who are below 150% of the poverty level (about
$24,000 for family of 4). For an office near you, contact
Salvation Army National Headquarters, 615 Slaters Lane, P.O.
Box 269, Alexandria, VA 22313; 703-684-5500; Fax: 703-684-
3478; {www.salvationarmy.org}.

10%-100% Off
On Your Glasses

Pearle Vision Centers offer 50% off either the lenses or frames
when you purchase a complete set of glasses to people 50-59,
60% off to those 60-69, 70% to those 70-79, and so on until
seniors reach 100 and they give them 100% off either the lenses
or frames when they purchase a complete set of glasses. Lens
Crafters and Eye Glass Factory also offer a 10% discount to
seniors, and Sears Optical Centers give 15% off to AARP
members. Now that makes seeing clearly less costly.

Money For Drugs and Health Care

3 Million Seniors & Disabled
Don't Apply for Their Free $1,000 For Health Care

Each year over 3 million eligible seniors and people with disabilities fail to apply for a little-known program that will give them up to an extra $1,051 in their Social Security check. That's how much the government deducts from their Social Security to pay for their Medicare premiums. It amounts to $87.60 a month for couples and $43.80 for individuals. There are three basic programs:

1) *Pays for Medicare premiums, deductibles and co-payments under the Qualified Medicare Beneficiaries (QMBs) plan.*
2) *Pays for Medicare Part B premiums under the Specified low income Medicare Beneficiaries (SLMBs) plan.*
3) *Pays for Medicare Part B premiums under the Qualified Individuals Plan for people with incomes up to $14,892.*

Studies show that only 5,000 of the 500,000 eligible apply for this program. With so few eligible people applying, it's understandable that many people don't know about this program.

Information USA, Inc.

Here's where to go. Contact your local Social Security Office. If they don't know, contact your state information operator listed in the Appendix and ask for your state Office of Social Services. You can also contact the Medicare Hotline and request the publication, *Guide to Health Insurance for People With Medicare*. Contact the Medicare Hotline at 800-638-6833; {www.medicare.gov}.

$1,300 Worth Of Free Dental Care

The National Foundation of Dentistry for the Handicapped started the Donated Dental Services program to help disabled and elderly persons who are low income by matching them with volunteer dentists. Homeless and mentally ill people are also helped.

Volunteer dentists agree to treat one or two people each year with dental problems, and dental laboratories that make dentures, crowns, and bridges also donate services. The program now serves over 500 people each year with each patient receiving an average of $1,300 worth of services. In some areas of the country, Dental House Call projects have been started where dentists will come to homes or centers to provide dental care.

FIGHT BACK — What to Do When Your HMO Says No

This booklet is free from The Center for Patient Advocacy, 1350 Beverly Road, Suite 108, McLean, VA 22101; 800-846-7444;
{www.patientadvocacy.org}.

To learn where services are located in your area, contact
National Foundation of Dentistry for the Handicapped, 1800
15th St., Unit 100, Denver, CO 80202; 303-534-5360, Fax: 303-
534-5290.

Free Seeing Eye Dogs, Training, Travel and Air Fare

Pilot Dogs gives its trained animals to the blind at absolutely no
charge. They also include four weeks of training in using the dog
and will pay for room and board, all equipment, and round trip
transportation. Other groups provide similar services:

* ***Pilot Dogs, Inc.***, 625 West Town Street, Columbus, OH
  43215; 614-221-6367; Fax: 614-221-1577;
  {www.pilotdogs.org/index.shtml}.

* ***Guide Dog Foundation for the Blind, Inc***, 371 East Jericho
  Tpke., Smithtown, NJ 11787; 800-548-4337; 516-265-2121;
  {www.guidedog.org}.

Alcohol and Drug Abuse Counseling & Treatment

Georgia provides outpatient counseling services, short-term
residential programs, and even school student assistance
programs. Florida provides substance abuse treatment programs
through a partnership with 102 public and private not-for-profit
community providers. Delaware contracts with private
organizations around the state to provide screening, outpatient
counseling, and detoxification, as well as short term and long

term treatment. Contact your state information operator listed in the Appendix and ask for your state Department of Health to see what your state has to offer.

There are also nonprofit organizations who, by themselves, offer free treatment to people, like the Center for Drug-Free Living in Orlando, Florida (5029 N. Lane, Suite 8, Orlando, FL 32808; 407-245-0012; {www.cfdfl.com}).

If your state can't help you get the information or treatment you need, one or both of the following hotlines should be able to help:

■ *National Drug and Treatment Routing Service*, Center for Substance Abuse Treatment, National Institute on Alcohol Abuse and Alcoholism (NIAAA), 600 Executive Blvd., Willco Bldg., Bethesda, MD 20892; 800-662-HELP; {www.niaaa.nih.gov}.

■ *The National Clearinghouse for Alcohol and Drug Information*, 11426 Rockville Pike, Suite 200, Rockville, MD 20852; 800-729-6686 24 hours a day; 301-468-2600 TDD; {www.health.org}.

MAKE $40,000 & GET FREE PRESCRIPTION DRUGS

Valium, Prozac, Dilantin, Insulin, the smoking patch and almost anything but Viagra, you can get FREE directly from the drug companies themselves.

That's right: drug companies don't want everybody to know this, but they will give their drugs free of charge to certain people who can't afford their medications. I guess they don't want to

tarnish their greedy bad guys image by publishing these benevolent programs.

So, what's the catch? It sounds too easy. All that many of these companies require is that your doctor write them a note stating that you will have difficulty paying for the drugs you need. Some companies have income requirements, but the income levels go up to $40,000.

Call the Pharmaceutical Research and Manufacturers of America hotline to receive a listing of the drug companies and their programs. Contact Pharmaceutical Manufacturers Association, 1100 15th St., NW, Washington, DC 20005; 800-PMA-INFO; {www.pharma.org}.

Free Mammograms & Cancer Tests

An estimated 2 million American women will be diagnosed with breast or cervical cancer in the 1990s, and half a million will lose their lives from these diseases. Screening could prevent up to 30% of these deaths for women over 40.

The government's Center for Disease Control will spend about $145 million a year to maintain a state-by-state program to establish greater access to screening and follow-up services. Each state runs their program a little differently. Most states have the following requirements:

➜ women starting at 40 or 50 years old,
➜ are underinsured or have no insurance

➔ have income below a certain level (usually $32,000 or
  $40,000 for family of 4)

Some states can adjust eligibility requirements for special cases.
States vary in the array of services covered but they normally
include:

➔ breast and cervical cancer screening
➔ mammograms
➔ treatment if diagnosed with cancer
➔ breast reconstruction or prosthesis

States that don't have direct funds for treatment often make
arrangements with other facilities to provide treatment for free. If
your screening has been done elsewhere, you can still receive
free treatment under this program. Men diagnosed with breast
cancer can also receive free treatment.

Contact your county office of public health listed in your
telephone book or contact your state information operator listed
in the Appendix and ask for your state Department of Health.
You can also contact the main office of this program at Division
of Cancer Prevention and Control, National Center for Chronic
Disease Prevention and Health Promotion, Center for Disease
Control and Prevention, 4770 Buford Highway, NE, MS K-64,
Atlanta, GA 30341, 770-488-4751; {www.cdc.gov/nccdphp/
dcpc/nbccedp/index.htm}.

More Free Mammograms

Not all insurance companies pay for mammograms, and not
every woman is eligible for the government's program described
earlier. The following organizations can help you identify free
and low cost mammograms in your area.

1) *The American Cancer Society*: contact your local office or the national office at 800-ACS-2345.
2) *YMCA's Encore Plus Program*: contact your local office or the national office at 800-95-EPLUS
3) *National Cancer Institute*: 800-4-CANCER
4) *State Office of Breast and Cervical Cancer*: contact your state information operator listed in the Appendix, and ask for your state Department of Health
5) *October is National Breast Cancer Awareness Month*: Many mammogram facilities offer their services at special fees during this period. Call and see what kind of deal you can get.
6) *Medicare coverage of mammograms*: call 800-638-6833

For a free copy of *How To Get A Low Cost Mammogram*, contact National Alliance of Breast Cancer Organizations, (NABCO) 9 East 37th Street, 10th Floor, New York, NY 10016; 800-719-9154; {www.nabco.org}.

Get Free Nursing Home Care Without Hiding Your Assets (Free Hospital Care)

Don't have money for your gall bladder surgery? What about that hospital visit you had two months ago? You might not have to pay a cent. Call the Hill-Burton Hotline.

Under this program, certain hospitals and other health care facilities provide free or low-cost medical care to patients who cannot afford to pay. You may qualify even if your income is up to double the Poverty Income Guidelines. That's $32,900 for a family of four! You can apply before or after you receive care, and even after the bill has been sent to a collection agency.

Call the Hotline to find out if you meet the eligibility
requirements and to request a list of local hospitals who are
participating. For more information, contact Hill-Burton Hotline,
Health Resources and Services Administration, 5600 Fishers
Lane, Room 11-19, Rockville, MD 20857; 800-638-0742; 800-
492-0359 (in MD); {www.hrsa.dhhs.gov/osp/
dfcr/about/aboutdiv.htm}.

Low Cost Immunizations for Travelers

In order to prevent contracting diseases like Yellow Fever,
Cholera or Japanese Encephalitis when traveling in other
countries, the government's Center for Disease Control
recommends that certain vaccines would eliminate your risk of
infection. Some local Public Health offices offer these vaccines
at a fraction of what you would pay at a doctor's office.

HOTLINE LOCATES WANDERING ALZHEIMER'S PATIENTS

Alzheimer's patients are known to wander away and even
wind up in other cities. My father, in his later years, went
for a drive that took him into someone's back yard.

Safe Return is a national clearinghouse that helps police
and private citizens locate and return lost Alzheimer's
patients. Contact The Alzheimer's Association, 919 N.
Michigan Ave., Suite 1000, Chicago, IL 60611; 800-272-
3900; {www.alz.org}.

To find your local county office of health, look in your telephone book or contact your state information operator listed in the Appendix and ask for your state Department of Health. For more information about disease and vaccines for travel, contact: Center for Disease Control and Prevention, National Center for Infectious Diseases, Division of Quarantine, 1600 Clifton Road, MS E-03, Atlanta, GA 30333; 404-638-8100; Fax: 404-639-2500; {www.cdc.gov/travel/index.htm}.

How To Fight Your Doctor, Hospital, Or Insurance Company

Well, not the actual Marines from the Department of Defense, dressed in fatigues and armed with high tech weapons. But you can call other government offices and advocacy groups that will do your fighting for you or give you the needed weapons to do your own fighting. Before you call a lawyer, call these free offices first:

♦ *State Insurance Commissioner*: will help you learn your legal rights regarding insurance.

♦ *State Medical Boards*: will review your complaint (including billing issues) and help resolve disputes.

♦ *State HMO boards*: will review your complaint (including billing issues) and help resolve disputes.

♦ *The Center for Patient Advocacy*, 1350 Beverly Road, Suite 108, McLean, VA 22101; 800-846-7444; {www.patientadvocacy.org}: provides free advice and publications on how to fight the system, also does advocacy work for patient's rights on Capitol Hill

♦ *Center for Medicare Advocacy, Inc*, P.O. Box 350, Willimantic, CT 06226; 860-456-7790;

{www.medicareadvocacy.org}: Attorneys, paralegals, and technical assistants provide legal help for elderly and disabled who are unfairly denied Medicare coverage in the states of Connecticut and New York. They will send materials to people in other states to learn how to fight for themselves.

♦ *American Self Help Clearinghouse*, Northwest Covenant Medical Center, 25 Pocono Road, Denville, NJ 07834; 973-625-9565; Fax: 973-635-8848; TTD 973-625-9053; {www.cmhc.com/selfhelp}: makes referrals to self-help organizations worldwide and helps people interested in starting their own self help group.

♦ *National Self-Help Clearinghouse*, c/o CUNY, Graduate School and University Center, 25 West 43rd St., Room 620, New York, NY 10036; 212-354-8525; Fax: 212-642-1956; {www.selfhelpweb.org}: makes referrals to self-help groups nationwide.

Grants and Fundraising Help For Transplant Patients

Organizations like The National Foundation for Transplants and National Transplant Assistance Fund assist patients, their families, and friends in raising significant amounts of money for the patient's transplant care when there is no public or private insurance that will cover all the costs. They also provide grants to help pay for medications required after a transplant, or money for transplant-related emergencies, and one-time assistance grants of $1,000.

Other transplant related nonprofits, like the Liver Foundation's Liver Transplant Fund, provide services and help for patients and families to raise money for an organ transplant.

- ☐ *National Foundation for Transplants*, 1102 Brookfield, Suite 200, Memphis, TN 38119; 800-489-3836, 901-684-1697, Fax: 910-684-1128; {www.transplants.org}.
- ☐ *National Transplant Assistance Fund*, 6 Bryn Mawr Avenue, P.O. Box 258, Bryn Mawr, PA 19010; 800-642-8399; Fax: 610-527-5210; {www.transplantfund.org}.
- ☐ *American Liver Foundation*, 75 Maiden Lane, Suite 603, New York, NY 10038; 800-GO LIVER; {www.liverfoundation.org}.

FREE HEALTH INSURANCE COUNSELING

Free one-on-one counseling is available to seniors and, in most areas, people with disabilities, to answer questions like:

- How much insurance is too much?
- If something sounds like fraud, where can I go for help?
- What's the best Medigap insurance plan?
- Do I qualify for government health benefits?
- Should I buy long-term care insurance?

The program is called **Health Insurance Counseling and Advocacy Program (HICAP)** and is sponsored by the

---

Free Video Describes What Medicare Covers For In-Home Health Care

Get a free VHS copy of *Home Health Care* from your local Medicare office or from 800-318-2596 or order online at {www.medicare.gov}.

U.S. Health Care Financing Administration. In most states, it is usually run by the state Department on Aging or the State Insurance Commissioner's office. Contact your state information operator listed in the Appendix and ask for your state office. If that fails, contact the Eldercare Locator hotline at 1-800-677-1116. They can give you the local number.

Low Cost Home Health Care

Montgomery County in Maryland provides home health care free or on a sliding scale, depending on income, through the local public health office. You don't have to be a senior to qualify.

A survey by the Center for Disease Control reports that about half of all local public health agencies provide similar services. To see what is available in your area, contact your county office of health listed in your telephone book or contact your state information operator listed in the Appendix and ask for your state Department of Health. If you cannot get satisfaction from these offices, contact the local office of your state or federal elected official.

Free Computers to People With Disabilities

Washington State chapter has a free loan program, and the chapters in Missouri offer computer classes. Contact your local Easter Seals Society to see what they may offer in the way of computers and computer skills for people with disabilities. If you can't find your local office, contact: Easter Seals, 230 West Monroe Street, Suite 1800, Chicago, IL 60606; 800-221-6825; 312-726-6200; Fax: 312-726-1494; {www.seals.com}.

For similar services for seniors, contact your local area agency on aging or your state information operator listed in the Appendix and ask for your state Department on Aging. If that fails, contact the Eldercare Locator hotline at 1-800-677-1116. They are available to help anyone identify services for seniors.

$$$$$ Money To Buy A Van, A Talking Computer Or Rubber Door Knob Grips

People with disabilities now have a place to turn to learn everything they need to know about how the latest in technology can improve their lives. It can be a specially equipped van, a talking computer, a special kitchen or eating aid, or adaptive toys for children. Or it may be a student with learning disabilities who needs special help getting through school.

A project funded by the U.S. Department of Education, called Technical Assistance Project has established an office in each state that can provide:

▲ *Information Services*: will help you identify the special products that are available to help you cope with your disability.

▲ *Equipment Loan Program*: allows people to borrow new technology devices for a number of weeks before they purchase them.

▲ *Recycling Program*: matches up people with needs for products with people who want to sell or donate products.

▲ *Funding Information*: collects information on the various sources of funding for this equipment from public and private sources.

▲ *Loans*: many states are offering special loans to help people purchase the necessary equipment; Ohio offers low interest loans up to $10,000, California has loans up to $20,000, North Carolina up to $15,000.

Contact your state information operator listed in the Appendix and ask for your state Office of Social Services or Vocational Rehabilitation. They should be aware of your state Assistance Technology Office.

If you have trouble locating your state office, you can contact the office that coordinates all state activities: Rehabilitation Engineering and Assertive Technology Society of North

National Immunization Information Hotline

This hotline tells you where you can go locally to get Free Immunization shots for your kids or flu shots for yourself. Immunizations for children can run as much as $335 per child.

This program is run by the U.S. Government's Center for Disease Control, which can answer almost any question you have about shots over the telephone or send you free publications. In most areas of the country, immunizations are available FREE for children. Adult services may be free or very low cost. Call 800-232-2522 (English); 800-232-0233 (Spanish); {www.cdc.gov/nip}.

America, (RESNA), 1700 North Moore Street, #1540, Arlington, VA 22209; 703-424-6686; Fax: 703-524-6630; TTY: 703-524-6639; {www.resna.org}.

Free Health Care By the Best Doctors In The World

Bob Dole and Sam Donaldson both knew where to go when they had cancer surgery — The National Institutes of Health (NIH).

Free Take Out Taxi

People 60 and over who are homebound because of illness, incapacity, or disability, or who are otherwise isolated can receive hot meals delivered to their home. The program is funded in every state by the Older Americans Act.

Contact your local area agency on aging or your state Department on Aging (your state information operator, listed in the Appendix, can help). If that fails, contact the Eldercare Locator hotline at 1-800-677-1116. They are available to help anyone identify services for seniors.

Each year, close to 75,000 patients receive free medical care by some of the best doctors in the world.

Medical research professionals receive millions of dollars each year to study the latest causes, cures, and treatments to various diseases or illnesses. If your health condition is being studied somewhere, you may qualify for what is called a "clinical trial" and get the treatment for free.

There are several ways to find out about ongoing clinical trials across the nation. Your first call should be to the National Institutes of Health Clinical Center. NIH is the federal government's focal point for

health research. The Clinical
Center is a 325-bed hospital that
has facilities and services to
support research at NIH. Your
doctor can call the Patient
Referral Line to find out if your
diagnosis is being studied and to
be put in contact with the
primary investigator who can
then tell if you meet the
requirements for the study.

You can also search their website for your diagnosis and
qualifying information. In addition, each Institute at NIH also
funds research that is conducted by universities, research
institutions, and others. To learn about those studies, contact the
Institute that handles your diagnosis. Or conduct a CRISP
(Computer Retrieval of Information on Scientific Projects)
search, which is a database of research projects and programs
supported by the U.S. Department of Health and Human
Services.

- ◆ **Clinical Center**, National Institutes of Health,
  Patient Recruitment, Building 61, 10 Cloister Court,
  Bethesda, MD 20892; 301-496-4891; 800-411-1222;
  {www.cc.nih.gov}.

- ◆ **National Institutes of Health**, Office of
  Communications, Building 1, Room 344, 1 Center Dr.,
  MSC0188, Bethesda, MD 20892; 301-496-4000;
  {www.nih.gov}.

- ◆ **CRISP**, Office of Reports and Analysis, Office of
  Extramural Research, 6700 Rockledge Dr., Room 3210,
  Bethesda, MD 20892-7772; 301-435-0656; {www-
  commons.cit.nih.gov/crisp/}.

How To Get A Break As A Caregiver

If you're the only caregiver for a sick child or relative and get frustrated because you cannot leave the patient alone, you can get someone to take over for a few hours or a few days while you get rest or run errands. The service is called Respite Care and, depending on your income, you can get this care for free or low cost through a number of different agencies:

★ *Your local public health services*: Contact your county office of health listed in your telephone book or your state

AFFORDABLE MENTAL HEALTH COUNSELING

The Community Institute for Psychotherapy is a nonprofit agency whose mission is to provide mental health counseling services to low income individuals in Marin County, CA so that they may re-establish mental and emotional well-being and live satisfying and productive lives. CIP offers outpatient psychotherapy on a sliding scale fee basis to adults, children, families, and couples who would otherwise be unable to afford such services.

To find out if similar programs like this exist in your area, contact your local Social Services Agency or your local health department (found in the blue pages of your phone book). Contact: Community Institute for Psychotherapy, 1330 Lincoln Avenue, Suite 201, San Rafael, CA 94901; 415-459-5999; Fax: 415-459-5602; {Email: cip@wenet.net}.

information operator listed in the Appendix and ask for your state Department of Health

★ *Your local office on aging*: Contact your local Area Agency on Aging or your state information operator listed in the Appendix and ask for your state Department on Aging. If that fails, contact the Eldercare Locator hotline at 1-800-677-1116

★ *Easter Seals office* or Easter Seals, 230 West Monroe Street, Suite 1800, Chicago, IL 60606; 800-221-6825; 312-726-6200; Fax: 312-726-1494; {www.seals.com}: This organization charges on ability to pay, but no person is refused service

★ *Respite Locator Service*: National Resource Center or Respite & Crisis Care, 800 Eastowne Drive, Suite 105, Chapel Hill, NC 27514; 800-7 RELIEF; {www.chtop.com/locator.htm}.

FREE HELP
Getting to the Doctor

Many seniors have to give up driving their cars, maybe because of the cost or illness. But then how do they get to the doctor, or the bank or the store? Many rely upon their friends and children to solve their transportation needs, but there are times when you need to come up with another alternative.

The *Eldercare Locator* provides access to an extensive network of organizations serving older people at state and local community levels. This service can connect you to information sources for a variety of services including transportation.

For more information, contact Eldercare Locator, National Association of Area Agencies on Aging, 1112 16th St., NW, Washington, DC 20024; 800-677-1116 between 9 a.m. and 8 p.m. EST; {www.aoa.dhss.gov}.

Find Out, FOR FREE, If You Have Diabetes

Sixteen million Americans have diabetes — one in three does not know it! Research proves that early detection and proper treatment for diabetes can lead to a longer, healthier life.

If you or the people you care about are at high risk for diabetes, you can call the American Diabetes Association's (ADA) "Diabetes Information and Action Line" (D.I.A.L.) where you can receive a free packet of information about diabetes and find out about free diabetes screenings and other diabetes alert activities in your area. D.I.A.L. is a national network of information and referral telephone lines for people with diabetes and their loved ones. This helpline can provide information on all aspects of diabetes management and refer callers to local diabetes programs and services, including diabetes education classes, year-round youth programs, counseling and support groups, and advocacy services.

Diabetes is more common in African Americans, Hispanics, Native Americans, Asian-Americans and Pacific Islanders. If you are a member of one of these ethnic groups, you need to pay special attention. Contact: American Diabetes Association, 1660

Duke Street, Alexandria, VA 22314; 800-DIABETES; 800-342-2383; {www.ada.org}.

Free Transportation To Medical Appointments For Your Mom

Mom has to get to a doctor's visit in the middle of the day and you can't take her. Or you have a disability that may cause you to miss an appointment if someone else doesn't drive. You may be able to get free transportation and escort services provided by either your local health office or local office on aging. Some communities even provide very low cost door-to-door services for seniors to go anywhere.

If you can't find your local area agency on aging or public health office in your telephone book, contact your state information operator listed in the Appendix and ask for your state

Free Directory Assistance For Customers with Disabilities

US West customers who have difficulty finding or remembering phone numbers can receive directory assistance services at no charge. To apply, call and ask for a Directory Assistance Exempt Certificate. It must be signed by your physician and returned to the phone company. Contact: US West - Customer Services, Bell Plaza, 1600 Seventh Ave, Room 2709, Seattle, WA 98191; 206 504-0670 Billing/Service; 206-555-1212 Directory Assistance; 411 Directory Assistance; TTY: 800-223-3131; Toll Free: 800-244-1111; Language: Interpreters available in 21 spoken languages and sign language {www.uswest.com}.

Department of Aging or Health. If that fails, contact the
Eldercare Locator Hotline at 1-800-677-1116. They are available
to help anyone identify services for seniors.

FREE CASH & FREE DRUGS FOR KIDNEY PATIENTS

The American Kidney Fund's (AKF) Individual Patient Grants
pay for urgently needed transportation to treatment, over-the-
counter medications, health insurance premiums and living
kidney donor expenses. The AKF Pharmacy Program provides
vital prescription medicines, nutritional supplements and medical
equipment to qualified kidney patients.

FREE CONSULTANTS HELP FIND MEDICAL & LIVING HELP FOR SENIORS

Looking for the local meals on wheels programs or
need a home health aide for mom? The *Eldercare
Locator* searches their database for the services for
seniors in any area of the country. These can include
transportation, legal assistance, housing options,
recreation and social activities, adult daycare, senior
center programs, and more.

Contact the Eldercare Locator, National Association
of Area Agencies on Aging, 1112 16th St., NW,
Washington, DC 20036; 800-677-1116 (9 a.m.- 8 p.m.
EST); {www.n4a.org}.

AKF establishes **Patient Emergency Funds** in dialysis and kidney transplant facilities. These funds enable facility staff to give immediate small cash grants to patients in emergency situations. AKF's Disaster Relief Program helps kidney patients get back on their feet when environmental crises strike their communities. AKF has helped victims of floods, hurricanes and earthquakes.

Contact: The American Kidney Fund, 6110 Executive Boulevard, Suite 1010, Rockville, MD 20852; 800-638-8299; 301-881-3052; Fax: 301-881-0898; {Email: helpline@ akfinc.org}; {www.akfinc.org}.

Money For MS Patients To Pay For Counseling

The Western Washington Chapter of the National Multiple Sclerosis Society offers financial assistance for counseling to people with Multiple Sclerosis and their families. This program is designed to assist individuals with MS and their families to cope with the disease by seeing a professional therapist for counseling. Financial assistance for counseling is limited to $300 per year for in-office counseling and $340 for in-home counseling.

Contact the Yakima office at P.O. Box 1093, Yakima, WA 98907; 509-248-2350; 800-736-7312; Fax: 509-248-2352; {Email: nmsswascw2@nwinfo.net}; {www.nmsswas.org/ living/counseling.html}.

Free and Low-Cost Dental Care

Don't let your teeth fall out just because you can't afford to go to a dentist. There are hundreds of programs across the country that offer free and low-cost dental care for seniors and practically anyone else who needs it, *often regardless of your income level*. If you know where and when to look, you may be able to get:

- free or low-cost dentures and repairs,
- automatic senior discounts of 15% to 80%,
- free at-home dental care if you can't get out,
- free dental implants by the best doctors in the world.

Most health insurance plans don't include dental coverage, and this means people often go without regular dental care simply because they think they can't afford it. But you may not be aware of the hundreds of programs that are designed for people like you — programs that actually require that you *don't* have dental insurance so that you can qualify to receive free or largely discounted dental care.

Here are some general examples of the kinds of programs funded all across the country. To identify which of these programs may be operating in your area, contact your state information operator listed in the Appendix and ask for all of the following:

- State Dental Society/Associations
- State Department of Health Dental Programs

Dental Care for the Elderly

You'll find that most states have special programs just for the elderly, especially those who have trouble finding money to pay for dental care on a limited income. Often dentists donate their time and services to make sure the elderly are taken care of.

Dental Schools for Everyone

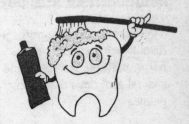

The best-kept secrets about low-cost dental care are the 53 dental schools across the country. They offer quality dental care at a fraction of the cost of private dentists. Many will even set up a repayment plan for you if you can't afford to pay the bill. Also, researchers at many dental schools receive big money from the federal government to do cutting edge dental research, and these researchers often need patients to work on for free. Be sure to ask about any clinical research underway at the dental school nearest you.

Free and Low Cost Dental Clinics

Many state and local health departments support dental clinics that offer their services for free or on a sliding fee scale basis. Services are usually limited to those with limited income or those with special needs.

Free & Low Cost County Care

Many of the local health offices provide dental services to children and to income-eligible adults on a sliding fee scale. Many states have special free or discount services just for seniors.

Free Dental Care For Children

Almost every state runs some kind of dental care program to make sure that kids keep their teeth in good shape. Many of these programs offer their services for free or at huge discounts, based upon your ability to pay. Your grandkids should know about this.

Dental Care for Disabled and Handicapped

There are special programs just for those with mental or physical disabilities, including those with mental retardation, cerebral palsy, multiple sclerosis, and much more. Many states also have special programs that offer free care for children born with cleft palates.

Free Tooth Implants and Impacted Molar Removal

These are just two of the many subjects that top dental researchers are studying at the National Institute of Dental Research which is part of the National Institutes of Health in Bethesda, Maryland. Also underway are studies on facial pain, taste disorders, herpes simplex, and dry mouth conditions.

Patients who participate in these clinical trials receive their dental care during that period free of charge. For information about the clinical studies program at the National Institutes of Health, you or your doctor can contact: Clinical Center, National Institutes of Health, Bldg. 10, 10 Center Dr., Bethesda, MD 20892; 301-496-2563, or the Patient Recruitment and Referral Center, Bldg. 61, 10 Cloister Ct., Bethesda, MD 20892; 301-402-6481; 800-411-1222; {www.cc.nih.gov}.

Dentists Who Get Government Grants to Do Work for Free

Washington is not the only place where doctors receive government grants to conduct dental research and treat patients for free. Each year hundreds of dental schools and other dental research facilities around the country receive money to work on everything from gum disease to denture satisfaction. You can contact the following office to receive information about ongoing or upcoming dental research in your area.

National Institute of Dental Research, Research Data and
    Management, Information Section, 45 Center Dr., Room
    4AF-19, MSC 2190, Bethesda, MD 20892-2290; 301-496-
    4261; {www.nidr.nih.gov}

Another method of finding these doctors is by contacting one of the Dental Schools across the country. Dental schools normally receive a good portion of available research.

Dental Societies — Dentists Who Volunteer

Each state's Dental Society keeps track of free and low-cost dental programs in their state, so it's a good idea to call them if you have any questions or if you're interested in learning about any new dental programs that start up.

Some Dental Societies also act as a clearinghouse for identifying dentists who volunteer their services to those facing emergencies or those who have other special problems.

Free Dentures for Seniors

Don't sit around with false teeth that keep falling out when you eat or hurt so badly that you can't keep them in your mouth. Many states have discount denture programs where you can receive big savings on false teeth, no matter what your age.

Dentists on Wheels

If you have trouble getting around because of a handicap or other infirmity, some states, like Illinois, Arizona, Missouri, New Jersey, and Colorado have mobile dental vans that will actually come to your home or nursing home and provide you with dental care right there on the spot.

Information Clearinghouse For All Types Of Disabilities

The Clearinghouse on Disability Information will answer your questions on a wide range of disability topics and send you all kinds of information about services for disabled and handicapped individuals at the national, state, and local levels.

They have several free publications, including *Office Of Special Education and Rehabilitative Services (OSERS) News In Print* newsletter, which describes OSERS programs, research, and topical information on a broad range of disability issues. The *Summary of Existing Legislation Affecting Persons With Disabilities* is available for all federal laws through 1991. The *Pocket Guide to Federal Help For Individuals with Disabilities* is a general, handy beginning reference.

Contact: Clearinghouse On Disability Information, Office Of Special Education and Rehabilitative Services, Communication

Choosing a Safe and Successful Weight-Loss Program
Very Low-Calorie Diets
Weight Loss for Life.

Weight-Control Information Network, 1 Win Way, Bethesda, MD 20892; 301-984-7378; 800-WIN-8098; {www.niddk.nih.gov}.

and Information Services, U.S. Department of Education, Room 3132 Switzer Bldg., Washington, DC 20202-2524; 202-205-8723, or 205-8241.

FREE MONEY AND HELP FOR LUPUS PATIENTS

The S.L.E. (LUPUS) Foundation (a Chapter of the Lupus Foundation of America) offers individual entitlement counseling showing families how to obtain Medicaid, Medicare, social security income/social security disability, food stamps, housing assistance and legal aid. They also have a Grant-in-Aid Program that provides mini-grants to help people with Lupus survive emergency and crisis situations.

Contact: The S.L.E. Foundation Inc., 149 Madison Avenue, Suite 205, New York, NY 10016; 212-685-4118; Fax: 212-545-1843; {Email: Lupus@LupusNY.org}; {www.lupusny.org/programs.htm}.

Hot Flash Hotline

Menopause doesn't have to be the hormonal hurricane women faced in the past. Taking estrogen and progesterone can help relieve the problems of menopause, although they may not be without problems of their own.

A free booklet entitled *Menopause* can answer many of your questions and outlines different forms of treatment. Contact: Information Center, National Institute on Aging, P.O. Box 8057, Gaithersburg, MD 20898; 800-222-2225; {www.nih.gov/nia}.

Local Free Health Services

Your local health department (found in the blue pages of your phone book) often operates free or sliding-fee scale clinics and screening centers to handle non-emergency health problems. Many operate prenatal and well-baby clinics as well. The

 services and fees vary from place to place, so contact the health department to find out about eligibility, hours of service, and services provided.

According to the National Association of Community Health Centers, federally sponsored community health centers serve six million people, and four to six million people are served at other-sponsored health centers. However, some problems exist. Because of the increase in demand for low-cost health care, many centers are closing off registration and are carrying waiting lists of 15 to 20 percent of their current case load. The demand and availability of local health centers do vary, so don't overlook this resource. To find out about local clinics, contact your State Department of Public Health.

One-On-One Help For Stroke Victims and Families

If you or someone you know has experienced stroke firsthand, call the American Heart Association's (AHA) *Stroke Connection* at 800-553-6321 or send an email to {strokeconnection@heart.org}. This is a network of over 1,600 stroke groups or clubs and more than 50,000 stroke survivors,

56

caregivers and professionals throughout the country. You can receive information regarding stroke, how it affects the lives of stroke survivors and their families, how to find a support group near you, how to subscribe to the *Stroke Connection Magazine*, or to talk to someone who understands. The phone line is manned by stroke families who want to help. They are there to answer your questions and offer options.

Contact: Stroke Connection, American Heart Association, National Center, 7272 Greenville Avenue, Dallas, TX 75231; 800-553-6321; {Email: strokeconnection@heart.org}; {www.americanheart.org}.

On-Line Database of 650,000 Doctors

The American Medical Association's (AMA) **Physician Select** provides on-line information on virtually every licensed physician in the United States and its possessions, including more than 650,000 doctors of medicine (MD) and doctors of osteopathy or osteopathic medicine (DO). 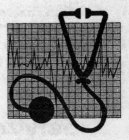 All physician credential data have been verified for accuracy and authenticated by accrediting agencies, medical schools, residency training programs, licensing and certifying boards, and other data sources. You can search this database by name or medical specialty. You will also find health information on specific conditions from AMA Health Insight, a reference library.

Contact: American Medical Association, 515 North State Street, Chicago, IL 60610; 312-464-5000; {www.ama-assn.org/aps/amahg.htm} (Physician Select).

FREE WHEELCHAIRS

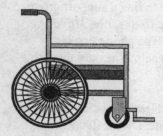

Easter Seals, the American Cancer Society and other helpful organizations provide free wheelchairs and other medical related equipment, like walkers, commodes, bathtub rails, bathtub chairs, crutches, transfer benches, electric wheelchairs and scooters, on a short- or long-term basis. Some programs require deposits that are completely refundable.

Check with your local office of Easter Seals and the American Cancer Society. You can also contact your state information operator listed in the Appendix and ask for your state Department of Health.

- *American Cancer Society, Inc.*, 1599 Clifton Road, NE, Atlanta, GA 30329; 800-ACS-2345; {www.cancer.org}.
- *Easter Seals*, 230 West Monroe Street, Suite 1800, Chicago, IL 60606; 800-221-6825; 312-726-6200; Fax: 312-726-1494; {www.seals.com}.

Service Organizations

Need help with child care, elderly services, substance abuse treatment? What about youth programs or disaster assistance? Many large service organizations have local offices that provide all this and more. Services vary depending upon the needs of the community, but before you fight your battles alone, contact these main offices to find out about local programs:

✦ *Catholic Charities USA*, 1731 King St., #200, Alexandria, VA 23314; 703-549-1390; {www.catholiccharitiesusa.org}.

✦ *Salvation Army*, 615 Slaters Lane, P.O. Box 2696, Alexandria, VA 22313; 703-684-5500; 800-SAL-ARMY; {www.salvationarmyusa.org}.

✦ *United Way of America*, 701 N. Fairfax St., Alexandria, VA 22314; 800-411-UWAY; {www.unitedway.org}.

BLADDER PROBLEMS

More than 13 million people in the United States — male and female, young and old — experience incontinence. It is often temporary and it always results from an underlying medical condition. Women experience incontinence twice as often as men. Pregnancy and childbirth, menopause, and the structure of the female urinary tract account for this difference. But both women and men can become incontinent from strokes, multiple sclerosis, and physical problems associated with old age.

Urinary Incontinence in Women is a free publication that looks at the causes of incontinence and describes treatments available and additional resources. For your copy, contact National Kidney and Urologic Diseases Information Clearinghouse, 3 Information Way, Bethesda, MD 20892; 301-654-4415; {www.niddk.nih.gov}.

Free Eye Care

If you or someone you love needs eye care, but cannot afford it, the following organizations can help:

♥ For those 65 and older: *National Eye Care Project*, American Academy of Ophthalmology (AAO), P.O Box 429098, San Francisco, CA 94142; 415-561-8500; 800-222-3937; {www.eyenet.org}.

♥ For low income families and children, applications are accepted on a first come-first serve basis in January with treatment following later in the year: *VISION USA*, American Optometric Association, 243 North Linbergh Blvd., St. Louis, MO 63141; 314-991-4100; 800-766-4466; {www.aoanet.org}.

♥ *Lions Clubs International*, 300 22nd St., Oak Brook, IL 60523; 630-571-5466; {www.lionsclubs.org}.

♥ *Glaucoma 2001*, American Academy of Ophthalmology (AAO), P.O Box 429098, San Francisco, CA 94142; 415-561-8500; 800-391-EYES; {www.eyenet.org}.

Free Eyeglasses, Cornea Transplants, and Glaucoma Screenings

Each year Lions Clubs around the country provide 600,000 free professional glaucoma screenings, perform 25,000 cornea transplants, collect over 3 million pairs of glasses, and provide thousands with free quality eye care. Services are provided based on need, and programs and services can be developed according to specific community needs. Lions Clubs conduct Hometown Day that brings people to Lenscrafters for eye exams and eyeglasses free of charge.

Consult your telephone directory for a Lions Club in your area or contact: Lions Club International, 300 22nd St., Oak Brook, IL 60523; 630-571-5466; Fax: 630-571-5735; {www.lionsclubs. org}.

Information USA, Inc.

Free Hotlines, Publications and Expertise on Any Health Topic

Don't know where to go or who to call? We have compiled a listing of resources you can call to receive information, support, assistance, and sometimes even treatment for a specific condition or disease! The following government and nonprofit organizations are experts in their specific areas and will help you online or on the telephone with free expertise, publications, and referrals. You are not alone. Help is just a phone call or a click away.

National Health Information Center
P.O. Box 1133
Washington, DC 20013
800-336-4797
301-565-4167
Fax: 301-984-4256
http://nhic-nt.health.org
Excellent phone referral service
Some publications available include:
- ★ *Toll-Free Numbers for Health Information*
- ★ *Federal Health Information Centers and Clearinghouses*
- ★ and many more

National Aging Information Center
U.S. Administration on Aging
330 Independence Avenue, NW
Room 4656
Washington, DC 20211
202-619-7501
Fax: 202-401-7620

www.aoa.dhhs.gov/naic/

Some publications available include:

★ *Older Persons with Mobility and Self-Care Limitations*

★ *Elder Abuse Prevention*

★ *Housing Options for Older Americans*

★ *Protecting the Rights of Older Americans*

★ and many more.

Extra Money
To Put In Your Pocket

Make $500 Turning In Annoying Telephone Solicitors

The Federal Communications Commission's (FCC) Consumer Protection Act says that you can collect $500 or more from telephone solicitors if:

✦ they call two or more times within a 12 month period after you tell them to stop

✦ they call you with a pre-recorded voice message to your home

✦ they call you at home before 8am or after 9pm

✦ they send you an unsolicited advertisement on your fax machine

✦ they tie up two or more lines on a multi-line business system with an automatic dialing machine

For more details on stopping telephone solicitors or how to collect your money, contact: *Federal Communications Commission*, Common Carrier Bureau, Consumer Complaints, Mail Stop 1600A2, Washington, DC 20554; 888-CALL-FCC; {www.fcc.gov/ccb/consumer_news/unsolici.html}.

You can get your telephone number taken off many of the major telephone solicitation lists by sending your name and telephone number to: *Telephone Preference Services*, Direct Marketing Association, P.O. Box 9014, Farmingdale, NY 11735; {www.the-dma.org/topframe/index1.html}.

Free Credit Repair

It always seemed strange to me that if you're in debt enough to need help with credit repair, why in the world would you spend more money on a credit repair service? You can do it for free, yourself!

Spending money needlessly is what got you there in the first place. And more importantly, federal and state regulators have been warning consumers against using credit counseling companies. Companies, lawyers and others will charge you $300 to $1000 for something you can do for free.

Here are some of the free reports you can get from the Federal Trade Commission:

- ❏ *Credit Repair: Self-Help May Be The Best*
- ❏ *Knee Deep in Debt*
- ❏ *How To Dispute Credit Reporting Errors*
- ❏ *How To Deal With Credit Problems*
- ❏ *How to Dispute Credit Report Errors*

For your copies, contact Public Reference, Room 130, Federal Trade Commission, Washington, DC 20580; 202-326-2222; 877-FTC-HELP; {www.ftc.gov}.

If you don't want to do it ALL yourself, you can ask for **FREE HELP**. The following nonprofit and government organizations provide free, or low-fee credit counseling services. You can contact them to find the office nearest you.

Some of these offices are financed by the bank and credit card industry, who are biased toward having you pay all your bills without using the bankruptcy option. So be sure that they explain your bankruptcy options.

❑ *National Foundation for Consumer Credit*, 8611 Second Avenue, Suite 100, Silver Spring, MD 20910; 800-388-2227; Spanish: 800-68AYUNDA; {www.credit.org}.

❑ Free Internet credit counseling services from the nonprofit organization, *Credit Counseling Center of America*, P.O. Box 830489, Richardson, TX 75083-0489; 800-493-2222; {www.cccamerica.org}.

❑ *County Cooperative Extension Service*: to find your local office, contact your state information operator listed in the Appendix.

GET EXTRA CASH FINDING LOST MONEY AND SURPLUS PROPERTY

Make $2,000 in 45 minutes. That's what the author, Mary Ann Martello, did when she searched state databases looking for old forgotten utility deposits and bank accounts set up by grandparents. Every state has an office that collects money in that state that has been abandoned, forgotten, or left unclaimed, including:

✓ Savings and checking accounts

✓ Uncashed payroll or cashiers checks

✓ Money orders and travelers checks

✓ Certificates of deposit

✓ Customer deposits or overpayment

✓ Paid up life insurance policies

✓ Health and accident insurance payments

✓ Uncashed death benefit checks

✓ Gift certificates and Christmas club accounts

✓ Stock and dividends

✓ Utility deposits

✓ Oil and gas royalty payments

The money could be a savings account that grandma set up for you when you were born. Or it could be a Christmas fund Great Aunt Rose contributed to before she passed away. Your father may have even had a safe deposit box he never told you existed.

According to reports, state agencies across the U.S. may be holding over $8 billion dollars in abandoned money. Although the rules vary from state to state, generally after two or more years without activity on an account (no deposits or withdrawals), the bank will try to contact you. If their efforts fail, the property is considered abandoned and transferred to the state of your last known address.

To locate funds, contact the unclaimed property office in the state (usually part of the state treasurer's department) where you or your benefactors have lived or conducted business. Most state agencies have websites, and many have searchable databases.

You can contact the National Association of Unclaimed Property Administrators, P.O. Box 7156, Bismarck, ND 58507; {www.unclaimed.org}. Not only does the website give you a listing of state offices, it also links you to those that have existing websites. Contact your state information operator listed in the Appendix and ask for your state Unclaimed Property Office.

Bargains on Toys, Books, Videos, CDs, TVs, VCRs, etc.

Did you ever wonder what happens to undeliverable mail? The U.S. Postal Service auctions it to willing buyers. Everything from the Christmas sweater you never received from grandma to the latest infomercial diet craze that never found its rightful dieter. Some people attend these auctions and collect bundles of items that they 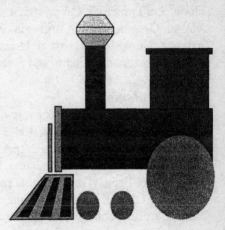 then resell for a profit at flea markets, garage sales, or retail stores.

Contact the Mail Recovery Centers listed below to learn more about the auctions in your area. You can be put on a mailing list to receive advance notice about the auctions. These auctions are held every six to eight weeks, with lots of similar goods being offered together. Although what is available varies from auction to auction, you will generally find anything that can be mailed — from CDs to televisions and books to jewelry and clothes. Call ahead to find out about payment procedures. Some require cash only, while others allow checks for those pre-approved.

Central Region

U.S. Postal Service Mail Recovery Center, 443 E. Fillmore Ave., St. Paul, MN 55017-9617; 612-293-3083. Includes Minnesota, Michigan, Wisconsin, North Dakota, South Dakota, Nebraska, Iowa, Illinois, Northern New Jersey, New Hampshire, Maine, Vermont, Rhode Island, Massachusetts, Kansas, Missouri, Connecticut, and New York.

Western Region

U.S. Postal Service Mail Recovery Center, 390 Main St., 4th Floor, San Francisco, CA 94105; 415-543-1826. Includes Alaska, Oregon, Idaho, California, Washington, Nevada, Utah, Arizona, New Mexico, part of Texas, Hawaii, Wyoming, Colorado, Montana, Guam, and Samoa.

Southern Region

U.S. Postal Service Mail Recovery Center, 730 Great Southwest Parkway, Atlanta, GA 30336; 404-344-1625. Includes Georgia, Florida, Louisiana, Tennessee, Arkansas, Mississippi, Oklahoma, part of Texas, Alabama, Mississippi, Virgin Islands, Puerto Rico, Pennsylvania, Southern New Jersey, Maryland, Delaware, Ohio, Kentucky, Indiana, Virginia, West Virginia, North Carolina, and South Carolina.

Buy From The Government at 2 Cents on the Dollar

If the U.S. Department of Defense buys a computer for $2,000, they sell it at auction for an average price of approximately $40 through the Defense Reutilization and Marketing Service (DRMS).

DRMS is responsible for the disposal of excess and surplus military personal property. Personal property is anything other than land, buildings, and real estate. It includes items such as tools, office furniture, camping equipment, appliances, furniture, computers, electronics, and much more.

DRMS offers four types of sales. Businesses can buy property in large quantities through the DRMS National Sales Office in Battle Creek, Michigan. Property is sold by auction, sealed bid sales, and in special circumstances, negotiated sales. These sales include such items as aircraft parts, ships, hazardous property, electronics, scrap bearing and hardware, and other property having wide commercial application.

Regional Sales offer deals for smaller businesses by selling smaller quantities of property through auction or sealed bids. This property includes vehicles and vehicular parts, furniture, appliances, material handling equipment, tools, and other property of interest.

DRMS also maintains DRMS Retail Sales Outlet Stores, where property is offered at a fixed price. You can also purchase items via the World Wide Web. Sales schedules, catalogs, and bid submissions information can be found on the website.

For more information on any of these items, contact the Defense Reutilization Marketing Service (DRMS), Federal Center, 74 N. Washington, Battle Creek, MI 49107; 800-GOVT-BUY; 888-352-9333; {www.drms.com}.

Get Forgotten Retirement Money

Did you work some place twenty years ago that is no longer in business? What about an old pension fund that was in financial trouble?

Don't give up. The Pension Benefit Guaranty Corporation (PBGC) monitors and sometimes takes over private sector-defined benefit plans. These are traditional pensions that promise a specified monthly benefit at retirement.

The PBGC operates a Pension Search Directory to find people who are owed pensions from the plans PBGC now controls. You can search by name, company worked for, or by state where the company is/was headquartered. In the last eighteen months, the directory found 1,400 people that were owed more that $4 million with the average benefit being $4,100. There is still $13 million just waiting to be claimed.

For more information, contact Pension Benefit Guaranty Corporation, Pension Search Program, 1200 K St., NW, Washington, DC 20005; 800-326-LOST; {www.pbgc.gov}.

MISSING MORTGAGE MONEY MEANS MORE MOULAS

If you ever purchased a home using a HUD/FHA insured mortgage, you may be eligible for a refund on part of your insurance premium or a share of the earnings. There are certain requirements you must have met.

To be eligible for a premium refund, you must have purchased your home after September 1, 1983, have paid an up front mortgage insurance premium at closing, and have not defaulted on your mortgage. To be eligible for an earnings dividend, you must have purchased your home before September 1, 1983 and made mortgage payments for more than 7 years.

Many people known as "Tracers" are locating this money for people and charging a finder's fee. HUD does state that people can do this for free, but many people are unaware that they are due a refund! You can search by a person's name or case number on the website.

For more information, contact U.S. Department of Housing and Urban Development, P.O. Box 23699, Washington, DC 20026; 800-697-6967; {www.hud.gov/wsrefund/html/page1.html}.

The IRS Has "GOOD NEWS" For 100,000 Taxpayers

Seems impossible, doesn't it? Close to 100,000 taxpayers are due a refund, yet their checks have been returned to the tune of over $62.6 million. The average check is $627.

What do you do if you think you or someone you love is missing a check? Contact the IRS toll-free hotline at 800-829-1040 and talk to a customer service representative. They can plug your name in the computer and see if your name pops up on their screen.

165,000 Unclaimed Social Security Checks

Social Security checks go out to 92% of those over the age of 65, so once in awhile, a check may go astray. If you think you are missing some checks, or if you find un-negotiated checks, contact your local Social Security Administration office. They can reissue the checks to the person or to the estate.
Social Security assures me that this occurs rarely, as they send out 612 million payments with only 165,000 checks that were not endorsed. Contact Social Security Hotline at 800-772-1213.

The same deal holds true with the Veterans Affairs Administration. If you feel you are missing checks or find checks that have not been endorsed, contact your local Veterans Affairs office so that checks can be reissued to you or to the estate of a loved one. Contact Veterans Affairs at 800-827-1000.

AN EXTRA $6,000 A YEAR IF YOU CAN'T WORK

Is your check too small to live on? If so, don't be discouraged. If you don't qualify for Social Security, or if your benefits are very low, you may qualify for Supplemental Security Income (SSI).

This program was established to help poor seniors over 65, as well as the blind and disabled, meet basic living needs. To qualify, you must meet a maximum monthly income test. Some of the income and services you receive are excluded when they calculate your monthly income in relation to your personal expenses.

Those who meet SSI's eligibility usually automatically qualify for Medicaid coverage and food stamp benefits. Studies have found that only between 40 and 60 percent of those who qualify for SSI actually receive benefits under the program. To find out if you qualify, contact your local Social Security office or call the Social Security Hotline at 800-772-1213.

Get Money While You're Waiting For Government Money

General Public Assistance or just Public Assistance (it is known by many different names) is a welfare program offered in 42 states. This is a program of last resort for people either waiting to qualify for other government programs such as disability benefits, or who do not qualify for any programs, yet need money to live.

The program eligibility and benefit levels vary within and across state lines. In some states, this benefit is only available in certain areas. There are strict income and asset levels that you must meet to qualify.

In Kansas, General Assistance pays families $278 per month while they are waiting for other government money. In California, the benefit is $225. Contact your local welfare office, your state Department of Social Service, or your state Temporary Assistance to Needy Families office to see what your state offers and the eligibility requirements. Your state information operator, listed in the Appendix, can help you locate your state offices.

Money For
Cars, Taxies and Rides

June Rapp of Massachusetts took her family van into a dealer to have it fixed and they wanted to charge her over $1000 to make the repairs. She called the U.S. Department of Transportation and found out that her problem was part of a manufacturer recall. Recalls have to be fixed for free and the repair shop didn't know that. To find out about recalls for any car, contact:

❑ **Auto Safety Hotline**, US Dept. of Transportation, NEF-11.2HL, 400 Seventh St., SW, Washington, DC 20590; 888-327-4236; {www.nhtsa.dot.gov/cars/problems/recall/recmmy1.cfm}

❑ The **Consumer Report** people have a searchable database for car recall information. Contact Consumers Union, 101 Truman Ave., Yonkers, NY 10702; 800-208-9699; {consumerreports.org}.

FREE RIDES TO VISIT A DOCTOR

Many seniors have to give up driving their cars, perhaps because of the cost or illness. But then how do they get to the doctor or the bank or the store? Many rely upon their friends and children to solve their transportation needs, but there are times when you need to come up with another alternative.

The Eldercare Locator provides access to an extensive network of organizations serving older people at state and local community levels. This service can connect you to information sources for a variety of services including transportation.

For more information, contact Eldercare Locator, National Association of Area Agencies on Aging, 1112 16th St., NW, Washington, DC 20024; 800-677-1116 between 9 a.m. and 8 p.m. EST; {www.aoa.dhss.gov}.

DISCOUNTS on Buses, Trains and Subways

If you are a senior citizen, you can usually ride most forms of transportation for about half-price. Amtrak and Greyhound offer discounts of 10-15% for the senior set. Children even get to take advantage of discount programs, with the youngest group often getting a free ride.

Don't forget to ask about a variety of reduced fare programs, including student and military discounts. Often job training programs will compensate you for your travel, so before you begin training, inquire about support services such as transportation and child care.

Cheap Air Fare To Visit A Sick Relative

Not free, but at least you don't have to pay full price. When a family member is very ill or has died, families have to make last minute airline reservations. Obviously you lose out on the 21-day advance purchase rates, but almost all airlines offer *bereavement* or *compassion* fares for domestic travel.

Generally the fares are available to close family members, and the discount on the full-fare rate varies from airline to airline. Many require that you provide the name of the deceased and the name, address and phone number of the funeral home handling the arrangements. In the case of a medical emergency, the name and address of the affected family member and the name, address and phone number of the attending physician or hospital are required.

Contact the airline of your choice to learn more about the "Bereavement/Compassion Fares." Full fare rate varies from airline to airline, but you could save up to 50%.

Free Cars and Air Travel To Go On Vacation

Not quite as easy as it sounds, but there are programs out there to help people move their cars. Most of the cars need to be driven across the country and in exchange, many car moving companies offer free gas and airline travel home.

This is not to say that you can take your family on a minivan vacation across the country. Certain rules and restrictions apply.

But I have known many a college kid that has gotten to drive across the U.S. for free.

Obviously, you do not get to pick your make and model, and you need to be flexible as to the departure time and destination, but this is one way to see America. Contact local moving companies to see what they have to offer. There is even a website for those interested in having their cars moved at {www.movecars.com}, and they may be able to provide you with information.

Air courier services operate the same way, but you are required to have a valid passport. Most air freight services don't do enough business to send a plane overseas each day.

As a courier, you carry a package checked as baggage to an overseas destination. There have been no incidences of contraband problems, and customs is familiar with this service.

You deliver the package to a company representative in the customs section of the airport, then you are on your own. In exchange, you get to fly to exotic ports for FREE or cheap. Children are not allowed to accompany couriers.

Contact companies listed in the air courier section of your phone book, do a web search using the terms "air courier service," or contact the Air Courier Association at 800-282-1202; or online at {www.aircourier.org}.

Get Discounts on
Boats, Limos, and Airplanes

The U.S. Marshals Service offers property for sale to the public that has been forfeited under laws enforced by the U.S. Department of Justice, the Drug Enforcement Administration, Federal Bureau of Investigation, and the Immigration and Naturalization Service. More than 6,000 items of forfeited real and personal property are sold annually with gross sales of $195 million.

The property offered for sale consists of residential and commercial real estate, business establishments, and a wide range of personal property such as motor vehicles, boats, aircraft, jewelry, art, antiques, collectibles, and livestock. The U.S. Marshals Service does not maintain a list of forfeited property for sale, nor a mailing list to notify prospective buyers of upcoming sales. The sales are handled through contract service providers.

The U.S. Marshals Service website provides information on the company/agency names, locations, and telephone numbers. This listing is also available by fax at 202-307-9777. For those without a fax or computer, the listing is available for 50 cents from the Consumer Information Center.

To learn how to order a copy, call the Federal Information Center at 800-688-9889. For more information on the sales, contact U.S. Marshals Service, Seized Assets Division, U.S. Department of Justice, 600 Army-Navy Dr., Arlington, VA 22202; 202-307-9237; {www.usdoj.gov/marshals/nsl.html}.

Money To Get A New Home Or Fix Up An Old One

Houston has a program that offers $4,000 in down payment and closing costs through their First-Time Homebuyers Program.

Iowa offers up to $2,750 in grants for a down-payment. You can be earning up to $65,000 a year and still be eligible for the money in their Down Payment/Closing Cost Grant Program.

Many cities, like Minneapolis, will offer interest free loans, called Equity Participation Loans, for up to 10% of the cost of the home. You pay back the money when you sell the house.

Programs vary from state to state and city to city. Contact your city government, your county government, and your local community development office to learn about local programs. If you have trouble locating your local community development office, the following organizations may be able to help:

❑ National Association of Housing and Redevelopment Officials, 630 I St., NW, Washington, DC 20001; 202-289-3500, Fax: 202-289-8181; {www.nahro.org}

❑ Information Center, Office of Community Planning and Development, P.O. Box 7189, Gaithersburg, MD 20898; 800-998-9999, Fax: 301-519-5027; {www.comcon.org}

❑ Also be sure to contact your state housing office. Your state information operator listed in the Appendix can help you.

"WOW!

...The Government Will Pay Your Mortgage"

You'd never have thought to ask, would you?

There are now programs that will make your mortgage payments for you when you get into financial trouble. For example, Pennsylvania law, 35 P.S. § 1680.401 et seq., states it will provide "*mortgage assistance payments to homeowners who are in danger of losing their homes through foreclosure and through no fault of their own and who have a reasonable prospect of resuming mortgage payments within the prescribed time frame.*" Pennsylvania calls it the ***"Homeowners' Emergency Mortgage Assistance Program."***

One of the best ways to find out if there are programs like this in your area is to contact the local HUD approved Housing Counseling agencies. To find your closest agency, contact your state housing office (your state information operator, listed in the Appendix, can help you), the Housing Counseling Center locator at 1-800-569-4287; {www.hud.gov/hsgcoun.html}, or Housing

Counseling Clearinghouse, P.O. Box 9057, Gaithersburg, MD 20898; 800-217-6970; Fax: 301-519-6655. If your local agency doesn't have money to pay your mortgage, they will certainly help you work out other arrangements with your mortgage company.

Make Money Going To Housing Classes

A HUD-approved housing counseling agency in Philadelphia offers $1,000 in settlement costs to certain people who attend pre-purchase house counseling sessions. A counseling agency in Boston offers new home buyers access to special low down payment mortgages if they attend pre-housing classes.

There are over 350 HUD-approved counseling agencies that offer free classes and help in housing related issues including:

> "The Best Way To Buy And Finance A Home"
> "Is A Reverse Mortgage For You?"
> "Foreclosure and Eviction Options"
> "The Best Way To Finance A Home Fix-Up"

These nonprofit agencies are trained and approved by the U.S. Department of Housing and Urban Development (HUD). To find your closest agency, contact your state housing office (your state information operator, listed in the Appendix, can help you), the Housing Counseling Center locator at 1-800-569-4287; {www.hud.gov/hsgcoun.html}, or Housing Counseling Clearinghouse, P.O. Box 9057, Gaithersburg, MD 20898; 800-217-6970, Fax: 301-519-6655.

Free Money To "Get The Lead Out"

If you are living in a house or apartment that was built before

1978, you, or even your landlord, may be eligible for grant money and other assistance to make sure that you do not suffer the effects of lead poisoning from lead-based paint.

Chips or dust from this type of paint can be highly dangerous to humans, especially children. The U.S. Department of Housing and Urban Development spends over $60 million a year helping home owners and apartment owners eliminate the problems that may be caused by lead paint.

Contact your state department of housing to see if your state has money for lead paint removal. Your state information operator listed in the Appendix can help you.

CUT YOUR RENT BY 50%

Studies show that people with less income pay a higher portion of their salary on housing than people in higher income categories. It is not unusual for a single mom to pay 70% of her salary in rent.

The government has a program called Section 8 Rental Assistance Program that offers vouchers and direct payments to landlords. This will, in turn, cut your rent down to only 30% of your income. Of course, there are income requirements for this program. For example, in Arlington County, VA, a one-person household with an income of $23,000 qualifies for the program. Arlington County also has housing grant rental assistance for low income elderly, disabled, and working families with children. Some of these programs have waiting lists, but it could be worth the wait.

To apply for these federal programs, contact your state housing authority (your state information operator, listed in the Appendix, can help you), your local housing authority, or a community services agency. If you have trouble getting the help you need, you can contact Information Center, Office of Community Planning and Development, P.O. Box 7189, Gaithersburg, MD 20898; 800-998-9999, Fax: 301-519-5027; {www.comcon.org}.

Free Money To Fix Up Your Home

States, cities, and counties, as well as local community development agencies are providing grants, loans, and even supplies and technical assistance for homeowners who want to fix up the inside or outside of their homes. Many of these have income requirements you must meet. Others offer forgivable loans if you stay in the house a certain number of years.

Programs vary from state to state and city to city. Contact your city government, your county government, and your local community development office to learn about local programs. If you have trouble locating your local community development office, the following organizations may be able to help:

❑ National Association of Housing and Redevelopment Officials, 630 I St., NW, Washington, DC 20001; 202-289-3500, Fax: 202-289-8181; {www.nahro.org}

❑ Information Center, Office of Community Planning and Development, P.O. Box 7189, Gaithersburg, MD 20898; 800-998-9999, Fax: 301-519-5027; {www.comcon.org}

❑ Also be sure to contact your state housing office. Your state information operator listed in the Appendix can help you.

Money For Buying a Condo Or Co-op

In 1999 the U.S. Department of Housing and Urban Development will finance about $9 billion for people to buy condominiums. This is almost double the amount financed in 1997. The program is called *Mortgage Insurance — Purchase of Units in Condominiums (234c)*. They also have a special program for units in co-op buildings called *Mortgage Insurance — Single Family Cooperative Housing (203n)*.

Contact your local office of Housing and Urban Development listed in the blue pages of your telephone book, or your state housing office, or the Housing Counseling Clearinghouse, P.O. Box 9057, Gaithersburg, MD 20898; 800-217-6970; {www.hudhcc. org}.

Your Rich Uncle Will Cosign A Loan To Buy or Fix Up a Home

Both the U.S. Department of Housing and Urban Development (HUD) and the Rural Housing Service of the U.S. Department of Agriculture offer loan guarantees to lending agencies around the county. A loan-guarantee assures the lending agency that the government will pay for the loan if you can't.

In addition, the Rural Housing Service has a direct loan program that provides loans to lower income families to buy, build, repair, renovate, or relocate their home. This is called the Section 502 Program.

★ To investigate the programs available in your area, contact your local HUD office listed in the blue pages of your telephone book, or U.S. Department of Housing and Urban Development (HUD), P.O. Box 6091, Rockville, MD 20850; 800-245-2691; {www.hud.gov}.

$2,000 GRANTS OR 2% INTEREST LOAN TO FIX UP YOUR HOME

A family of 4 can be making close to $30,000/year and still be eligible for a 2% interest loan from local Community Action Agency. Some agencies also offer grants or are aware of other local organizations that provide grants. There are about 1,000 of them around the country to help neighborhoods.

To find an agency near you, contact National Association of Community Action Agencies, 1100 17th St., NW, Washington, DC 20036, 202-265-7546; Fax: 202-265-8850; {www.nacaa.org}; {www.nemaine.com/whca/housing.htm}.

✶ To find your local Rural Housing Service, look in the blue pages of your telephone book, or contact Single Family Housing Programs, USDA Rural Housing Service, 1400 Independence Ave., SW, Washington, DC 20250; 202-720-5177; {www.rurdev.usda.gov/agency/rhs/rhs.html}.

✶ In addition, you may contact your state housing office. Your State Information Operator listed in the Appendix can help you.

Money For Seniors And Those With A Disability To Buy or Fix Up A Home

The city of Houston offers $5,000 fix up money for the disabled and elderly in their Emergency Repair Program. Minneapolis offers home repair grants of $10,000 to people with disabilities who have incomes under $18,000. Nebraska has a special low interest loan program to help people with disabilities buy a home.

The Rural Housing Service of the U.S. Department of Agriculture offers special grants through their Section 504 program of up to $7,500 if you're over 62, and need to fix up your home. Programs vary from state to state and city to city, and obviously, many have eligibility requirements.

Contact your city government, your county government and your local community development office to learn about local programs. If you have trouble locating your local community development office, contact *National Association of Housing and Redevelopment Officials*, 630 I St., NW, Washington, DC 20001; 202-289-3500, Fax: 202-289-8181; {www.nahro.org}, or

Information Center, Office of Community Planning and Development, P.O. Box 7189, Gaithersburg, MD 20898; 800-998-9999, Fax: 301-519-5027; {www.comcon.org}.

To find your local *Rural Housing Service*, look in the blue pages of your telephone book, or contact Single Family Housing Programs, USDA Rural Housing Service, 1400 Independence Ave., SW, Washington, DC 20250; 202-720-5177; {www.rurdev.usda.gov/agency/rhs/rhs.html}. In addition, you may contact your state housing office. Your State Information Operator listed in the Appendix can help you.

Money To Buy Or Fix Up A Mobile Home

The city of Sunnyvale, Ca will lend you up to $7,500 at 0-5% interest for a mobile home. New York State offers loans to help you buy a mobile home park or the land your mobile home sits on through their *Manufactured Home Cooperative Fund Program.* And the U.S. Department of Agriculture has what is called *Section 504 funds* that allow loans of up to $20,000 to fix a mobile home or to move it from one site to another.

Here is how to contact the major programs for manufactured (mobile) homes.

VA-Guaranteed Manufactured Home Loan

Contact your local office of the Department of Veterans Affairs, or U.S. Department of Veterans Affairs, 1120 Vermont Avenue, Washington, DC 20420; 800-827-1000; {www.va.gov/programs.htm}.

FHA Insured Title I Manufactured Home Loan

Contact your local office of Housing and Urban Development listed in the blue pages of your telephone book, or your state housing office, or the Housing Counseling Clearinghouse, P.O. Box 9057, Gaithersburg, MD 20898; 800-217-6970; {www.hudhcc.org}

Section 504 Rural Housing Loans and Grants

To find your local Rural Housing Service, look in the blue pages of your telephone book, or contact Single Family Housing Programs, USDA Rural Housing Service, 1400 Independence Ave., SW, Washington, DC 20250; 202-720-5177; {www.rurdev.usda.gov/agency/rhs/rhs.html}.

FREE HOUSES

Well, maybe they're not free, but they can cost you as little as a few hundred dollars a month. And maybe they're not in good shape, but many of the programs will also offer you a low interest loan to fix up the house.

Some states refer to the program as an *Urban Homesteading Act*.
The idea of the program is

> **Urban Homesteading Act**

that the government gets you a home for next to nothing and you agree to live there for a certain number of years. Minnesota has a program. Baltimore had a very active program for many years. Davenport, Iowa purchases homes, completely rehabs them, and then offers the houses in a lottery each May. You must get a

Information USA, Inc.

mortgage, but your monthly payments are under $400 a month for a completely rebuilt house!

There are some states, like Alaska, that still offer wilderness land for homesteading. Because the houses are so cheap, there is usually a lottery for eligible buyers. Contact your city government, your county government and your local community development office to learn about local programs.
If you have trouble finding your local community development agency, the following organizations may be able to help:

◆ National Association of Housing and Redevelopment Officials, 630 I St., NW, Washington, DC 20001; 202-289-3500, Fax: 202-289-8181; {www.nahro.org}

◆ Information Center, Office of Community Planning and Development, P.O. Box 7189, Gaithersburg, MD 20898; 800-998-9999; Fax: 301-519-5027; {www.comcon.org}

◆ You can also contact your state housing office. Your state information operator listed in the Appendix can help you.

Get Money For Down Payments And Closing Costs

There were many examples of financial assistance programs offered by states, cities and counties at the time we were doing our initial research for this book. Be aware that these programs are constantly changing and all have some form of eligibility requirements, but don't let that stop you! New ones are added and old ones may be discarded.

To be sure that you are aware of all the programs available in your area, contact your state office on housing (your state information operator, listed in the Appendix, can help you), your city housing office, your county housing office, as well as any local community development offices that may be in your area. If you need help locating your community development office, the following may be of assistance: National Association of Housing and Redevelopment Officials, 630 I St., NW, Washington, DC 20001; 202-289-3500; Fax: 202-289-8181: {www.nahro.org}.

Use Your Sweat as a Down Payment

One of the biggest providers of this type of program is the nonprofit organization called **Habitat for Humanity**. You've probably seen them in the news with Ex-President Jimmy Carter helping them build houses. They have even received government money to help support their program.

The typical arrangement is for people with incomes between $9,000 and $30,000. You and your family work an average of 300 to 500 hours building your home or other people's homes, and in return you get a home with no down payment and a very low mortgage payment.

Because people provide free labor to build the home, you only pay about $60,000 for a $100,000 home, and you get the money interest free. A typical bank loan can cost you over $700 per month, but through this program you pay only about $200 a month.

Other local or national organizations may run similar programs in your area, with or without government financing. To find programs in your area, you can contact:

⇨ Habitat for Humanity International, 121 Habitat Street, Americus, GA 31709; 912-924-6935; {www.habitat. org}. To find a local affiliate, cali 912-924-6935, ext. 2551 or ext. 2552
⇨ Information Center, Office of Community Planning and Development, P.O. Box 7189, Gaithersburg, MD 20898; 800-998-9999, Fax: 301-519-5027; {www.comcon.org}.

Volunteers Will Fix Up Your Home For Free

Many service organizations have begun to organize community service days, where the town is beautified along with certain homes in need of repair.

Christmas in April is a national organization with over 185 affiliates that gather together volunteers to help rehabilitate the homes of low income homeowners. The work is done for free with the goal being to provide a safe and secure home for those in need.

An example of a program in the Dallas area is the Volunteer Home Repair and Weatherization Program. This program provides home repairs that improve the health, safety, and energy efficiency of a home for low income homeowners.

Contact your city government, your county government and your local community development office to learn about local programs.

✓ In the Dallas area, contact Volunteer Home Repair and Weatherization Program, Center for Housing Resources, 3103 Greenwood, Dallas, TX 75204; 214-828-4380, Fax: 214-828-4412; {www.chrdallas.org}

✓ Christmas in April, 1536 Sixteenth St., NW, Washington, DC 20036; 202-483-9083; {www.pdi.com/cina-usa/index.html}.

GOVERNMENT FORECLOSED LAND

No, they are not giving away the kitchen sink, but you may be able to find some good deals nonetheless.

The government sells foreclosed homes all across the country, and even in your neighborhood. You don't need to know someone to get in on these deals. All are sold through real estate agents.

Contact your agent, ask about government repossessed homes and they can do a search for you. These are not just HUD homes, but also those from the VA, Fannie Mae, IRS, Federal Deposit Insurance Corporation, and more.

I want to be able to say that they give you these houses at 50% off, but I can't. Most want fair market value, but the government does not want to carry the real estate taxes for all these houses either. You can make a deal that works out best for everyone.

For more information, contact HUD USER, P.O. Box 6091, Rockville, MD 20850; 800-245-2691; {www.hud.gov/homesale.html} (Note: this website has links to all the major government home sale programs); U.S. Department of Veterans Affairs, 810 Vermont Ave., NW, Washington, DC 20420; 800-827-1000; {www.va.gov}.

Free Weatherization, Fuel Bills, and Rent for Incomes Up to
$50,000

If you are within a certain income and need help paying your heating bills, need money to make your house more energy efficient, or need funds for urgent repairs, call your local Community Action Agency. There are about 1,000 of them around the country to help neighborhoods. They will also come out and check if your home or apartment needs to be more energy efficient.

To find an agency near you, contact National Association of Community Action Agencies, 1100 17th St., NW, Washington, DC 20036; 202-265-7546; Fax: 202-265-8850; {www.nacaa.org}. Also, your local utility can provide you with or refer you to other programs in your area to analyze your energy usage, recommend energy saving measures, provide fuel and utility assistance to retain or restore service, establish payment discounts based on income and usage, or establish affordable payment plans if you are in arrears. Contact your local utility company to take advantage of these services.

Real Estate Property As Low As $500

Failed commercial banks often own businesses, land, or real estate that they must sell. Although a booklet of all available properties is not available, the Federal Deposit Insurance Corporation (FDIC) makes an effort to keep their website up-to-date showing available properties under the button, "**Asset Info**".

You can search the site for a specific location, business, price parameter, and more. A contact number is available for each listing. Look under *Special Sales, FDIC Bargain Properties*, for the deals that go as low as $500. Property sales are handled through each regional FDIC office.

For more information on asset sales, contact Federal Deposit Insurance Corporation, 550 17th St., NW, Washington, DC 20429; 800-934-FDIC; {www.fdic.gov}.

FREE HOME REPAIRS

Need money to widen your doorway for wheelchairs, install ramps or grab bars, or even put on a new roof? There's a free money program that awards grants of at least $1000 to help a senior citizen fix up and repair their home.

As part of the HOME Investment Partnership Program, the *HOME Repair/Modification Programs for Elderly Homeowners* program makes funds available to low income individuals for home repair services. Money is distributed through over 500 sites, so to locate the closest program and application information, contact the Community Connections, P.O. Box 7189, Gaithersburg, MD 20898; 800-998-9999.

State Money To Buy, Build Or Fix Up A House

While affordable housing has long held an important place on the Federal government's policy agenda, budget cutbacks in recent years have forced the government to turn over many housing responsibilities to the states. Housing finance agencies (HFAs) have been created by states to issue tax-exempt bonds to finance mortgages for lower income first-time home buyers and to build multifamily housing.

States are involved in a host of initiatives throughout the broad spectrum of housing finance and development. Interim construction financing programs which can reduce the basic costs of lower income housing projects have been initiated in a number of states, together with innovative home ownership programs and programs directed toward rehabilitation and improved energy conservation.

States are also venturing into areas which have not received as much public sector attention until recently. By encouraging non-traditional types of housing, such as accessory units, shelters, and single room occupancy housing, states are addressing important elements of the housing market.

In Colorado, the state Housing and Finance Authority (CHFA) has issued more than $2.6 billions of bonds and notes since its establishment in 1973, providing housing for more than 47,000 families and individuals of low and moderate income, 27,200 first-time home buyers and over 20,500 rental housing units. In recent years, the state has broadened CHFA's authority to allow it to develop finance programs to assist the growth of small business, help exports with insurance on goods sold overseas, and similar projects.

Colorado has done more than simply help its citizens find housing: the programs have resulted in construction employment of more than 20,000 jobs, with wages estimated at almost $20 million in new local real estate taxes and an indirect gain of $1.6 billion for the state.

Wisconsin, Maine and New York each have between 18 and 20 programs including special ones for women and minorities, for disabled persons, and for environmental hazard removal.

Maryland operates 26 programs, including those to help people with closing costs and settlement expenses. It also has special

Neighborhood Revitalization

funds available for the elderly and is developing an emergency mortgage fund to help people who have fallen behind in their payments. Nonprofit developers can also tap the state for money to build low cost rental units.

Among Michigan's 29 programs and Minnesota's 25 are several for neighborhood revitalization.

Minnesota also offers programs targeting the needs of urban Indians and migrant farm workers. Alaska, Oregon and Vermont offer financing for tenant acquisition of mobile home parks.

Funds are also available for persons who take steps to make their homes more energy efficient, for homeowners and landlords who remove lead paint from dwelling units, for houses without plumbing or those with plumbing that is dysfunctional, for handicapped persons, and to help landlords defray the costs of bringing low income housing into compliance with state and local housing codes. There are also funds for nonprofit organizations to acquire or renovate existing houses and apartments for use as group homes for special needs such as the mentally retarded.

In many states, elderly homeowners can look to the HFA to obtain financing and/or support services they need to remain in their homes and avoid institutionalization. Some of the states have more than one agency dedicated to housing. Also, many cities and counties have quasi-federal/quasi-local "housing authorities" with additional programs. Check your local government listings for these.

To find out what your state has to offer, contact your State Housing Finance Office. Your state information operator listed in the Appendix can help you.

Free Money To Renovate Historic Homes

Renovating an old house can be very time consuming and expensive. If only there were a way to get someone else to pay for all that time consuming work...well, there is, if you know where to look. About 20 states offer some kind of grant or loan program for individual homeowners who are renovating historic homes. Here are a few examples:

- Iowa offers matching grants for renovation projects
- Kansas offers up to $75,000 in matching grants for renovation
- South Carolina offers up to $25,000 in matching grants.
- Maryland offers low interest loans for historic renovation
- Tennessee offers 50/50 matching grants for renovation

To qualify for these grant and loan programs, you first need to have your house qualify for the National Register of Historic Places. This isn't as difficult as it might seem. Your house doesn't have to have national significance, such as at one time being George Washington's weekend retreat. It can have local historic or architectural significance to qualify for the National Register. It could be an early example of 18th century Greek Revival style--or have been owned at one time by a locally significant family. You'd be surprised how many older houses have some sort of local significance, and that might be just enough to qualify for these programs. Contact your State Office of Historic Preservation for more information about how to get your property qualified for historic status.

Federal Tax Credits

If you happen to live in one of the 30 states that don't offer renovation grants to individual homeowners, you still may be able to qualify for some types of financial benefits. Under the Federal Tax Credit Program, individuals who have rehabilitated an income producing building used for commercial or industrial purposes can receive a 20% tax credit on expenses incurred during that renovation. To be eligible for funding, buildings must be listed on the National Register of Historic Places or be eligible for membership into that organization.

What this means is that if you renovate your house and use part of it to run your own business, like a gift shop, you may be able to receive a federal tax deduction of 20% of the renovation costs. If you spent $50,000 on renovations, that comes out to a $10,000 tax deduction on next year's taxes. Not bad. Not only would you get the benefit of writing off 20% of your renovation expenses, but you'll also be able to write off part of your mortgage as a business expense.

Nonprofits Get The Breaks

Starting up a nonprofit, or looking to relocate an existing one? Think of moving into an historic building in need of renovation. Most states offer nonprofits matching grant money and low interest loans to buy and renovate historic buildings. Yes, that's right — some states actually offer nonprofits money to buy historic buildings.

Check In Often

The availability of money for historic renovation changes from year to year, depending on the state in which you live. Just because your state isn't awarding grants or loans this year, they may change within the next year or two, so continue to check the resources. Don't forget that some states, like South Dakota and Iowa, allow renovating homeowners of historic places up to 8 years of not having to pay property taxes — in the long run that could be even better for you than getting grant money.

To find out what your state has to offer, contact your State Historic Preservation Officer. Your state information operator listed in the Appendix can help you.

Money To Train For A
Job You Love

(See Also Money For Classes, Degrees & PhD's)

Separated, Divorced, Widowed Women Get Free Help From 1200 Offices

Single mothers deserve respect, as does any woman who suddenly needs to become a principal breadwinner for her family. It's a leap of faith, but looking for career opportunities has never been easier for women than it is today. There are over 1,200 offices across the country that provide job training for single moms and other women who need to start making money because of dramatic changes in their lives due to:

- separation
- divorce
- widowhood
- loss of public assistance
- a husband's long term unemployment or disability

Women Work! is a national network of over 1500 programs sponsored by the National Network for Women's Employment.

Information USA, Inc.

Money To Train For A Job You Love

Services are available to all women, but especially those who are widowed, divorced, homeless, battered, or abandoned. Most programs provide career training, job search, and counseling services. What else? Other types of assistance include:

- safe havens
- ways to become self-sufficient
- connections to employers
- counseling
- skills training
- internships

- support networks
- improved self esteem
- financial management skills
- workshops
- job placement assistance
- tuition assistance

Funded by federal and state money, community resources, and private contributions, these programs are often located in women's centers, local YWCAs, community colleges, universities, and vocational education institutions. Women Work! maintains the most up-to-date catalog of programs in your area.

Women Work! has a number of publications to help displaced homemakers and other women seeking job training dollars. In addition to individual publications on such topics as career options for younger women and programs for displaced homemakers, members can order special discount packages on multiple books and booklets that explain various state and federal targeted employment programs for women. For additional information, call toll free:

Women Work!
National Network for Women's Employment
1625 K St., Suite 300
Washington, DC 20006
800-235-2732

Job Training Programs Just For Seniors

(Job Training Partnership Act (JTPA) - 17.250)

The Job Training Partnership program trains and places older workers in full- and part-time jobs with private businesses.

Program participants not only receive experience on a job, but also an opportunity to develop valuable employment skills and good work habits.

Additional services available to older workers in this program include employment counseling, resume writing help, job searches, and classroom training. Participating businesses who hire JTPA graduates receive financial and tax incentives for doing so. To be eligible for employment assistance, you just need to be facing some obstacles in finding adequate employment.

Over 420,000 total participants will be served with $1,054,813,000 set aside to fund the program. To learn more about JTPA, contact your state capitol operator listed in the Appendix and ask for your State Commission on Aging and Job Training Partnership Program. You can also contact the Office of Job Training Programs, Employment and Training Administration, U.S. Department of Labor, 200 Constitution Ave., NW, Room N4459, Washington, DC 20210; 202-219-6236.

Free Computer and Computer Training

In 1997, over 75% of those with incomes over $75,000 had a home computer but only 23% of those making less than $25,000 had home computers according to the National Telecommunications & Information Administration {www.ntia.doc.gov/ntiahome/ net2/charts.html}.

There are hundreds of organizations helping families so they will not fall through the net. Tech Corps of Georgia (2801 R. N. Martin St., East Point, GA 30344; 404-768-9990; {www.techcorpsga.org}) provides refurbished computers and training to low income families with school age children for a very low cost. Mindshare Collaborative in Massachusetts recycles computers for nonprofits who work with kids, those  physically impaired or adults trying to get a job {www.citysource.com/mindshare/}.

If you have trouble finding a local center near you, there is an association of these organizations called: Community Technology Centers' Network, 55 Chapel Street, Newton, MA 02158; 617-969-7100, ext. 2727; Fax: 617-332-4318; {www.ctcnet.org}.

Free Training To Get A New Job
(Senior Community Service Employment)
(Title V - 17.235)

Title V of the Older Americans Act offers a special program for the elderly who are in search of employment. This program offers part-time training and employment opportunities for low income persons 55 years of age and older in a variety of public or private nonprofit community service settings, such as senior centers, nutrition programs, social service agencies, libraries, environmental projects, and many others.

The program provides older persons with minimum wage income and with the opportunity to acquire new skills or upgrade the ones they already have. The program also helps enrollees make an easier transition to the private job market through training, job finding, support, and counseling.

Typical program participants work at jobs such as:

activities coordinator	janitor
bookkeeper	mechanic
cashier	museum guard
clerk typist	park ranger
custodian	receptionist
data entry clerk	salesperson
day care worker	school aide
driver	security guard
food service worker	teacher's aide
grounds keeper	

You can be making up to $30,000 a year and still be eligible for this program. In 1996, 67,000 jobs were subsidized with $410,500,000 obligated exclusively for this program. For more information about the Senior Community Service Employment

Program, contact Office of Special Targeted Programs, Employment and Training Administration, U.S. Department of Labor, Room N4641, 200 Constitution Ave., NW, Washington, DC 20210; 202-219-5500.

GOVERNMENT HIRES RETIREES FOR SPECIAL PROJECTS
(Jobs With the Federal Government)

The Federal government is obviously an equal employment opportunity employer, but two agencies make a special effort to employ seniors 55 and over in part time to full time positions. These jobs are not only in Washington, DC, but throughout the United States at Environmental Protection Agency (EPA) and Forest Service regional offices. There are a couple of differences between the programs. The EPA hires

people at all skill and professional levels and recruits people through six senior citizen organizations. The Forest Service takes part in the Senior Community Service Employment Program described earlier in this chapter. Seniors must be 55 or older and meet income eligibility guidelines. This program is designed to help seniors receive training or skill upgrading, and pays at least minimum wage. Read on to learn more about these important programs for seniors.

JOBS WITH THE EPA

(Senior Environmental Employment Program (SEE) - 66.508)

Senior Environmental Employment Program (SEE)
U.S. Environmental Protection Agency
Office of Research and Development of Exploratory Research
Washington, DC 20460
202-260-2574

The Environmental Protection Agency (EPA) has a special
program for hiring senior citizens 55 years and over. When an
EPA regional office has a shortage of workers, they notify one of
the organizations listed below, which in turn recruit workers.
Senior citizens get involved in all kinds of activities from
conducting national surveys to fulfilling general administrative
tasks. The jobs carry national unemployment, workmen's
compensation, Social Security, and health benefits. There are four
levels of pay:

Level 1- Xerox operators, messengers, telephone assistants:
$6-8/hour
Level 2- secretaries, administrative assistance; $7.25-10/hour
Level 3- writers and editors: $8.50-11/hour
Level 4- professionals with relevant degrees: $10.50-15/hour

For general information, contact the Senior Environmental
Employment Program office at the address listed above.

For recruitment information contact:

American Association of Retired Persons, 601 E St., NW,
Washington, DC 20049; 202-434-6153.

National Association for Hispanic Elderly, 2727 West 6th St.,
Los Angeles, CA 90057; 213-487-1922.

National Caucus and Center on Black Aged, Suite 500, 144 K St.,
NW, Washington, DC 20005; 202-637-8400.

National Council of Senior Citizens, 1331 F St., NW, Washington, DC 20004; 202-347-8800.

National Council on the Aging, 409 Third St., SW, Washington, DC 20024; 202-479-1200.

National Pacific/Asian Resource Center on Aging, Suite 410, 2033 6th Ave., Seattle, WA 98121; 206-448-0313.

Get A Job With The Forest Service

U.S. Forest Service
U.S. Department of Agriculture
Human Resource Programs
P.O. Box 96090
Washington, DC 20090
703-235-8855.

If you are over 55 years of age and meet some income eligibility guidelines, you may be a candidate for the Senior Community Service Employment Program (SCSEP).

This program provides part-time outdoor and indoor employment and training opportunities, while providing community services to the general public. Employees work an average of 20 hours per week at a nearby Forest Service Office in their local community. They are paid at least the federal or state minimum wage, receive training and skill upgrading, health programs, and more.

SCSEP supplements the permanent Forest Service workforce. You can be assigned a variety of jobs including visitor information, receptionist, computer aide, carpenter, researcher, or more. Over 5,600 seniors are employed through this program with $26,100,000 set aside for their salaries. To learn about the program, contact your local Forest Service office or the office listed above.

Become A Journeyman

Getting a good job does not always mean that you must attend college or trade school, but no one will readily admit that. There are apprenticeship programs all over the country that will provide free on-the-job training — and you will learn while you earn.

Apprentices learn each skill of a job by carrying it out step by step under the close supervision of a skilled craft worker. An apprenticeship involves planned, day-by-day supervised training on the job, combined with technical instruction. Length of training varies depending on the job and is determined by standards adopted by a particular industry. The minimum term of apprenticeship is one year, but can be as long as four.

Currently there are over 800 apprenticeable occupations, including cook, air craft mechanic, electrician, computer programmer, tool maker, and welder. For more information, contact your state information operator listed in the Appendix and ask for the Bureau of Apprenticeship located in your state, or you may contact Bureau of Apprenticeship and Training, U.S. Department of Labor, 200 Constitution Ave., NW, Room N4649, Washington, DC 20210; 202-219-5921; {www.doleta.gov/indiv/apprent.htm}.

State Contacts

Alabama
U.S. Department of Labor
Bureau of Apprenticeship and
Training
950 22nd St., North

Birmingham, AL 35203
205-731-1308

Alaska
U.S. Department of Labor

Bureau of Apprenticeship and
Training
3301 C St., Suite 201
Anchorage, AK 99503
907-271-5035

Arizona
Department of Economic Security
438 W. Adams St.
Phoenix, AZ 85003
602-252-7771 Ext. 114

U.S. Department of Labor
Bureau of Apprenticeship and
Training
Suite 302
3221 North 16th St.
Phoenix, AZ 85016
602-640-2964

Arkansas
U.S. Department of Labor
Bureau of Apprenticeship and
Training
700 West Capitol St.
Little Rock, AR 72201
501-324-5415

California
Division of Apprenticeship
Standards
Department of Industrial Relations
45 Freemont St.
Suite 1040
San Francisco, CA 94105
415-975-4251

U.S. Department of Labor
Bureau of Apprenticeship and
Training
Suite 1090-N
1301 Clay St.
Oakland, CA 94612
510-637-2951

Colorado
U.S. Department of Labor
Bureau of Apprenticeship and
Training
721 19th St., Room 469
Denver, CO 80202
303-844-4826

Connecticut
Apprenticeship Program Manager
Connecticut Labor Department
200 Folly Brook Blvd.
Wethersfield, CT 06109
860-566-2450

U.S. Department of Labor
Bureau of Apprenticeship and
Training
135 High St., Room 367
Hartford, CT 06103
203-240-4311

Delaware
Apprenticeship and Training
Section
Division of Employment and
Training
4425 N. Market St.
Station 313
P.O. Box 9828
Wilmington, DE 19809
302-761-8121

U.S. Department of Labor
Bureau of Apprenticeship and
Training
844 King St.
Wilmington, DE 19801
302-573-6113

District of Columbia
D.C. Apprenticeship Council
500 C St., NW, Suite 241
Washington, DC 20001
202-724-7246

Florida

Apprentice Section
Bureau of Job Training
Department of Labor
1320 Executive Center Dr.
Atkins Building, Suite 200
Tallahassee, FL 32399
850-488-9250

Apprenticeship

U.S. Department of Labor
Bureau of Apprenticeship and
Training
227 North Bronough St.
Tallahassee, FL 32301
850-942-8336

Georgia

U.S. Department of Labor
Bureau of Apprenticeship and
Training
61 Forsyth St., SW
Atlanta, GA 30303
404-562-2323

Hawaii

Apprenticeship Division
Department of Labor and
Industrial Relations
830 Punchbowl St., Room 334
Honolulu, HI 96813
808-586-8877

U.S. Department of Labor
Bureau of Apprenticeship and
Training
300 Ala Moana Blvd.
Honolulu, HI 96850
808-541-2519

Idaho

U.S. Department of Labor
Bureau of Apprenticeship and
Training
3050 North Lakeharbor Lane
Boise, ID 83703
208-334-1013

Illinois

U.S. Department of Labor
Bureau of Apprenticeship and
Training
230 South Dearborn St.
Room 708
Chicago, IL 60604
312-353-4690

Indiana

U.S. Department of Labor
Bureau of Apprenticeship and
Training
46 East Ohio St.
Room 414
Indianapolis, IN 46204
317-226-7592

Iowa

U.S. Department of Labor
Bureau of Apprenticeship and
Training
210 Walnut St., Room 715
Des Moines, IA 50309
515-284-4690

Kansas

Apprenticeship Director
Department of Human Resources
401 S.W. Topeka Blvd.
Topeka, KS 66603
785-296-4161

U.S. Department of Labor
Bureau of Apprenticeship and
Training

444 SE Quincy St.
Room 247
Topeka, KS 66683
785-295-2624

Kentucky
Apprenticeship Director
Division of Employment
Standards and Mediation
Kentucky Labor Cabinet
1047 U.S. 127 South, Suite 4
Frankfort, KY 40601
502-564-2784

U.S. Department of Labor
Bureau of Apprenticeship and
Training
600 Martin Luther King Place
Louisville, KY 40202
502-582-5223

Louisiana
Director of Apprenticeship
Louisiana Department of Labor
1001 North 23rd St.
P.O. Box 94094
Baton Rouge, LA 70804
504-342-7820

U.S. Department of Labor
Bureau of Apprenticeship and
Training
501 Magazine St.
New Orleans, LA 70130
504-589-6103

Maine
Apprenticeship Standards
Department of Labor
Bureau of Employment Services
55 State House Station
Augusta, ME 04333
207-624-6431

U.S. Department of Labor
Bureau of Apprenticeship and
Training
68 Sewall St., Room 401
Augusta, ME 04330
207-622-8235

Maryland
Apprenticeship and Training
Council
1100 North Eutaw St., Sixth Floor
Baltimore, MD 21201
410-767-2968

U.S. Department of Labor
Bureau of Apprenticeship and
Training
300 West Pratt St., Room 200
Baltimore, MD 21201
410-962-2676

Massachusetts
Division of Apprentice Training
Dept. of Labor and Workforce
100 Cambridge St., Room 1107
Boston, MA 02202
617-727-3488

U.S. Department of Labor
Bureau of Apprenticeship and
Training
Room E-370
JFK Federal Building
Boston, MA 02203
617-565-2288

Michigan
U.S. Department of Labor
Bureau of Apprenticeship and
Training
801 South Waverly, Room 304
Lansing, MI 48917
517-377-1746

Minnesota
Division of Apprenticeship
Department of Labor and Industry
443 Lafayette Rd.
4th Floor
St. Paul, MN 55155
651-296-2371

U.S. Department of Labor
Bureau of Apprenticeship and
Training
316 Robert St., Room 134
St. Paul, MN 55101
651-290-3951

Mississippi
U.S. Department of Labor
Bureau of Apprenticeship and
Training
100 West Capitol St.
Jackson, MS 39269
601-965-4346

Missouri
U.S. Department of Labor
Bureau of Apprenticeship and
Training
1222 Spruce St.,
St. Louis, MO 63103
314-539-2522

Montana
Apprenticeship and Training
Program
Montana Department of Labor
715 Front St.
Helena, MT 59620
406-447-3210

U.S. Department of Labor
Bureau of Apprenticeship and
Training
301 South Park Ave.
Room 396- Drawer #10055

Helena, MT 59626
406-441-1076

Nebraska
U.S. Department of Labor
Bureau of Apprenticeship and
Training
106 South 15th St., Room 801
Omaha, NE 68102
402-221-3281

Nevada
Labor Commissioner
Nevada Apprenticeship Council
555 E. Washington Ave.
Suite 4100
Las Vegas, NV 89101
702-486-2660

U.S. Department of Labor
Bureau of Apprenticeship and
Training
301 Stewart Ave., Room 311
Las Vegas, NV 89101
702-388-6396

New Hampshire
Director of Apprenticeship
State Office Park South
95 Pleasant St.
Concord, NH 03301
603-271-6297

U.S. Department of Labor
Bureau of Apprenticeship and
Training
143 North Main St., Room 205
Concord, NH 03301
603-225-1444

New Jersey
U.S. Department of Labor
Bureau of Apprenticeship and
Training

Parkway Towers
Building E, 3rd Floor
485 Route #1, South
Iselin, NJ 08830
908-750-9191

New Mexico
Apprenticeship Director
New Mexico Department of Labor
501 Mountain Rd., NE
Albuquerque, NM 87102
505-841-8989

U.S. Department of Labor
Bureau of Apprenticeship and
Training
505 Marquette, Room 830
Albuquerque, NM 87102
505-766-2398

New York
Apprentice Coordinator
NYS Department of Labor
State Campus Building #12
Room 140
Albany, NY 12240
518-457-4391

U.S. Department of Labor
Bureau of Apprenticeship and
Training
Leo O'Brien Federal Building
Room 809
North Pearl & Clinton Ave.
Albany, NY 12207
518-431-4008

North Carolina
Apprenticeship Division
Department of Labor
4 West Edenton St.
Raleigh, NC 27601
919-733-7540

U.S. Department of Labor
Bureau of Apprenticeship and
Training
Somerset Park, Suite205
4407 Bland Rd.
Raleigh, NC 27609
919-790-2801

North Dakota
U.S. Department of Labor
Bureau of Apprenticeship and
Training
New Federal Building
304 East Broadway, Room 332
Bismarck, ND 58501
701-250-4700

Ohio
Director of Apprenticeship
State Apprenticeship Council
Bureau of Apprenticeship Services
145 S. Front St.
Columbus, OH 43215
614-644-2242

U.S. Department of Labor
Bureau of Apprenticeship and
Training
200 North High St., Room 605
Columbus, OH 43215
614-469-7375

Oklahoma
U.S. Department of Labor
Bureau of Apprenticeship and
Training

1500 South Midwest Blvd.
Suite 202
Midwest City, OK 73110
405-732-4338

Oregon
Apprenticeship and Training
Division
Bureau of Labor and Industry
800 NE Oregon St.
Room 32
Portland, OR 97232
503-731-4891

U.S. Department of Labor
Bureau of Apprenticeship and
Training
1220 SW 3rd Ave.
Portland, OR 97204
503-326-3157

Pennsylvania
Apprenticeship and Training
Council
Labor and Industry Building
7th and Forster St.
Room 1301
Harrisburg, PA 17120
717-787-4763

U.S. Department of Labor
Bureau of Apprenticeship and
Training
Federal Building
228 Walnut St., Room 773
Harrisburg, PA 17108
717-221-3496

Rhode Island
Apprenticeship Training Programs
Department of Labor
610 Manton Ave.
Providence, RI 02909
401-457-1859

U.S. Department of Labor
Bureau of Apprenticeship and
Training
Federal Building
100 Hartford Ave.
Providence, RI 02909
401-528-5198

South Carolina
U.S. Department of Labor
Bureau of Apprenticeship and
Training
Strom Thurmond Federal Building
1835 Assembly St.
Room 838
Columbia, SC 29201
803-765-5547

South Dakota
U.S. Department of Labor
Bureau of Apprenticeship and
Training
Oxbow I Building, Room 204
2400 West 48th St.
Sioux Falls, SD 57105
605-330-4326

Tennessee
U.S. Department of Labor
Bureau of Apprenticeship and
Training
1321 Murfreesboro Rd.
Suite 541
Nashville, TN 37210
615-781-5318

Texas
U.S. Department of Labor
Bureau of Apprenticeship and
Training
2320 LaBranch St.
Houston, TX 77004
713-750-1696

Utah
U.S. Department of Labor
Bureau of Apprenticeship and
Training
1600 West 2200 South
Suite 101
Salt Lake City, UT 84119
801-975-3650

Vermont
Apprenticeship and Training
Department of Labor and Training
5 Green Mountain Dr.
P.O. Box 488
Montpelier, VT 05620
802-828-5082

U.S. Department of Labor
Bureau of Apprenticeship and
Training
11 Elmwood Ave., Room 612
Burlington, VT 05401
802-951-6278

Virginia
Apprenticeship Director
Department of Labor and Industry
13 South 13th St.
Richmond, VA 23219
804-786-2381

U.S. Department of Labor
Bureau of Apprenticeship and
Training
700 Centre, Suite 546
704 East Franklin St.
Richmond, VA 23219
804-771-2488

Washington
Apprenticeship Program Manager
Department of Labor and
Industries
P.O. Box 44530

46 Legion Way S.E.
Olympia, WA 98504
360-902-5320

U.S. Department of Labor
Bureau of Apprenticeship and
Training
1400 Talbot Rd. South
Renton, WA 98055
206-277-5214

West Virginia
U.S. Department of Labor
Bureau of Apprenticeship and
Training
1108 Third Ave., Suite 203
Huntington, WV 25301
304-528-7540

Wisconsin
Dept of Workforce Develp
Division of Workforce Excellence
Bureau of Apprenticeship
Standards
7201 E. Washington Ave.
Room 211
P.O. Box 7972
Madison, WI 53707
608-266-3133

U.S. Department of Labor
Bureau of Apprenticeship and
Training
212 East Washington Ave.
Room 303
Madison, WI 53703
608-264-5377

Wyoming
U.S. Dept. of Labor Bureau of
Apprenticeship and Training
1912 Capitol Ave.#508
Cheyenne, WY 82001
307-772-2448

FREE TRAINING
IF YOU ARE LAID OFF

If you have found yourself on the losing end of a plant closing or mass layoff, apply for money and re-training under the Economic Dislocation and Worker Adjustment Assistance Act. The program is administered by each state, and because of that, the program differs from state to state. Under certain circumstances, states may also authorize service for displaced homemakers.

Workers can receive classroom, occupational skills, and/or on-the-job training to qualify for jobs in demand. Basic and remedial education, entrepreneurial training, and instruction in literacy or English-as-a-second-language may be provided. For more information contact you state information operator listed in the Appendix and ask for your state Department of Labor, or you may contact Office of Worker Retraining and Readjustment Programs, U.S. Department of Labor, Room N-5426, 200 Constitution Ave., NW, Washington, DC 20210; 202-219-5577; {www.doleta.gov/programs/factsht/edwaa.htm}.

State Dislocated Worker Contacts

Alabama
Workforce Development Division
Alabama Department of Economic
and Community Affairs
401 Adams Ave.
P.O. Box 5690
Montgomery, AL 36103
334-242-5300
800-562-4916

Alaska
Division of Community and Rural
Development
Department of Community and
Regional Affairs
333 West 4th Ave., Suite 220
Anchorage, AK 99501
907-269-4658

Arizona
Dislocated Worker Coordinator
Job Training Partnership Act
1789 West Jefferson
Site Code 920Z
Phoenix, AZ 85005
602-542-2484

Arkansas
Arkansas Employment Security
Department
P.O. Box 2981
Little Rock, AR 72203
501-682-3137

California
Displaced Worker Services
Section
Job Training Partnership Division
Employment Development
Department
P.O. Box 826880
Sacramento, CA 94280
916-654-8275

Colorado
Dislocated Worker Unit
Governor's Job Training Office
720 S. Colorado Blvd., Suite 550
Denver, CO 80222
303-620-4200
800-388-5515

Connecticut
CT Department of Labor
Dislocated Worker Unit
200 Folly Brook Blvd.
Wethersfield, CT 06109
203-566-4290

Delaware
Division of Employment and
Training
Delaware Department of Labor

4425 North Market St.
Wilmington, DE 19809
302-761-8117

District of Columbia
Dislocated Worker Unit
Department of Employment
Services
500 C St., NW
Washington, DC 20001
202-724-7130

Florida
Bureau of Workforce Program
Support
Division of Labor, Employment
and Training
1320 Executive Center Dr.
Atkins Building, Room 200
Tallahassee, FL 32399
850-488-9250
800-633-3572

Georgia
Georgia Department of Labor
Sussex Place
Suite 440
148 International Blvd., NE
Atlanta, GA 30303
404-656-6336

Hawaii
Workforce Development Division
Department of Labor and
Industrial Relations
830 Punchbowl St., Room 329
Honolulu, HI 96813
808-586-8812

Idaho
Dept. of Employment
317 Main St.
Boise, ID 83735
208-334-6298

Money To Train For A Job You Love

Illinois
Job Training Division
Department of Commerce and
Community Affairs
620 East Adams St.
Springfield, IL 62701
217-785-6006

Dislocated
Worker Unit

Indiana
Indiana Dept. of Employment and
Training Services
Program Operations Division
10 North Senate Ave.
Indianapolis, IN 46204
317-232-7461
800-437-9136

Iowa
Division of Workforce
Development
Iowa Department of Economic
Development
1000 East Grand Ave.
Des Moines, IA 50319
515-281-5365
800-562-4692

Kansas
Job Training Director
Department of Human Resources
Division of Employment and
Training
401 SW Topeka Blvd.
Topeka, KS 66603
785-296-7876

Kentucky
Office of Training and
Reemployment

Workforce Development Cabinet
275 East Main
3 Floor West
Frankfort, KY 40601
502-564-5360

Louisiana
Special Programs Section Office
of Labor Federal Training
Program
P.O. Box 94094
Baton Rouge, LA 70804
504-342-7637

Maine
Dislocated Worker Unit
Hallow/Annex Central Building
55 State House Station, 2nd Floor
Augusta, ME 04330
207-624-6390

Maryland
Department of Labor, Licensing
and Regulations
Office of Employment and
Training
1100 North Eutaw St.
Room 310
Baltimore, MD 21201
410-767-2803

Massachusetts
Corporation for
Business, Work and Learning
The Schrafft Center
529 Main St., Suite 400
Boston, MA 02129
617-727-8158 ext. 319

Michigan
Dislocated Worker Unit
Michigan Jobs Commission
201 N. Washington Square
Lansing, MI 48913
517-373-6234

Information USA, Inc.

Money To Train For A Job You Love

Minnesota
State Dislocated Worker Unit
Minnesota Department of Jobs and
Training
390 North Robert St., First Floor
St. Paul, MN 55101
612-296-7918
800-438-5627

Mississippi
Employment and Training
Division
Mississippi Department of
Economic and Community
Development
301 West Pearl St.
Jackson, MS 39203
601-949-2234
800-762-2781

Missouri
Division of Job Development and
Training
Department of Economic
Development
P.O. Box 1087
Jefferson City, MO 65102
314-751-7796
800-877-8698

Montana
Dislocated Worker Unit
State Job Training Bureau
Montana Department of Labor and
Industry
P.O. Box 1728
Helena, MT 59624
406-444-4500

Nebraska
Job Training Program Division
Nebraska Department of Labor
550 South 16th St.
Lincoln, NE 68509
402-471-9903

Nevada
State Job Training Office
Capitol Complex
400 West King St., Suite 108
Carson City, NV 89710
702-687-4310
800-900-4614

New Hampshire
New Hampshire Job Training
Coordinating Council
64-B Suncock Rd.
Concord, NH 03301
603-228-9500

New Jersey
Rapid Response Team
Labor Management Committee
New Jersey Department of Labor,
CN 058
Trenton, NJ 08625
800-343-3919

New Mexico
EDWAA Coordinator
P.O. Box 4218
Santa Fe, NM 87502
505-827-6866

New York
Dislocated Worker Unit
NY State Department of Labor
State Office Campus, Bldg. 12
Albany, NY 12240
518-457-3101

North Carolina
Division of Employment and
Training
NC Department of Commerce
441 N. Harrington St.
Raleigh, NC 27603
919-733-6383, ext. 212
800-562-6333

North Dakota
Job Training Division
Job Service North Dakota
1000 E. Divide Ave.
P.O. Box 5507
Bismarck, ND 58502
701-328-2843
800-247-0981

Ohio
Dislocated Worker Unit
Ohio Bureau of Employment
Services
145 South Front St.
P.O. Box 1618
Columbus, OH 43215
614-466-3817

Oklahoma
Oklahoma Employment Security
Commission
Will Rogers Bldg., Room 408
2401 North Lincoln Blvd.
Oklahoma City, OK 73104
405-557-7294

Oregon
Dislocated Worker Unit
Economic Development
Department
255 Capitol St., NE, 3rd Floor
Salem, OR 97310
503-373-1995

Pennsylvania
Dislocated Worker Unit
Labor and Industry Building
12th Floor, 7th and Forester Sts.
Harrisburg, PA 17120
717-772-0781

Rhode Island
EDWAA Coordinator
Department of Employment and
Training

109 Main St.
Pawtucket, RI 02860
401-828-8283

South Carolina
Manpower Training Unit
P.O. Box 1406
Columbia, SC 29202
803-737-2601
800-922-6332

South Dakota
Job Training Partnership Act
Administrator
South Dakota Department of
Labor
Kneip Building
700 Governors Dr.
Pierre, SD 57501
605-773-5017
800-952-2316

Tennessee
Tennessee Department of Labor
Gateway Plaza
4th Floor
710 James Robertson Pkwy.
Nashville, TN 37243
615-741-1031
800-255-5872

Texas
Work Force Development
Division
Texas Workforce Commission
211 East 7th St., Suite 1000
Austin, TX 78701
512-936-0474
888-562-7489

Utah
Utah Department of Workforce
Services
140 East 300 South, Suite 500

Salt Lake City, UT 84114
801-526-4312
888-848-0688

Vermont
Dislocated Worker Unit
Department of Employment and
Training
P.O. Box 488
Montpelier, VT 05602
802-828-4177

Virginia
Virginia Employment
Commission
P.O. Box 1358
Richmond, VA 23218
804-786-3037

Washington
Dislocated Worker Unit
Employment Security Department
Employment Security Bldg.
P.O. Box 9046
Olympia, WA 98507
360-438-4629

West Virginia
Governor's Administered
Programs
Bureau of Employment Programs
Job Training Programs Div.
112 California Ave.
Charleston, WV 25305
304-558-1847

Wisconsin
Department of Labor, Industry and
Human Relations
201 E. Washington Ave.
P.O. Box 7972
Madison, WI 53707
608-266-0745
888-822-5246

Wyoming
Job Training Program
Department of Employment
100 West Midwest
P.O. Box 2760
Casper, WY 82601
307-235-3601
800-730-9725

Free Training If You Lose Your Job From Increased Imports

Ever notice how so many products have gotten less expensive over the last ten years? Shirts that once cost $30 are now sold for $15. Televisions and VCRs — not to mention computers — have never been cheaper.

Almost everything we now buy in the U.S. is being made overseas. If you lost your job because of imports, you can get help looking for a new job, or get paid to get more training. The

Trade Adjustment Assistance program will help
you learn more marketable job skills, so
you can move to greener employment
pastures. You can receive up to 104 weeks of
on-the-job and classroom training; you can receive
52 weeks of benefits after your unemployment
expires if you are part of a job training program;
you can receive $800 to travel for job hunting
purposes, $800 to relocate for a job, and
transportation expenses to job training programs.

For more information, contact your local
employment services office in the blue pages of your phone
book, or Office of Trade Adjustment Assistance, Employment
and Training Assistance, U.S. Department of Labor, Room
C4318, 200 Constitution Ave., NW, Washington, DC 20210;
202-219-5555; {www.doleta.gov}. For a listing of state contacts,
see the list located after the next item.

CHECK YOUR STATE FOR TRAINING MONEY AND HELP

Each and every state also has a number of training
programs that can provide money and help for people of any
age looking to get the job they always wanted. For example,
Maine has a program that trains people who are not eligible
for any other program. Massachusetts provides tuition to
attend college classes. Alabama works one-on-one to get
people trained on how to get the job they want. California
even trains people to work for themselves.

Find out what your state has to offer by contacting your
State Department of Labor, located in your state capitol. See
the Appendix for your state information operator.

Free Training For Those Who Lose Their Jobs Because Of Increased Trade With Mexico or Canada

NAFTA is not a dirty word, but a lot of U.S. workers swear it is a plan to put them out of work and ship their jobs where labor costs are cheaper — Canada, but more significantly to Mexico and other Latin American countries.

In a dog-eat-dog global economy, there are no real borders. If you were laid off or lost your job because of the North American Free Trade Agreement (NAFTA), the government wants to help you find a new one, and probably one that pays you more than your last job. The **NAFTA Transitional Adjustment Assistance Program** is like a job skills and retraining SWAT team geared to provide rapid and early response to the threat of unemployment. The program includes on-site services to let workers know they are eligible; assessment of skills; financial and personal counseling; career counseling; job placement assistance; child care; transportation; income support for up to 52 weeks after the worker has exhausted unemployment compensation while the worker is enrolled in training; relocation allowance; and more.

For more information, contact your local employment services office in the blue pages of your phone book, or Office of Trade Adjustment Assistance, Employment and Training Assistance, U.S. Department of Labor, Room C4318, 200 Constitution Ave., NW, Washington, DC 20210; 202-219-5555; {www.doleta.gov}.

State TAA-NAFTA Contacts

Alabama
Department of Industrial Relations
649 Monroe St., Room 330A
Montgomery, AL 36131
334-242-8635

Alaska
Employment Security Division
P.O. Box 25509
Juneau, AK 99802
907-465-5954

Arizona
Department of Employment
Security
P.O. Box 6666
Phoenix, AZ 85005
602-495-1861

Arkansas
Arkansas Employment Security
Department
P.O. Box 2981
Little Rock, AR 722-3
501-682-3747

California
Employment Development
Department
P.O. Box 826880
Attn: MIC40
Sacramento, CA 94280
916-654-9305

Colorado
Department of Labor and
Employment
Two Park Central, Suite 400

1515 Arapahoe St.
Denver, CO 80202
303-620-4201

Connecticut
Connecticut Department of Labor
Employment Security Division
200 Folly Brook Blvd.
Wethersfield, CT 06109
860-566-2424

Delaware
Division of Employment and
Training
P.O. Box 9828
4425 North Market St.
Wilmington, DE 19809
302-761-8117

District of Columbia
Office of Unemployment
Compensation
D.C. Department of Employment
Services
500 C St., NW, Room 515
Washington, DC 20001
202-724-7274

Florida
Department of Labor and
Employment Security
1320 Executive Center Dr.
Room 200, Atkins Building
Tallahassee, FL 32399
850-488-9250

Georgia
Georgia Department of Labor
148 International Blvd., Room 440
Atlanta, GA 30303
404-656-6336

Hawaii
Department of Labor and Industry
830 Punchbowl St., Room 329
Honolulu, HI 96813
808-586-8820

Idaho
Idaho Department of Labor
317 Main St.
Boise, ID 83735
208-334-6314

Illinois
Department of Employment
Security
401 South State St., 7th Floor
Chicago, IL 60605
312-793-6805

Indiana
Department of Workforce
Development
10 North Senate Ave.
Indianapolis, IN 46204
317-232-7186

Iowa
Department of Workforce
Development
1000 E. Grand Ave.
P.O. Box 10332
Des Moines, IA 50306
515-281-4981

Kansas
Department of Human Resources
512 SW 6th Ave.
Topeka, KS 66603
785-291-3470

Kentucky
Dept. of Employment Services
2nd Floor West, CHR Building
275 E. Main St.
Frankfort, KY 40621
502-564-5334

Louisiana
Louisiana Department of Labor
1001 N. 22nd St.

P.O. Box 94094
Baton Rouge, LA 70804
504-342-8753

Workforce Development

Maine
Maine Department of Labor
Bureau of Employment Services
55 State House Station
Augusta, ME 04330
207-624-6390

Maryland
Department of Labor, Licensing
and Regulations
Division of Employment and
Training
1100 N. Eutaw St.
Baltimore, MD 21201
410-767-2832

Massachusetts
Corporation for Business, Work
and Learning
Schrafft Center
529 Main St.
Boston, MA 02129
617-727-8158

Michigan
Employment Security Agency
7310 Woodward Ave.
Detroit, MI 48202
313-876-5374

Mississippi
Employment Security
Commission
P.O. Box 1699

Jackson, MS 39215
601-961-7544

Missouri
Department of Labor and
Industrial Relations
Division of Employment Security
P.O. Box 59
Jefferson City, MO 65104
573-751-3784

Montana
Department of Labor and Industry
Job Service Division
P.O. Box 1728
Helena, MT 59624
406-444-3351

Nebraska
Department of Labor
P.O. Box 94600
Lincoln, NE 68509
402-471-3406

New Hampshire
New Hampshire Employment
Security
P.O. Box 9505
Manchester, NH 03108
603-656-6608

New Jersey
Department of Labor
Central Regional Office
506 Jersey Ave.
New Brunswick, NJ 08901
732-937-6249

New Mexico
Department of Labor
P.O. Box 1928
Albuquerque, NM 87103
505-841-8452

New York
Department of Labor
State Office Building
Campus #12, Room 156
Albany, NY 12240
518-457-3101

North Carolina
Employment Security
Commission
Workforce Development Division
P.O. Box 26988
Raleigh, NC 27611
919-733-6745

North Dakota
Job Service of North Dakota
1000 East Divide Ave.
P.O. Box 5507
Bismarck, ND 58506
701-328-2817

Ohio
Bureau of Employment Services
145 South Front St.
P.O. Box 1618
Columbus, OH 43216
614-644-2706

Oklahoma
Employment Security
Commission
Will Rogers Memorial Office
Building
2401 North Lincoln
P.O. Box 52003
Oklahoma City, OK 73152
405-557-7274

Oregon
Job Training Administration
Attn: DWU
255 Capitol St.
Salem, OR 97310
503-947-1665

Pennsylvania
Department of Labor and Industry
7th and Forster Sts., Room 1100
Harrisburg, PA 17120
717-783-8050

Rhode Island
Department of Labor and Training
175 Main St.
Pawtucket, RI 02860
401-277-3450

South Carolina
Employment Security
Commission
P.O. Box 1406
Columbia, SC 29202
803-737-3096

South Dakota
Department of Labor
Kniep Building
700 Governors Dr.
Pierre, SD 57501
605-773-5017

Tennessee
Dept. of Employment Security
Davy Crockett Bldg., 11th Floor
500 James Robertson Parkway
Nashville, TN 37245
615-741-1948

Texas
Texas Workforce Commission
101 E. 15th St.
Austin, TX 78778
512-305-9638

Utah
Department of Workforce
Services
140 East 300 South
P.O. Box 45249

Salt Lake City, UT 84145
801-526-4309

Vermont
Dept. of Employment Security
P.O. Box 488
5 Green Mountain Dr.
Montpelier, VT 05602
802-828-4177

Virginia
Virginia Employment Security
703 East Main St., Room 308
Richmond, VA 23219
804-786-8825

Washington
Employment Security Department
P.O. Box 9046
Mail Stop 6000
Olympia, WA 98507
360-438-4645

West Virginia
Division of Employment Service
Bureau of Employment Programs
112 California Ave.
Charleston, WV 25305
304-558-2850

Wisconsin
Department of Workforce
Development
201 E. Washington
P.O. Box 7946
Madison, WI 53707
608-266-0745

Wyoming
Department of Employment
200 West Midwest
P.O. Box 2760
Casper, WY 82602
307-235-3284

Free Training If You Are Laid Off Due To Defense Cutbacks

Thousands of communities around the country have felt the fallout of the end of the Cold War. And the fallout has been economic, not nuclear. Base closings mean no jobs — pure and simple. Fortunately, the Defense Conversion Adjustment (DCA) Program provides retraining and other assistance for workers hurt by defense cutbacks.

The DCA Program offers retraining and readjustment services tailored to meet each individual participant. Long-term training, including educational and occupational, is encouraged. Those eligible include workers who lose their jobs because of plant closings or mass layoffs due to reduced U.S. defense expenditures or closed military facilities.

For more information, contact your state job training office, contact your state information operator listed in the Appendix and ask for your State Dislocated Worker Contact, or contact Office of Worker Retraining and Adjustment Programs, Employment and Training Administration, U.S. Department of Labor, Room N5426, 200 Constitution Ave., NW, Washington, DC 20210; 202-219-5577; {www.doleta.gov}.

Free Training If You Are Laid Off By A Defense Contractor

If you have been laid off or fired because the company you worked for was on the wrong end of cutbacks at the U.S. Department of Defense, you may qualify to be retrained for another job.

Information USA, Inc.

The Defense Diversification Program (DDP) provides retraining and readjustment assistance to workers and military personnel dislocated by defense cutbacks and base closings, as well as career planning support and assistance. Those eligible for the program include civilian employees of the Department of Defense, Department of Energy, and defense contractors who have been terminated or laid off, or have a notice of termination or layoff.

For more information, contact your state job training office, contact your state information operator listed in the Appendix and ask for your State Dislocated Worker Contact, or contact Office of Worker Retraining and Adjustment Programs, Employment and Training Administration, U.S. Department of Labor, Room N5426, 200 Constitution Ave., NW, Washington, DC 20210; 202-219-5577; {www.doleta.gov}.

One-Stop to Money and Help To Train For a New Job

Whether it's learning about programs that offer $9,000 to train for a new job, free courses on how to search the Internet for jobs, or even free use of computers, run, don't walk, to your local One-Stop Career Center. This is a joint Federal and local government program that finances these services. They are all over the country. I found three in my neighborhood! To find a center near you, call 1-877-2US-JOBS, or go to {www.servicelocator.org/}.

Money For Classes, Degrees or PhD's

350 COLLEGES YOU CAN GO TO FOR FREE

Believe it or not, more than 350 colleges and universities all across the country have special programs for seniors who are interested in going back to school. This often means free or low-cost tuition, discounts on fees and books, and even special deals on housing, if you feel like living in a dorm and blasting your Benny Goodman records to all hours of the night!

Anyone interested should contact the school they wish to attend to find out how to apply for a discount or waiver. Some limitations and restrictions may apply, such as residency and space availability.

Alabama
Gadsden State Community College
Gadsden, AL 35902-0227

Jefferson State Community College
Birmingham, AL 35215-3098

Livingston University
Livingston, AL 35470

University of Montevallo
Montevallo, AL 35115

Alaska
Prince William Sound Community College
Valdez, AK 99686

University of Alaska/ Anchorage
Anchorage, AK 99508

University of Alaska/ Fairbanks
Fairbanks, AK 99775-0060

University of Alaska/ Southeast
Juneau, AK 99801

Arizona
Arizona Western College
Yuma, AZ 85366-0929

Central Arizona College
Coolidge, AZ 85228

Arkansas
Arkansas State University
Jonesboro, AR 72467-1630

Arkansas State University: Beebe Branch
Beebe, AR 72012

Arkansas Tech University
Russelville, AR 72801-2222

East Arkansas Community College
Forest City, AR 72335-9598

Garland County Community College
Hot Springs, AR 71913

Henderson State University
Arkadelphia, AR 71999-7534

Northern Arkansas Community College
Harrison, AR 72601

Phillips County Community College
Helena, AR 72342

California
California State University - Sacramento
Sacramento, CA 95819-6048

Colorado
Adams State College
Alamosa, CO 81102

Colorado Moutain College: Alpine Campus
Steamboat Springs, CO 80487

Colorado State University
Ft. Collins, CO 80523

Metropolitan State College of Denver
Denver, CO 80217

University of Colorado, Boulder
Boulder, CO 80309

University of Colorado at Denver
Denver, CO 80217-3364

University of Northern Colorado
Greeley, CO 80639

Connecticut
Asnuntuck Community College
Enfield, CT 06082

Central Connecticut State University
New Britain, CT 06050

Eastern Connecticut State University
Willimantic, CT 06226

University of Connecticut, Storrs
Storrs, CT 06269-3088

University of Hartford
West Hartford, CT 06117-0395

Western Connecticut State University
Danbury, CT 006810

Delaware
Delaware State College
Dover, DE 19901-2277

Delaware Technical and Community
College: Jack F. Owens Campus
Georgetown, DE 19947

Delware Technical and Community College:
Stanton/Wilmington Campus
Wilmington, DE 19801

Deleware Technical and Community
College: Terry Campus
Dover, DE 19901

District of Columbia
University of the District of Columbia
Washington, DC 20008

Florida
Broward Community College, Ft.
Lauderdale
Ft. Lauderdale, FL 33301

Florida Atlantic University
Boca Raton, FL 33431-0991

Florida International University
Miami, FL 33199

Florida State University
Tallahassee, FL 32306-1009

Santa Fe Community College
Gainesville, FL 32602

University of Central Florida
Orlando, FL 32816-0111

Georgia
Albany State College
Albany, GA 31705

Armstrong State College
Savannah, GA 31419

Athens Area Technical Institute
Athens, GA 30610-3099

Bainbridge College
Bainbridge, GA 31717

Brunswick College
Brunswick, GA 31520-3644

Clayton State College
Morrow, GA 30260

Columbus College
Columbus, GA 31907-5645

Georgia College
Milledgeville, GA 31061

Georgia Southern University
Statesboro, GA 30460-8024

Georgia Southwestern College
Americus, GA 31709-4693

Georgia State University
Atlanta, GA 30302-4009

Hawaii
University of Hawaii: Hawaii Community
College
Hilo, HI 96720

University of Hawaii: Honolulu Community
College
Honolulu, HI 96817

University of Hawaii: Kapiolani Community
College
Honolulu, HI 96816

University of Hawaii: Kauai Community
College
Lihue, HI 96766

University of Hawaii: Leeward Community
College
Pearl City, HI 96782

University of Hawaii at Manoa
Honolulu, HI 96822

University of Hawaii: Maui Community
College
Kahului, HI 96732

University of Hawaii: Windward
Community College
Kaneohe, HI 96744

Idaho
Boise State University
Boise, ID 83725

College of Southern Idaho
Twin Falls, ID 83303-1238

Idaho State University
Pocatello, ID 83209

Lewis Clark State College
Lewiston, ID 83501

North Idaho College
Coeur d'Alene, ID 83814

Illinois
Belleville Area College
Belleville, IL 62221

Chicago State University
Chicago, IL 60628

Money For Classes, Degrees or PhDs

College of Du Page
Glen Ellyn, IL 60137

Illinois State University
Normal, IL 61790-2200

Northern Illinois University
Dekalb, IL 60115-2857

Indiana
Ball State University
Muncie, IN 47306

Indiana University at Kokomo
Kokomo, IN 46904-9003

Indiana University-Purdue University at Fort
Wayne
Fort Wayne, IN 46805

Indiana University Southeast
New Albany, IN 47150

University of Southern Indiana
Evansville, IN 47712

Iowa
Clinton Community College
Clinton, IA 52732-6299

Des Moines Area Community College
Ankeny, IA 50021

Indian Hills Community College
Ottumwa, IA 52501

Iowa Western Community College
Clarinda, IA 51632

Kansas
Allen County Community College
Iola, KS 66749

Barton County Community College
Great Bend, KS 67530-9283

Butler County Community College
Eldorado, KS 67042

Cloud County Community College
Concordia, KS 66901-1002

Coffeyville Community College
Coffeyville, KS 67337

Emporia State University
Emporia, KS 66801-5087

Fort Hays State University
Hays, KS 67601-4099

Garden City Community College
Garden City, KS 67846

Hutchinson Community College
Hutchinson, KS 67501

Kentucky
Ashland Community College
Ashland, KY 41101

Eastern Kentucky University
Richmond, KY 40475-3101

Elizabethtown Community College
Elizabethtown, KY 42701

Lexington Community College
Lexington, KY 40506-0235

Madisonville Community College
Madisonville, KY 42431

Maysville Community College
Maysville, KY 41056

Morehead State University
Morehead, KY 40351

Murray State University
Murray, KY 42071-0009

Northern Kentucky University
Highland Heights, KY 41099-7010

University of Kentucky
Lexington, KY 40506-0054

University of Louisville
Louisville, KY 40292

Louisiana
Delgado Community College
New Orleans, LA 70119

Grambling State University
Grambling, LA 71245

Louisiana State University and Agricultural
and Mechanical College
Baton Rouge, LA 70803

Louisiana State University at Alexandria
Alexandria, LA 71302-9633

Money For Classes, Degrees or PhDs

Louisiana State University - Baton Rouge
Baton Rouge, LA 70803

Louisiana State University at Eunice
Eunice, LA 70535

Louisiana State University in Shreveport
Shreveport, LA 71115

Louisiana Tech University
Ruston, LA 71272

McNeese State University
Lake Charles, LA 70609

Nicholls State University
Thibodaux, LA 70310

Northeast Louisiana University
Monroe, LA 71209-1110

Northwestern State University
Natchitoches, LA 71497

Southeastern Louisiana University
Hammond, LA 70402-0752

Maine
University of Maine
Orono, ME 04469

University of Maine at Augusta
Augusta, ME 04330

University of Maine at Farmington
Farmington, ME 04938

University of Maine at Fort Kent
Fort Kent, ME 04743

Maryland
Alleghany Community College
Cumberland, MD 21502

Baltimore City Community College
Baltimore, MD 21215

Bowie State University
Bowie, MD 20715

Coppin State College
Baltimore, MD 21216

Frostburg State University
Frostburg, MD 21532-1099

Salisbury State University
Salisbury, MD 21801-6862

St. Mary's College of Maryland
St. Mary's City, MD 20686

University of Maryland - College Park
College Park, MD 20742

Massachusetts
Berkshire Community College
Pittsfield, MA 01201

Boston University
Boston, MA 02215

Bridgewater State College
Bridgewater, MA 02325

Briston Community College
Fall River, MA 02720

Bunker Hill Community College
Boston, MA 02129-2991

Cape Cod Community College
West Barnstable, MA 02668-1599

Salem State College
Salem, MA 01970

North Adams State College
North Adams, MA 01247

Michigan
Alpena Community College
Alpena, MI 49707

Central Michigan University
Mount Pleasant, MI 48859

Charles Stewart Mott Community College
Flint, MI 48503

Delta College
University Center, MI 48710

Glen Oaks Community College
Centreville, MI 49032

Macomb Community College
Sidney, MI 48885-0300

Oakland Community College
Bloomfield Hills, MI 48304-2266

Information USA, Inc.

Money For Classes, Degrees or PhDs

Wayne State University
Detroit, MI 48202

Western Michigan University
Kalamazoo, MI 49008-5120

University of Michigan - Ann Arbor
Ann Arbor, MI 48109-1316

Minnesota

Anoka-Ramsey Community College
Coon Rapids, MN 55433

Austin Community College
Austin, MN 55912

Bemidji State University
Bemidji, MN 56601

Brainerd Community College
Brainerd, MN 56401

Fergus Falls Community College
Fergus Falls, MN 56537

Hibbing Community College
Hibbing, MN 55746

Minnesota Universities - Twin Cities
Minneapolis, MN 55455

Mississippi

Copiah-Lincoln Community College
Wesson, MS 39191

Delta State University
Cleveland, MS 38733

East Central Community College
Decatur, MS 39327

Holmes Community College
Goodman, MS 39079

Itawamba Community College
Fulton, MS 38843

Jones County Junior College
Ellisville, MS 39437

Meridian Community College
Meridian, MS 39307

Mississippi Gulf Coast Community College:
Jackson County Campus
Gautier, MS 39553

Missouri

Crowder College
Neosho, MO 64850

East Central College
Union, MO 63048

Jefferson College
Hillsboro, MO 63050

Lincoln University
Jefferson City, MO 65102-0029

Longview Community College
Lee's Summit, MO 64081

Maple Woods Community College
Kansas City, MO 64156

Missouri Southern State College
Joplin, MO 64801-1595

Missouri Western State College
St. Joseph, MO 64507

Moberly Area Community College
Moberly, MO 65270

St. Louis Community College
Kirkwood, MO 63122

Montana

Dawson Community College
Glendive, MT 59330

Flathead Valley Community College
Kalispell, MT 59901

Fort Belknap College
Harlem, MT 59526

Fort Peck Community College
Poplar, MT 59255

Miles Community College
Miles City, MT 59301

Montana College of Mineral Science and
Technology
Butte, MT 59701

Northern Montana College
Havre, MT 59501

Western Montana College at the University
of Montana
Dillon, MT 59725

University of Montana
Missoula, MT 59812

Nebraska
Chadron State College
Chadron, NE 69337

McNook Community College
McNook, NE 69001

Metropolita Community College
Omaha, NE 68103

Mid-Plains Community College
North Platte, NE 69101

Nebraska Indian Community College
Mayce, NE 42837

Southeast Community College: Beatrice
Campus
Beatrice, NE 68310

Southeast Community College: Lincoln
Campus
Lincoln, NE 68520

Southeast Community College: Milford
Campus
Milford, NE 68405

Nevada
Community College of Southern Nevada
North Las Vegas, NV 89030

Northern Nevada Community College
Elko, NV 89801

Truckee Meadows Community College
Reno, NV 89512

University of Nevada: Las Vegas
Las Vegas, NV 89154-1021

University of Nevada: Reno
Reno, NV 89557

Western Nevada Community College
Carson City, NV 89703

New Hampshire
New Hampshire Technical College: Berlin
Berlin, NH 03570

New Hampshire Technical College:
Claremont
Claremont, NH 03743

New Hampshire Technical College:
Manchester
Manchester, NH 03102

New Hampshire Technical College: Nashua
Nashua, NH 03063

New Hampshire Technical College:
Stratham
Stratham, NH 03885

New Hampshire Technical Institute
Concord, NH 03301-7412

Notre Dame College
Manchester, NH 03104

Plymouth State College of the University
System of New Hampshire
Plymouth, NH 03264-1600

School for Lifelong Learning
Concord, NH 03301

University of New Hampshire at Manchester
Manchester, NH 03102

New Jersey
Atlantic Community College
Mays Landing, NJ 08330

Bergen Community College
Paramus, NJ 07652

Brookdale Community College
Lincroft, NJ 07738

Burlington County College
Pemberton, NJ 08068

Camden County College
Blackwood, NJ 08012

County College of Morris
Randolf, NJ 07869

Essex County College
Newark, NJ 07102

Rowan State College
Glassboro, NJ 08028

Gloucester County College
Sewell Post Office, NJ 08080

Jersey City State College
Jersey City, NJ 07305

Kean College of New Jersey
Union, NJ 07083

Mercer County Community College
Trenton, NJ 08690-1099

Middlesex County College
Edison, NJ 08818

Montclair State College
Upper Montclair, NJ 07043

Ocean County College
Toms River, NJ 08754

Ramapo College of New Jersey
Mahwah, NJ 07430

State University of New Jersey - Rutgers
New Brunswick, NJ 08903-2101

New Mexico
Clovis Community College
Clovis, NM 88101

New Mexico State College at Carlsbad
Calrsbad, NM 88220

New Mexico State University
Las Cruces, NM 88003

New Mexico State University at
Alamogordo
Alamogordo, NM 88311

New Mexico State University at Grants
Grants, NM 87020

University of New Mexico
Albuquerque, NM 87131

New York
Adirondack Community College
Queensbury, NY 12804

Broome Community College
Binghamton, NY 13902

Cayuga County Community College
Auburn, NY 13021

City University of New York: Baruch
College
New York, NY 10010

City University of New York: Bronx
Community College
New York, NY 10453

City University of New York: Brooklyn
College
Brooklyn, NY 11210

City University of New York: City College
New York, NY 10031

City University of New York: College of
Staten Island
Staten Island, NY 10314

City University of New York: Hostos
Community College
Bronx, NY 10451

City University of New York: Hunter
College
New York, NY 10021

City University of New York: Kingsborough
Community College
Brooklyn, NY 11235

North Carolina
Alamance Community College
Graham, NC 27253

Anson Community College
Polkton, NC 28135

Appalachian State University
Boone, NC 28608

Beaufort County Community College
Washington, NC 27889

Bladen Community College
Dublin, NC 28332

Blue Ridge Community College
Flat Rock, NC 28731

Brunswick Community College
Supply, NC 28462

Cape Fear Community College
Wilmington, NC 28401-3993

Carteret Community College
Morehead City, NC 28557

Catawba Valley Community College
Hickory, NC 28602

North Carolina University - Raleigh
Raleigh, NC 27695-7401

University of North Carolina - Chapel Hill
Chapel Hill, NC 27599

North Dakota
North Dakota State University
Fargo, ND 58105

North Dakota State University: Bottineau
and Institute of Forestry
Bottineau, ND 58318

Standing Rock College
Fort Yates, ND 58538

University of North Dakota: Lake Region
Devils Lake, ND 58301-1598

University of North Dakota: Williston
Williston, ND 58801

Valley City State University
Valley City, ND 58072

Ohio
Belmont Technical College
St. Clarisville, OH 43950

Bowling Green State University
Bowling Green, OH 43403

Bowling Green State University - Firelands
College
Huron, OH 44839

Central Ohio Technical College
Newark, OH 43055

Central State University
Wilberforce, OH 45384

Cuyahoga Community College District
Cleveland, OH 44115

Kent State University
Kent, OH 44242-0001

Ohio State University
Columbus, OH 43210

University of Akron
Akron, OH 44325-2001

University of Cincinnati
Cincinnati, OH 45221-0091

University of Toledo
Toledo, OH 43606-3398

Oklahoma
Cameron University
Lawton, OK 73505

Carl Albert State College
Poteau, OK 74953-5208

Connors State College
Warner, OK 74469

Oklahoma Panhandle State University
Goodwell, OK 73939

Oklahoma State University
Stillwater, OK 74078

University of Oklahoma
Norman, OK 73019

Oregon
Blue Mountain Community College
Pendleton, OR 97801

Central Oregon Community College
Bend, OR 97701

Chemeketa Community College
Salem, OR 97305

Clackamas Community College
Oregon City, OR 97045

Clatsop Community College
Astoria, OR 97103

Lane Community College
Eugene, OR 97405

Linn-Benton Community College
Albany, OR 97321-3779

Mount Hood Community College
Gresham, OR 97030

Oregon Institute of Technology
Klamath Falls, OR 97601-8801

Oregon State University
Corvallis, OR 97331

Portland Community College
Portland, OR 97280-0990

Portland State University
Portland, OR 97207-0751

Pennsylvania
Bloomsburg University of Pennsylvania
Bloomsburg, PA 17815

Bucks County Community College
Newtown, PA 18940

Butler County Community College
Butler, PA 16003-1203

California University of Pennsylvania
California, PA 15419

Clarion University of Pennsylvania
Clarion, PA 16214

Community College of Beaver County
Monaca, PA 15061

Pennsylvania State University
University Park, PA 16802

University of Pennsylvania
Philadelphia, PA 19104

University of Pittsburgh
Pittsburgh, PA 15260

Rhode Island
Community College of Rhode Island
Warwick, RI 02886

Rhode Island College
Providence, RI 02908

University of Rhode Island
Kingston, RI 02881-0806

South Carolina
Aiken Technical College
Aiken, SC 29802-0696

Chesterfield-Marlboro Technical College
Cheraw, SC 29520

The Citadel
Charleston, SC 29409

Clemson University
Clemson, SC 29634-5307

College of Charleston
Charleston, SC 29424

Denmark Technical College
Denmark, SC 29042

Florence-Darlington Technical College
Florence, SC 29501-0548

Francis Marion College
Florence, SC 29501-0547

Greenville Technical College
Greenville, SC 29606-5616

Horry-Georgetown Technical College
Conway, SC 29526

Lander College
Greenwood, SC 29649

Midlands Technical College
Columbia, SC 29202

South Dakota
Black Hills State University
Spearfish, SD 57799-9502

Dakota State University
Madison, SD 57042

Northern State University
Aberdeen, SD 57401

South Dakota School of Mines and
Technology
Rapid City, SD 57701-3995

University of South Dakota
Vermillion, SD 57069-2390

Tennessee
Austin Peay State University
Clarksville, TN 37044

Chattanooga State Technical Community
College
Chattanooga, TN 37406

Cleveland State Community College
Cleveland, TN 37320

Columbia State Community College
Columbia, TN 38402-1315

Dyersburg State Community College
Dyersburg, TN 38025-0648

East Tennessee State University
Johnson City, TN 37614

Jackson State Community College
Jackson, TN 38301

Memphis State University
Memphis, TN 38152

Middle Tennessee State University
Murfreesboro, TN 37132

Motlow State Community College
Tullahoma, TN 37388-8100

University of Tennessee
Knoxville, TN 37996-0341

Texas
Alvin Community College
Alvin, TX 77511-4898

Amarillo College
Amarillo, TX 79176

Angelina College
Lufkin, TX 75902

Bee County College
Beeville, TX 78102

Southwest Texas State University
San Marcos, TX 78666-4603

University of Houston - Central Campus
Houston, TX 77204-2160

University of North Texas
Denton, TX 76203

University of Texas - Austin
Austin, TX 78712-1157

Utah
Brigham Young University
Provo, UT 84602

College of Eastern Utah
Price, UT 84501

Dixie College
St. George, UT 84770

Salt Lake Community College
Salt Lake City, UT 84130

Snow College
Ephraim, UT 84627

Southern Utah University
Cedar City, UT 84720

University of Utah
Salt Lake City, UT 84112

Utah State University
Logan, UT 84322-1600

Utah Valley State College
Orem, UT 84058

Weber State University
Ogden, UT 84408-1015

Money For Classes, Degrees or PhDs

Vermont

Castleton State College
Castleton, VT 05735

Community College of Vermont
Waterbuty, VT 05676

Johnson State College
Johnson, VT 05656

Lyndon State College
Lyndonville, VT 05851

University of Vermont
Burlington, VT 05401

Virginia

In the State of Virginia the following rule
applies: If annual federal taxable income is
less than $10,000, tuition and application
fees are waived (audit only).

Blue Ridge Community College
Weyers Cave, VA 24486-9989

Central Virginia Community College
Lynchburg, VA 24502

Clinch Valley College of the University of
Virginia
Wise, VA 24293

College of William and Mary
Williamsburg, VA 23187-8795

Dabney S. Lancaster Community College
Clifton Forge, VA 24422

Danville Community College
Danville, VA 24541

Eastern Shore Community College
Melfa, VA 23410-9755

George Mason University
Fairfax, VA 22030

Germanna Community College
Locust Grove, VA 22508

James Madison University
Harrisonburg, VA 22807

Northern Virginia Community College
Annandale, VA 22003

University of Virginia
Charlottesville, VA 22903

Washington

Bellevue Community College
Bellevue, WA 98007

Big Bend Community College
Moses Lake, WA 98837

Central Washington University
Ellensburg, WA 98926

Centralia College
Centralia, WA 98531

Clark College
Vancouver, WA 98663

University of Washington
Seattle, WA 98195

West Virginia

Apparently, Legislature has been proposed
several times to no avail. We were unable to
find any schools who offered a discount to
senior citizens.

Wisconsin

Chippewa Valley Technical College
Eau Claire, WI 54701

Madison Area Technical College
Madison, WI 53704-2599

Mid-State Technical College
Wisconsin Rapids, WI 54494-5599

Milwaukee Area Technical College
Milwaukee, WI 53233

Northcentral Technical College
Wausau, WI 54401

Northeast Wisconsin Technical College
Green Bay, WI 54307-9042

Wyoming

Casper College
Casper, WY 82601

Central Wyoming College
Riverton, WY 82501

Money For Classes, Degrees or PhDs

Eastern Wyoming College
Torrington, WY 82240

University of Wyoming
Laramie, WY 82071

Laramie County Community College
Cheyenne, WY 82007

Western Wyoming Community College
Rock Springs, WY 82901

Tuition and basic fees are based on the lowest fees (in-state, in-district, in-county, non-degree seeking, undergraduate etc.). Special fees may apply to some classes. Generally, lab, books and materials are additional, and vary depending upon class. Some other additional fees include parking, health insurance, and a fee for degree seeking and graduate students.

An interested individual should contact the school they wish to attend to find out how to apply for a discount or waiver. Qualifications vary from school to school. Some limitations and restrictions apply such as an income limit, residency, and space availability.

Over 400 Programs Worth
$3 Billion In State Aid For Students

There are close to 400 programs worth almost $3 billion dollars in financial aid available through all 50 states. Just because you don't have the money to pay for college, that doesn't mean your dream of a college degree will never happen. Even if you do have the money, financial assistance from one of these programs could make things a little easier for all concerned.

Did you know that there are state money programs which:

- ◆ Pay for a singing degree?
- ◆ Give you money to study wildlife?
- ◆ Give you $2000 to go to vocational school?
- ◆ Pay for your nursing, teaching, or law degree?
- ◆ Give you $7,000 to study marine sciences?

The advantage of many of these programs is that most people don't even know they exist, so your competition will be less. Each state has different requirements for their various programs, so you may need to do some checking on what specific programs might fit your needs. Some programs are exclusive to residents of a particular state, whereas others have no limitations. In addition, some programs will award money to a student, and put no limitation on what school the student chooses to attend. In some cases, for teachers or health professionals, a service requirement may exist which says that the student will practice in a particular state after graduation for a certain period of time.

Contact each state below for a listing of available programs. This will allow you to shop around for the best program to suit your individual needs. By remaining flexible and adjusting your educational goals to fit the program that most appeals to you, chances are you might find yourself pursuing the college education that you always thought was beyond your reach. Using this information might be an important first step in building a successful future for yourself.

Alabama
Alabama Commission on Higher Education
P.O. Box 30200
Montgomery, AL 36130-2000
334-242-2274

Alaska
Alaska Commission on Postsecondary
Education
3030 Vintage Blvd.
Juneau, AK 99801
907-465-2962

Arizona
Arizona Commission for Postsecondary
Education
2020 North Central
Suite 275
Phoenix, AZ 85004
602-229-2590

Arkansas
Arkansas Department of Higher Education
114 East Capitol
Little Rock, AR 72201
501-371-2000

California
California Student Aid Commission
P.O. Box 510845
Sacramento, CA 94245-0845
916-445-0880

Colorado
Colorado Commission on Higher Education

1300 Broadway, 2nd Floor
Denver, CO 80203
303-866-2723

Connecticut
Department of Higher Education
61 Woodland St.
Hartford, CT 06105-2391
860-566-8118

Delaware
Commission on Higher Education
Carvel State Office Building
820 N. French St.
Wilmington, DE 19801
302-577-3240
Fax: 302-577-6765

District of Columbia
Office of Postsecondary Education
2100 Martin Luther King, Jr., Ave., SE
Suite 401
Washington, DC 20020
202-727-3685

Florida
Florida Office of Student Financial
Assistance
255 Collins
Tallahassee, FL 32399-0400
904-488-1034
Fax: 904-488-3612

Georgia
Student Finance Commission

2082 E. Exchange Place, Suite 200
Atlanta, GA 30084
770-414-3006
770-414-3224

Hawaii
Systems Group
641-18th Ave., V201
Honolulu, HI 96816
808-733-9124

Idaho
Office of the State Board of Education
P.O. Box 83720
Boise, ID 83720-0037
208-334-2270

Illinois
Illinois Student Assistance Commission
1755 Lake Cook Drive
Deerfield, IL 60015
708-948-8550

Indiana
State Student Assistance Commission of
Indiana
150 W. Market St., Suite 500
Indianapolis, IN 46204
317-232-2350

Iowa
Iowa College Student Aid Commission
200 Tenth, 4th Floor
Des Moines, IA 50309-3609
515-281-3501

Kansas
Kansas Board of Regents
700 SW Harrison, Suite 1410
Topeka, KS 66603
913-296-3517

Kentucky
Kentucky Higher Education Assistance
Authority
1050 U.S. 127 South
Frankfort, KY 40601
502-564-7990

Louisiana
Office of Student Financial Assistance
P.O. Box 91202
Baton Rouge, LA 70821-9202
504-922-1011

Maine
Finance Authority of Maine (FAME)
Maine Education Assistance Division
119 State House Station
One Weston Court
Augusta, ME 04333
1-800-228-3734 (In Maine)
207-626-8200
207-626-3263/2717
Fax: 207-626-8208

Higher Education

Maryland
Maryland Higher Education Commission
State Scholarship Administration
The Jeffrey Building
16 Francis Street, Suite 209
Annapolis, MD 21401-1781
410-974-5370
Fax: 410-974-5994

Massachusetts
Board of Regents of Higher Education
Scholarship Office
330 Stuart Street
Boston, MA 02116
617-727-9420

Michigan
Michigan Department of Education
Student Financial Assistance Services
Higher Education Authority
P.O. Box 30462
Lansing, MI 48909
517-373-3394

Minnesota
Minnesota Higher Education Programs
Capitol Square Building, Suite 400
550 Cedar Street
St. Paul, MN 55101
612-296-3974

Mississippi
Mississippi Institution of Higher Education
3825 Ridgewood Rd.
Jackson, MS 39211-6453
601-982-6663

Missouri
Missouri Coordinating Board of Higher
Education
P.O. Box 1438
3515 Amazonia St.
Jefferson City, MO 65109
573-751-2361

Montana
Office of the Commissioner of Higher
Education
P.O. Box 20301
Helena, MT 59620-3101
406-444-6594

Nebraska
Nebraska Coordinating Commission For
Postsecondary Education
140 N. Eighth St., Suite 300
P.O. Box 95005
Lincoln, NE 68508
402-471-2847

Nevada
Nevada Department of Education
Student Incentive Grant Program
700 E. 5th Street
Carson City, NV 98701-9050
702-687-9200

New Hampshire
New Hampshire Postsecondary Education
Commission
2 Industrial Park Drive
Concord, NH 03301
603-271-2555

New Jersey
New Jersey Department of Higher Education
Office of Student Assistance
4 Quakerbridge Plaza, CN 540
Trenton, NJ 08625
609-588-3288

New Mexico
New Mexico Commission On Higher
Education
1068 Cerrillos Road
Santa Fe, NM 87501
505-827-7383

New York
New York Higher Education Services
Corporation

Grants and Scholarship Information
99 Washington Ave.
Albany, NY 12255
518-474-1137

North Carolina
North Carolina State Education Assistance
Authority
P.O. Box 2688
Chapel Hill, NC 27515-2688
919-549-8614
Fax: 919-549-8481

North Dakota
University Systems
600 E. Boulevard
Bismarck, ND 58505
701-328-2962

Ohio
Ohio Board of Regents
Ohio Student Aid Commission
State Grants and Scholarship Department
309 S. 4th Street
P.O. Box 182452
Columbus, OH 43218
614-466-7420
Fax: 614-752-5903

Oklahoma
Oklahoma State Regents for Higher
Education
500 Education Building
State Capitol Complex
Oklahoma City, OK 73105
405-524-9100

Oregon
Oregon State Scholarship Commission
1500 Valley River Dr.
Suite 100
Eugene, OR 97401
503-687-7400

Pennsylvania
Pennsylvania Higher Education Assistance
Agency
1200 N. 7th Street
Harrisburg, PA 17102
717-720-2850

Rhode Island
Rhode Island Higher Education Assistance
Authority
560 Jefferson Boulevard

Warwick, RI 02886
401-736-1100

South Carolina
South Carolina Commission on Higher
Education
1333 Main Street, Suite 200
Columbia, SC 29201
803-737-2260

South Dakota
South Dakota Department of Education And
Cultural Affairs
Office of the Secretary
7000 Governors Drive
Pierre, SD 57051
605-773-3134

Tennessee
Tennessee Student Assistance Corporation
404 James Robertson Parkway
Suite 1950, Parkway Towers
Nashville, TN 37243-0820
615-741-1346

Texas
Texas Coordinating Board on Higher
Education
Box 12788, Capitol Station
Austin, TX 78711-2788
512-483-6100

Utah
Utah System of Higher Education
355 West North Temple
3 Triad, Suite 550
Salt Lake City, UT 84180-1205
801-321-7100

Vermont
Vermont Student Assistance Corporation

P.O. Box 2000
Champlain Mill
Winooski, VT 05404
800-798-8722
802-655-4050

Virginia
Virginia State Council of Higher Education
Office of Financial Aid
James Monroe Building
101 North 14th St., 10th Floor
Richmond, VA 23219
804-786-4690
Fax: 804-225-2604

Washington
Higher Education Coordinating Board
917 Lakeridge Way
P.O. Box 43430
Olympia, WA 98504
360-753-7800

West Virginia
West Virginia Higher Education Program
1018 Kanawha Blvd. East
Suite 700
Charleston, WV 25301
304-558-4614

Wisconsin
State of Wisconsin Higher Educational Aids
Board
P.O. Box 7885
Madison, WI 53707-7885
608-267-2206

Wyoming
Wyoming Department of Higher Education
Hathaway Building
Cheyenne, WY 82002
307-777-6213

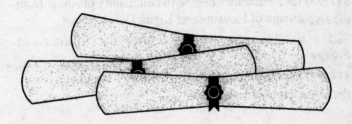

78 Federal Money Programs For Education Worth $30 Billion

Most people have heard of the Federal government's largest money programs for students like the Pell Grant program and the Guaranteed Student Loan program. But did you know that the Federal government is the single largest source of money for students — whether they show financial need or not? It's true, but very few people are aware of the many grant programs in place and just waiting to give money to those students smart enough to find out about them. These little known programs provide students with:

- ♠ $15,000 to do graduate studies in housing related topics from the Department of Housing and Urban Development

- ♠ Money to finance a graduate degree in criminal justice from the Department of Justice

- ♠ $5,000 to study to be a librarian from the Department of Education

- ♠ $11,000 for a bachelor's degree in community planning from the Department of Housing and Urban Development

- ♠ $800 to travel to energy conferences from the Department of Energy

- ♠ $14,000 to get a graduate degree in foreign languages from the Department of Education

♠ Money to finance a graduate degree in mathematics from the Department of Defense

♠ $2,500 towards a degree in history from the National Endowment for the Humanities

♠ $8,800 plus tuition and expenses to be a nurse from the Department of Health and Human Services

♠ Grants to study child development and violence training from the Department of Health and Human Services

How To Apply

Requirements and application procedures vary widely from program to program. Some programs accept applications once a year, while others award money on a year round basis. Some programs require you to apply directly to the main funding office in Washington, DC, while other programs distribute the money to local organizations, which then distribute funds to individuals. Whenever possible, we have provided a current listing of those local organizations that you may contact directly to obtain money. It should be noted that these lists can change and students might find it useful to also check the main Washington office just to inquire about new organizations which may have been recently added to the list. Like most things connected to the government, organizations are formed, changed, and even shut their doors on a frequent basis.

All these federal programs are listed in the *Catalog of Federal Domestic Assistance*, which is available in most libraries. The program name and number in parenthesis refer to this publication.

Money To Study Farming, Flowers, Clothing And Food
(Special Emphasis Outreach Grants 10.140)
Don Green, Special Emphasis Outreach Programs, Civil Rights Enforcement, U.S. Department of Agriculture, 14th and Independence Ave., SW, Washington, DC 20250, 202-720-7002

Fellowships To Study Food And Agriculture Science
(Food and Agricultural Science National Needs Graduate Fellowship Grants 10.210)
Grant Programs Manager, Office of Higher Education Programs, CSREES, U.S. Department of Agriculture, Administrative Building, Room 338A,

14th and Independence Ave., SW, Washington, DC 20250, 202-720-7854

Help Prepare For College Math And Science
(Youth Competency, Math and Science 11.449)
Dr. James L. Rasmussen, Environmental Research Laboratories, 1335 East-West Hwy., Silver Spring, MD 20910, 301-713-2474, ext. 107

Money From The Department Of Defense To Study Mathematics
(Mathematical Sciences Grants Program 12.901)
Dr. Charles F. Osgood, National Security Agency, ATTN: R51A, U.S. Department of Defense, Fort George G. Meade, MD 20755-6000, 301-688-0400

Money To Study Community Planning And Development
(Community Development Work-Study Program)
John Hartung, U.S. Department of Housing and Urban Development, Community Planning and Development, Office of University Partnerships, 451 7th St., SW, Room 8130, Washington, DC 20410, 202-708-3061, ext. 261

Money To Study Housing Issues
(Doctoral Dissertation Research Grant Program)
Ann Weeks, Division of Budget, Contracts, and Program Control, Office of Policy Development and Research, U.S. Department of Housing and Urban Development, 451 7th St., SW, Room 8230, Washington, DC 20410, 202-708-0544

Money For Members Of Indian Tribes To Go To College
(Indian Education - Higher Education Grant Program 15.114)
Terry L. Porta, Bureau of Indian Affairs, Office of Indian Education Programs, Code 522, Room MS 3512-MIB, U.S. Department of the Interior, 1849 C St., NW, Washington, DC 20240, 202-208-4871

Money For Graduate Students In Criminal Justice
(Criminal Justice Research and Development - Graduate Research Fellowships 16.562)
National Institute of Justice, 633 Indiana Ave., SW, Washington, DC 20531, 202-307-2942

Money For Graduate Students Who Want To Study The Break Up Of The USSR
(Russian, Eurasian, and East European Research and Training 19.300)
Program Officer, Eurasian and East European Research and Training Program, INR/RES, U.S. Department of State, Suite 404, Box 19, 1250 23rd St., NW, Washington, DC 20037, 202-736-4386

$3,000 A Year To Study At A State School To Become A Merchant Marine
(State Marine Schools 20.806)
Taylor E. Jones II, Director, Office of Maritime Labor and Training, Maritime Administration, U.S. Department of Transportation, 400 7th St., SW, Washington, DC 20590, 202-366-5755

All Expenses Plus $543 A Month To Study At The Merchant Marine Academy
(U.S. Merchant Marine Academy 20.807)
Taylor E. Jones II, Director, Office of Maritime Labor and Training, Maritime Administration, U.S. Department of Transportation, 400 Seventh St., SW, Washington, DC 20590, 202-366-5755

$4,000 To Study The Humanities For The Summer
(Promotion of the Humanities - Summer Stipends 45.121)
Division of Research Programs, Summer Stipends, National Endowment for the Humanities, 1100 Pennsylvania Ave., NW, Room 316, Washington, DC 20506, 202-606-8551

Money For Ph.D. Students In Humanities To Complete Their Dissertation
(Promotion of the Humanities - Dissertation Grants 45.157)
Division of Research Programs, Dissertation Grants, National Endowment for the Humanities, 1100 Pennsylvania Ave., NW, Room 316, Washington, DC 20506, 202-606-8465

Money For Social, Behavioral, And Economic Sciences Students
(Social, Behavioral, and Economic Sciences 47.075)
Assistant Director, Social, Behavioral, and Economic Research (SBER), National Science Foundation, 4201 Wilson Blvd., Arlington, VA 22230, 703-306-1700

Money For Science, Math, And Engineering Students
(Education and Human Resources 47.076)
Assistant Director, Education and Human Resources, National Science
Foundation, 4201 Wilson Blvd., Arlington, VA 22230, 703-306-1700

Money For Disabled Veterans To Go To College
(Vocational Rehabilitation For Disabled Veterans 64.116)
Department of Veterans Affairs, Central Office, Washington, DC 20420,
800-827-1000

Money For Spouses And Children Of Deceased Or Disabled Veterans To Go To School
(Survivors and Dependents Educational Assistance 64.117)
Department of Veterans Affairs, Central Office, Washington, DC 20420,
800-827-1000

Money For Veterans Who Served Between 1977-1985 To Go To School Or Receive Training
(Post-Vietnam Era Veterans' Educational Assistance 64.120)
Department of Veterans Affairs, Central Office, Washington, DC 20420, 800-827-1000

Money For Retired Veterans To Get Two Years Of Training To Start A New Career
(Vocational Training For Certain Veterans Receiving VA Pensions 64.123)
Department of Veterans Affairs, Central Office, Washington, DC 20420,
800-827-1000

Money For Retired Veterans To Go To School
(All-Volunteer Force Educational Assistance 64.124)
Department of Veterans Affairs, Central Office, Washington, DC 20420,
800-827-1000

Volunteer And Earn Money To Pay For School
(AmeriCorps 94.006)
Corporation for National Service, 1201 New York Ave., NW, Washington,
DC 20525, 202-606-5000, ext. 474

Money For Science And Engineering Students To Travel To And Work In Energy Labs
(University-Laboratory Cooperative Program 81.004)
Larry L. Barker, Postsecondary Programs Division, Office of University

and Science Education Programs, Office of Science and Technology, U.S.
Department of Energy (DoE), Washington, DC 20585, 202-586-8947

Money For Minority Students To Go To Energy Related Conferences

(Minority Educational Institution Research Travel Program)
Annie Whatley, Office of Minority Economic IMPACT, MI-1, U.S.
Department of Energy, Forrestal Building, Room 5B-110, Washington, DC
20585, 202-586-0281

Money For Minority Students At Junior Colleges Who Are Energy Majors

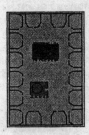

(Minority Technical Education Program 81.082)
The Minority Energy Information Clearinghouse,
Minority Economic IMPACT, Office of Economic
Impact and Diversity, U.S. Department of Energy,
Forrestal Building, Washington, DC 20585, 202-586-
5876

Spend A Semester In A Department Of Energy Lab

(Science and Engineering Research Semester 81.097)
Donna Prokop, Postsecondary Programs Division, Office of University and
Science Education Programs, Office of Science and Technology, U.S.
Department of Energy, Washington, DC 20585, 202-586-8949

$15,000 For Graduate Students To Study Overseas

(Educational Exchange - Graduate Students 82.001)
Institute of International Education, 809 United Nations Plaza, New York,
NY 10017, 212-984-5330

$4,000 Grant For Students Having Trouble Paying For Tuition

(Federal Supplemental Educational Opportunity Grants 84.007)
Division of Assistance to States, Office of the Assistant Secretary for
Special Education and Rehabilitation Services, U.S. Department of
Education, 400 Maryland Ave., SW, Washington, DC 20202,
202-708-4690

Money For A Foreign Language Degree

(National Resource Centers and Fellowships Program For Language and
Area or Language and International Studies 84.015)
Christine Corey, International Studies Branch, Center for International
Education, Office of Postsecondary Education, U.S. Department of
Education, Seventh and D St., SW, Washington, DC 20202-5332, 202-401-
9783

Money For Classes, Degrees or PhDs

Money For Students And Teachers To Travel Overseas
(Fulbright-Hays Training Grants - Group Projects Abroad 84.021)
Office of Assistance Secretary for Postsecondary Education, U.S. Department of Education, ROB-3, Seventh and D St. SW, Washington, DC 20202, 202-732-6061

Money For Ph.D. Students To Do Research Overseas
(Fulbright-Hays Training Grants - Doctoral Dissertation Research Abroad 84.022)
Karla Ver Bryck Block, Advanced Training and Research Branch, Center for International Education, Office of Assistant Secretary for Postsecondary Education, U.S. Department of Education, 600 Independence Ave., SW, Washington, DC 20202, 202-708-7283

Money To Study To Be A Special Education Teacher
(Special Education - Special Education Personnel Development and Parent Training 84.029)
Max Mueller, Division of Personnel Preparation, Special Education Programs, Office of Assistant Secretary for Special Education and Rehabilitative Services, U.S. Department of Education, Washington, DC 20202, 202-205-9554

Guaranteed Student Loans
(Guaranteed Student Loans 84.032)
Pamela Moran, Division of Policy Development, Policy, Training, and Analysis Service, Office of Assistant Secretary for Postsecondary Education, U.S. Department of Education, Washington, DC 20202, 202-708-8242

Get Loans Directly From Your School
(Federal Direct Student Loan Program)
Division of Policy Development, Policy, Training, and Analysis Service, Office of Assistant Secretary for Postsecondary Education, U.S. Department of Education, Washington, DC 20202, 800-433-3243

Work-Study Programs To Pay For School
(Federal Work-Study Program 84.033)
Division of Policy Development, Student Financial Assistance Programs, Office of Assistant Secretary for Postsecondary Education, U.S. Department of Education, 400 Maryland Ave., SW, Washington, DC 20202, 202-708-9167

Money For Classes, Degrees or PhDs

Grants To Study Library Science
(Library Education and Human Resource Development Fellowships 84.036)
Louise Sutherland, Discretionary Library Programs Division, Library Programs, Office of Educational Research and Improvement, U.S. Department of Education, 555 New Jersey Ave., NW, Washington, DC 20208, 202-219-1315

Low-Interest Student Loans
(Federal Perkins Loan Program - Federal Capital Contributions 84.038)
Division of Policy Development, Student Financial Assistance Programs, Office of Assistant Secretary for Postsecondary Education, U.S. Department of Education, 600 Independence Ave., Washington, DC 20202, 202-708-9167

Get Help To Study
(Upward Bound 84.047)
Prince O'Teal, Jr., Division of Student Services, Education Outreach Branch, Office of Postsecondary Education, U.S. Department of Education, 600 Independence Ave., SW, Room 3060, Regional Office Bldg. 3, Washington, DC 20202, 202-708-4804

$2,300 Grants To Go To School
(Federal Pell Grant Program 84.063)
Division of Policy Development, Student Financial Assistance Programs, Office of Postsecondary Education, U.S. Department of Education, 600 Independence Ave., SW, Washington, DC 20202, 202-708-4607

$5,000 From Your State To Go To College
(Grants to States For State Student Incentives 84.069)
Fred Seller, Division of Policy Development, Student Financial Assistance Programs, Office of Postsecondary Education, U.S. Department of Education, 600 Independence Ave., SW, ROB-3, Washington, DC 20202, 202-708-4607

Money For Students Interested In Helping People With Disabilities
(Rehabilitation Training 84.129)
Tim Muzzio, Rehabilitation Services Administration, Office of Special Education and Rehabilitation Services, U.S. Department of Education, Washington, DC 20202-2649, 202-205-8926

Aid For Students Who Want To Be Interpreters For The Deaf

(Training Interpreters For Individuals Who Are Deaf and Individuals Who Are Deaf-Blind 84.160)

Deafness and Communicative Disorders Branch, Rehabilitation Services Administration, U.S. Department of Education, 330 C St., SW Room 3228, Washington, DC 20202-2736, 202-205-9152, TTY: 202-205-8352

$12,200 Per Year For Ph.D. Students

(Jacob K. Javits Fellowships 84.170)

John DeCleene, Division of Higher Education Incentive Programs, Office of Postsecondary Education, U.S. Department of Education, Washington, DC 20202-5329, 202-260-3574

$20,000 For Students Who Want To Become Teachers

(Douglas Teacher Scholarships 84.176)

Valerie Hurry, U.S. Department of Education, Office of Assistant Secretary for Postsecondary Education, Division of Higher Education Incentive Programs, 600 Independence Ave., SW, Washington, DC 20202, 202-260-3392

$1,500 Per Year Grants To College Students

(Robert C. Byrd Honors Scholarships 84.185)

U.S. Department of Education, Office of Student Financial Assistance, Office of the Assistant Secretary for Postsecondary Education, Division of Higher Education Incentive Programs, The Portals, Suite C-80, Washington, DC 20024, 202-260-3394

Money To Graduate Students Who Are Studying In Areas Of National Need

(Graduate Assistance In Areas Of National Need 84.200)

John E. Bonas, Division of Higher Education Incentive Programs, Office of Postsecondary Education, U.S. Department of Education, Washington, DC 20202-5329, 202-260-3265

Grants For Undergraduate And Graduate Students Who Have Trouble Paying Tuition

(Ronald E. McNair Post Baccalaureate Achievement 84.217)

Eileen Bland, U.S. Department of Education, Division of Student Services, Office of Postsecondary Education, 600 Independence Ave., SW, Washington, DC 20202, 202-708-4809

Money For Students Interested In Careers In Public Service

(Harry S. Truman Scholarship Program 85.001)

Louis Blair, Executive Secretary, Truman Scholarship Foundation, 712 Jackson Place, NW, Washington, DC 20006, 202-395-4831

Part-Time Jobs In The Government For Students 16 And Older Who Have Trouble Paying Tuition

(Student Temporary Employment Program 27.003)
Staffing Reinvention Office, Employment Service, Office of Personnel Management, 1900 E St., ~~NW~~, Washington, DC 20415, 202-606-0830

Summer Jobs In The Government For College And High School Students

(Federal Summer Employment 27.006)
Staffing Operations Division, Career Entry Group, Office of Personnel Management, 1900 E St., NW, Washington, DC 20415

Internships For Graduate Students To Work At 54 Government Agencies

(Presidential Management Intern Program 27.013)
Office of Personnel Management, Philadelphia Service Center, Federal Building, 600 Arch St., Philadelphia, PA 19106, 215-597-7136

Health Education Assistance Loans

(Health Education Assistance Loans 93.108)
Stephen J. Boehlert, Chief, Division of Student Assistance, Bureau of Health Professions, Health Resources and Service Administration, Public Health Service, U.S. Department of Health and Human Services, Room 8-48, 5600 Fishers Lane, Rockville, MD 20857, 301-443-1540

Health Professions Scholarships For American Indians

(Health Professions Pregraduate Scholarship Program For Indians 93.123)
Rose Foley, IHS Scholarship Program, Indian Health Service (IHS), Public Health Service, U.S. Department of Health and Human Services, Twinbrook Metro Plaza, Suite 100A, 12300 Twinbrook Parkway, Rockville, MD 20852, 301-443-6197

Money To Train To Become A Nurse Anesthetist

(Nurse Anesthetist Traineeships 93.124)
Donna English, Division of Nursing, Bureau of Health Professions, Health Resources and Services Administration, Public Health Service, U.S. Department of Health and Human Services, Parklawn Building, Room 9-36, 5600 Fishers Lane, Rockville, MD 20857, 301-443-5763

Money For Classes, Degrees or PhDs

Financial Assistance For Disadvantaged Health Professions Students
(Financial Assistance For Disadvantaged Health Professions Students 93.139)
Bruce Baggett, Division of Student Assistance, Bureau of Health Professions, Health Resources and Services Administration, Public Health Service, U.S. Department of Health and Human Services, Parklawn Building, Room 8-34, 5600 Fishers Lane, Rockville, MD 20857, 301-443-4776

Money For Minorities Pursuing A Health Professions Education
(Programs of Excellence In Health Professions Education For Minorities 93.157)
A. Roland Garcia, Ph.D., Division of Disadvantaged Assistance, Bureau of Health Professions, Health Resources and Services Administration, Public Health Service, U.S. Department of Health and Human Services, Room 8A-09, Parklawn Building, 5600 Fishers Lane, Rockville, MD 20857, 301-443-4495

Money For Health Professionals To Repay Their Student Loans
(National Health Service Corps Loan Repayment 93.162)
National Health Service Corps, Loan Repayment Program, 2070 Chain Bridge Rd., Suite 450, Vienna, VA 22182, 800-221-9393

Money For Health Professionals To Repay Their Student Loans If They Serve With The Indian Health Service
(Indian Health Service Loan Repayment Program 93.164)
Mr. Charles Yepa, Loan Repayment Program, Indian Health Service, Public Health Service, U.S. Department of Health and Human Services, 12300 Twinbrook Parkway, Suite 100, Rockville, MD 20852, 301-443-6197

Money For Disadvantaged Students To Study Nursing
(Nursing Education Opportunities For Individuals From Disadvantaged Backgrounds 93.178)
Division of Nursing, Bureau of Health Professions, Health Resources and Services Administration, Public Health Service, U.S. Department of Health and Human Services, Room 8C-26, Parklawn Building, 5600 Fishers Lane, Rockville, MD 20857, 301-443-6880

Grants For Podiatric Primary Care Residency Training
(Grants For Podiatric Primary Care Residency Training 93.181)
John R. Westcott, Division of Medicine, Bureau of Health Professions, Health Resources and Services Administration, Public Health Service, U.S.

Department of Health and Human Services, Room 8C-26, Parklawn Building, 5600 Fishers Lane, Rockville, MD 20857, 301-443-6880

Money For Health Care Students Who Want To Train In Rural Areas

(Interdisciplinary Training For Health Care For Rural Areas 93.192) Division of Associated, Dental and Public Health Professions, Bureau of Health Professions, Health Resources and Services Administration, Room 8C-26, Parklawn Building, 5600 Fishers Lane, Rockville, MD 20857, 301-443-6880

Money For Health Care Students To Study Job Safety And Health

(Occupational Safety and Health - Training Grants 93.263) Dr. Bernadine Kuchinski, National Institute for Occupational Safety and Health (NIOSH), Centers for Disease Control and Prevention, Public Health Service, U.S. Department of Health and Human Services, D-40, 1600 Clifton Rd., Atlanta, GA 30333, 404-639-3525

Scholarships For National Health Service Corps

(National Health Service Corps Scholarship Program 93.288) National Health Service Corps Scholarships, Division of Scholarships and Loan Repayments, Bureau of Primary Health Care, Health Resources and Services Administration, Public Health Service, U.S. Department of Health and Human Services, 4350 East-West Hwy., 10th Floor301-594-4410, Bethesda, MD 20814, 800-638-0824

Health Professionals Student Loans

(Health Professions Student Loans, Including Primary Care Loans/ Loans For Disadvantaged Students 93.342) Bruce Baggett, Division of Student Assistance, Bureau of Health Professions, Health Resources and Services Administration, Public Health Service, U.S. Department of Health and Human Services Administration, Parklawn Building, Room 8-34, 5600 Fishers Lane, Rockville, MD 20857, 301-443-4776

Money To Train To Be A Professional Nurse

(Professional Nurse Traineeships 93.358) Erin Stevens, Division of Nursing, Bureau of Health Professions, Health Resources and Services Administration, Public Health Service, U.S. Department of Health and Human Services, Room 9-36, Parklawn Building, 5600 Fishers Lane, Rockville, MD 20857, 301-443-5763

Nursing Student Loans

(Nursing Student Loans 93.364)
Bruce Baggett, Division of Student Assistance,
Bureau of Health Professions, Health Resources
and Services Administration, Public Health Service,
U.S. Department of Health and Human Services,
Parklawn Building, Room 8-34, 5600 Fishers Lane,
Rockville, MD 20857, 301-443-4776

Grants For Graduate Training In Family Medicine

(Grants For Graduate Training In Family Medicine
93.379)
Division of Medicine, Bureau of Health
Professions, Health Resources and Services
Administration, Public Health Service, U.S.
Department of Health and Human Services, Room
9A27, 5600 Fishers Lane, Rockville, MD 20857, 301-443-6190

Scholarships For Students of Exceptional Financial Need

(Scholarships For Students Of Exceptional Financial Need 93.820)
Bruce Baggett, Division of Student Assistance, Bureau of Health
Professions, Health Resources and Services Administration, Public Health
Service, U.S. Department of Health and Human Services, Room 8-34,
Parklawn Building, 5600 Fishers Lane, Rockville, MD 20857,
301-443-4776

Health Careers Opportunity Program

(Health Careers Opportunity Program 93.822)
Mario A. Manecci, Division of Disadvantaged Assistance, Bureau of
Health Professions, Health Resources and Services Administration, Public
Health Service, U.S. Department of Health and Human Services, Room
8A-09, 5600 Fishers Lane, Rockville, MD 20857, 301-443-4493

Money For Dental Students For Advanced Residency Training

(Residency Training And Advanced Education In General Practice Of
Dentistry 93.897)
Dr. Kathy L. Hayes, Dental Education and Special Initiatives Branch,
Division of Associated Dental and Public Health Professions, Bureau of
Health Professions, Health Resources and Services Administration, Public
Health Service, U.S. Department of Health and Human Services, 5600
Fishers Lane, Rockville, MD 20857, 301-443-6880

Money For Classes, Degrees or PhDs

Grants For Nurse Anesthetists

(Grants For Nurse Anesthetist Faculty Fellowships 93.907)
Marcia Starbecker, Division of Nursing, Bureau of Health Professions,
Health Resources and Services Administration, Public Health Service,
Room 9-36, Parklawn Building, 5600 Fishers Lane, Rockville, MD 20857,
301-443-6193

**Money For Nursing Students To Repay Their Loans By Working At
A Public Health Facility After Graduation**

(Nursing Education Loan Repayment Agreements For Registered Nurses
Entering Employment At Eligible Health Facilities 93.908)
Loan Repayment Programs Branch, Division of Scholarships and Loan
Repayment, Bureau of Primary Health Care, Health Resources and
Services Administration, 4350 East-West Highway, Rockville, MD 20857,
301-594-4400

**Scholarships And Money To Repay Loans Of Disadvantaged
Health Professionals**

(Disadvantaged Health Professions Faculty Loan Repayment and
Fellowship Program 93.923)
Lafayette Gilchrist, Division of Disadvantaged Assistance, Bureau of
Health Professions, Health Resources and Services Administration, Public
Health Service, Parklawn Building, Room 8A-09, 5600 Fishers Lane,
Rockville, MD 20857, 301-443-1503

**Grants To States To Give Scholarships To Those Who Want To
Serve The Community**

(Demonstration Grants To States For Community Scholarships 93.931)
Division of National Health Service Corps, Bureau of Primary Health Care,
Health Resources and Services Administration, Public Health Service, 4350
East-West Highway, Rockville, MD 20814, 301-594-4400

Money For Health Professionals Who Want To Be In Public Health

(Public Health Traineeships 93.964)
Anne Kahl, Public Health Branch, Division of Associated, Dental, and
Public Health Professions, Bureau of Health Professions, Health Resources
and Services Administration, Public Health Service, Parklawn Bldg., Room
8C-09, 5600 Fishers Lane, Rockville, MD 20857, 301-443-6896

**Money For American Indians Who Want To Be Health Care
Professionals**

(Health Professions Recruitment Program For Indians 93.970)
Mr. Larry S. Thomas, Director, Division of Health Professions Recruitment
and Training, Indian Health Service, Public Health Service, U.S.

Department of Health and Human Services, Twinbrook Metro Plaza, 12300
Twinbrook Parkway, Suite 100, Rockville, MD 20852, 301-443-7813

Money For American Indians Who Need Extra Studies Before Acceptance Into A Health Care Program

(Health Professions Preparatory Scholarship Program For Indians 93.971)
Rosh Foley, Indian Health Service Scholarship Program, Indian Health
Service (IHS), U.S. Department of Health and Human Services, Twinbrook
Metro Plaza, Suite 100, 12300 Twinbrook Parkway, Rockville, MD 20852,
301-443-6197

Scholarships For Health Care Professionals

(Health Professions Scholarship Program 93.972)
Rosh Foley, Indian Health Service Scholarship Program, Indian Health
Service (IHS), U.S. Department of Health and Human Services, Twinbrook
Metro Plaza, Suite 100A, 12300 Twinbrook Parkway, Rockville, MD
20852, 301-443-6197

Loans For Health Service Corps Doctors To Enter Private Practice

(Special Loans For National Health Service Corps Members To Enter
Private Practice 93.973)
National Health Service Corps, Health Resources and Services
Administration, Public Health Service, U.S. Department of Health and
Human Services, 4350 East-West Hwy., 8th Floor, Bethesda, MD 20814,
301-594-4130

How To Get A GED and More Adult Education

People drop out of or fail to complete high school for many different reasons. But one thing is clear; getting your high school diploma or GED is the key to advancement. You can join the privileged ranks of people like Bill Cosby, Mary Lou Retton, and 10 million other people famous and not so famous who have obtained their GED.

What is a GED and how do you get one? GED stands for General Educational Development. When you take a GED test, it tests your knowledge and ability in five different areas: writing skills, social studies, science, interpreting literature and the arts, and mathematics. This is a way for you to earn your GED diploma which you can then use to apply for jobs, enter training programs, or even attend college!

GED tests are given at sites all across the United States. There are several ways to learn where the nearest GED test site is located. You can contact your local Board of Education, your State Department of Adult Education, or the GED Information Hotline at 800-62-MY-GED. This hotline is operated by the American Council on Education (P.O. Box 81826, Lincoln, NE 68501) which administers the GED tests.

You can take the GED without studying if you feel prepared. However, many people who have been out of school for awhile may need a little time to study. There are different ways to do this. Your local library or bookstore offers a variety of GED study books, many of which come with practice tests. The GED hotline listed above can also provide you with information on how to purchase a practice test. Many local school boards, community organizations, and community colleges offer adult education courses. Your local public television station may also run programs to help you study for the test.

Another wonderful resource is the National Literacy Hotline at 800-228-8813 (Contact Center, P.O. Box 81826, Lincoln, NE 68501). This hotline maintains a database of resources and organizations that focus on literacy and can connect you to literacy resources and contacts in your area.

Other Resources

Clearinghouse on Adult Education and Literacy
400 Maryland Ave., SW
Washington, DC 20202
202-205-9996
This clearinghouse can direct you to state contacts for assistance and has publications which review different types of training and education programs.

ERIC Clearinghouse on Adult, Career and Vocational Education
Ohio State University
Center on Education and Training for Employment
1900 Kenny Rd.
Columbus, OH 43210
614-292-4353
800-848-4815
This clearinghouse has literature and relevant materials covering the topics of adult and continuing education, ranging from basic literacy training through professional skill upgrading. They can conduct a database search for materials on a specific subject of interest and have a publications list of resource summaries.

State Directors of Adult Education

Most of us learned the basics —
reading, writing, and math — in school.
But there are millions of Americans
who never learned how to read, much
less mastered any of the other
fundamental skills necessary to survive
in the world today. Without the ability
to read, one can't check the want ads,
fill out a job application, or attempt to
take a job placement test. The road to
literacy is never easy, but it's even more
difficult as you get older. It takes a great
deal of time and effort to achieve your
goal of literacy, but reading is the only way to get ahead.

There are many ways to learn what you missed in high school.
Nonprofits across this country have been established to deal with
illiteracy. They have programs throughout the United States where
volunteers work one on one with participants to improve their
reading and math skills. The National Literacy Hotline at 800-228-
8813 is designed to put callers in touch with literacy programs
close by. You may also contact some of the nonprofits listed
below to help a loved one learn to read and enjoy a more
satisfying life.

* Literacy Volunteers of America, 5795 Widewaters Parkway,
  Syracuse, NY 13214; 315-445-8000.

* Reading is Fundamental, Smithsonian Institution, 600
  Maryland Ave. SW, Suite 500, Washington, DC 20560; 202-
  287-3220.

⋆ National Institute for Literacy, 800 Connecticut Ave., NW, Suite 200, Washington, DC 20202; 202-632-1500.

⋆ Barbara Bush Foundation for Family Literacy, 1002 Wisconsin Ave., NW, Washington, DC 20007; 202-338-2006.

The Federal government supports programs as well. The local board of education may provide classes, as may the nearest community college. The following is a list of state Adult Education Directors. Contact the Director for your state if you are having trouble locating the services you need, or you may contact the headquarters at Clearinghouse on Adult Education and Literacy, Division of Adult Education and Literacy, U.S. Department of Education, 400 Maryland Ave., SW, Washington, DC 20202; 202-205-9996.

Alabama
Mr. Bobby B. Dees
State Administrator
GED Testing Program
Adult Basic Education Section
Division of Federal Administrative Services
Department of Education
Gordon Persons Building, Room 5343
50 North Ripley St.
Montgomery, AL 36130
334-242-8181
Fax: 334-242-2236

Alaska
Ms. Constance Munro, State Supervisor
Adult Basic Education
Department of Education
801 West 10th, Box F
Juneau, AK 99801
907-465-8714
Fax: 907-465-3396

American Samoa
Ms. Fa'au'uga Achica
Dean of Continuing and Adult Education
American Samoa Community College
Board of Higher Education
Mapusaga Campus
Pago Pago, AS 96799
011-684-699-9155
Fax: 011-684-699-2062

Arizona
Dr. Gary A. Eyre
State Administrator
Adult Education Services
Department of Education
1535 West Jefferson
Phoenix, AZ 85007
602-542-5280
Fax: 602-542-1849

Arkansas
Mr. Garland Hankins
Deputy Director
Adult Education Section
Department of Education
Luther S. Hardin Building, #506
Third Capitol Mall
Little Rock, AR 72201-1083
501-682-1970/1978
Fax: 501-682-1982

California
Dr. Gerald Kilbert
State Director
Adult Education
Department of Education
P.O. Box 944272
Sacramento, CA 94244-2720
916-322-6535
Fax: 916-327-4239

Money For Classes, Degrees or PhDs

Colorado
Ms. Dian Bates
State Director, ABE
Division of Adult Education
201 E. Colfax Ave.
Denver, CO 80203
303-866-6611
Fax: 303-830-0793

Connecticut
Ms. Roberta Pawloski
Director, Division of Vocational Technical
and Adult Education
Department of Education
25 Industrial Park Rd.
Middletown, CT 06457
203-638-4035
Fax: 203-638-4156/4062

Delaware
Dr. Fran Tracy-Mumford
State Supervisor
Adult and Community Education
Department of Public Instruction
P.O. Box 1402
J.G. Townsend Building
Dover, DE 19901
302-739-4681
Fax: 302-739-3744

District of Columbia
Dr. Otho E. Jones
Assistant Superintendent
District of Columbia Public Schools
Browne Administrative Unit
26th and Benning Rd., NE
Washington, DC 20002
202-724-4178
Fax: 202-724-4750

Federated States of Micronesia
Dr. Catalino L. Cantero
Secretary, Department of Education
P.O. Box P.S. 87
Palikir, Pohnpei, FM 96941
011-691-320-2609
Fax: 11-691-320-5510

Florida
Dr. John E. Lawrence, Chief
Bureau of Adult and Community Education
FEC Building
Department of Education
325 W. Gains St., Room 1244
Tallahassee, FL 32399-0400
850-487-4929
Fax: 850-487-6259

Adult Education

Georgia
Dr. Jean DeVard-Kemp
Assistant Commissioner for Adult Literacy
Department of Technical and Adult Education
1800 Century Place
Atlanta, GA 30345-4304
404-679-1635
Fax: 404-679-1630

Guam
Mr. John T. Cruz, Director
Occupational Education Services, Academic
Education Services and Student Services
Guam Community College
P.O. Box 23069
Main Postal Facility
Guam, 96921
011-671-734-4311
Fax: 011-671-734-5238

Hawaii
Mr. Kenneth Yamamoto
Administrator, Youth and Early Childhood Section
Department of Education
Hahaione Elementary School
595 Pepeekeo St., H-2
Honolulu, HI 96825
808-395-9451
Fax: 808-395-1826

Idaho
Dr. Shirley Spencer
Director, A.E.
Department of Education
Len B. Jordon Office Building
650 W. State St.
Boise, ID 83720
208-334-2187
Fax: 208-334-2228

Money For Classes, Degrees or PhDs

Illinois
Mrs. Noreen Lopez, Director, A.E.
Adult, Vocational and Technical Education
State Board of Education
100 N. First St., E-439
Springfield, IL 62777
217-782-3370
Fax: 217-782-9224

Indiana
Ms. Carlotta Anderson
Director, Division of Adult Education
Department of Education
Room 229, State House
Indianapolis, IN 46204
317-232-0522
Fax: 317-232-9121

Iowa
Mr. Donald L. Wederquist
Chief, Adult Education
Department of Education
Grimes State Office Building
Des Moines, IA 50319-0146
515-281-3671
Fax: 515-242-5988

Kansas
Ms. Janet Stotts
Director, Adult Education
Department of Education
120 East 10th St.
Topeka, KS 66612
913-296-3191
Fax: 913-296-7933

Kentucky
Ms. Teresa Suter
Office Head
Adult Education Services
Department for Adult and Technical
Education
Capital Plaza Tower, 3rd Floor
500 Mero St.
Frankfort, KY 40601
502-564-5114
Fax: 502-564-5316

Louisiana
Mr. Glenn Gossett
Director, Bureau of Adult and Community
Education
Department of Education
P.O. Box 94064
Baton Rouge, LA 70804-9064

504-342-3510
Fax: 504-342-7316

Maine
Dr. Paul (Randy) Walker, Director
Adult and Community Education
Department of Education
State House Station 23
Augusta, ME 04333
207-289-5854
Fax: 207-287-5894

Maryland
Mr. Charles Talbert, Director
Adult Education and Literacy Services
Branch
Division of Career Technology and Adult
Learning, 3rd Floor
Maryland State Department of Education
200 West Baltimore St.
Baltimore, MD 21201
410-767-0162
Fax: 410-333-2379

Massachusetts
Mr. Robert Bickerton, Director
Adult and Community Service
Department of Education
350 Main St., 4th Floor
Malden, MA 02148
617-388-3300, ext. 353
Fax: 617-388-3394

Michigan
Dr. Ronald M. Gillum, Director
Adult Extended Learning Services
Department of Education
P.O. Box 30008
Lansing, MI 48909
517-373-8425
Fax: 517-335-3630

Minnesota
Mr. Brian Kanes, Coordinator
Adult Basic Education
Department of Education
997 Capitol Square Building
550 Cedar St.
St. Paul, MN 55101
651-296-8311
Fax: 615-297-5695

Mississippi
Ms. Eloise Johnson
Director of Literacy

168   *Information USA, Inc.*

State Board for Community and Junior
Colleges
Education and Research Center
3825 Ridgewood Rd.
Jackson, MS 39211
601-982-6344
Fax: 601-359-2326

Missouri
Mr. Elvin Long
Director, Adult Education
Department of Elementary and Secondary
Education
P.O. Box 480
Jefferson City, MO 65102
314-751-0887
Fax: 314-751-1179

Montana
Dr. Robert Ruthemeyer
Director, Adult Education
State Office of Public instruction
Office of the State Superintendent
State Capitol Building
Helena, MT 59602
406-444-4443
Fax; 406-444-3924

Nebraska
Mr. Burney Bouslough
Director, Adult and Community Education
Department of Education
301 Centennial Mall South
P.O. Box 94987
Lincoln, NE 68509
402-471-4807
Fax: 402-471-0117

Nevada
Ms. Phyllis Rich
Adult Basic Education Consultant
State GED Administrator
Department of Education
Adult and Continuing Education
400 W. King St.
Capitol Complex
Carson City, NV 89710
702-687-3134
Fax: 702-687-5660

New Hampshire
Mr. Art Ellison
Supervisor, ABE
Department of Education
101 Pleasant St.

Concord, NH 03301
603-271-6698
Fax: 603-271-1953

New Jersey
Mr. Harry Van Houten
Director, A.E.
Department of Education
225 West State St.
Trenton, NJ 08625-0500
609-777-0577
Fax: 609-633-9825

New Mexico
Ms. Muriel Lawler
State Director, ABE
Department of Education
Education Building
300 Don Gaspar
Santa Fe, NM 87501
505-827-6672
Fax: 505-827-6696

New York
Mr. Garrett W. Murphy
Director, Division of Continuing Education
State Education Department
Washington Ave.
Albany, NY 12234
518-474-5808
Fax: 518-474-2801

North Carolina
Mr. Bobby Anderson
Director, Continuing Education
Department of Community Colleges
200 West Jones
Raleigh, NC 27063-1337
919-733-4791
Fax: 919-733-0680

North Dakota
Mr. G. David Massey
Director, Adult Education
Department of Public Instruction
600 Boulevard Ave. East
9th Floor, State Capitol Building
Bismarck, ND 58505-0440
701-224-2393/3600
Fax: 701-224-2461

Northern Mariana Islands
Ms. Fe Calixterio
Director, Adult Education
Northern Marianas College

Commonwealth of the Northern Mariana
Islands
Box 1250
Saipan, MP 96950
011-670-234-3690
Fax: 011-670-234-0759

Ohio
Mr. James A. Bowling
State Director, Adult Education
Department of Education
933 High St., Suite 210
Worthington, OH 43085-4087
614-466-5015
Fax: 614-752-1640 (466-2372)

Oklahoma
Mr. Al Underwood
Director, Lifelong Learning
Department of Education
Oliver Hodge Memorial Education Building
2500 N. Lincoln Blvd., Room 180
Oklahoma City, OK 73105-4599
405-521-3321
Fax: 405-521-6205

Oregon
Dr. Donna M. Lane
Assistant Commissioner, Office of
Community College Services
255 Capitol St., NE
Salem, OR 97310
503-378-8585
Fax: 503-378-8434

Literacy

Palau
Mr. Masa-Aki N. Emesiochi
Grant Coordinator
Chief, Division of Curriculum
Public School System
Department of Social Services
P.O. Box 189
Koror, Palau 96940
011-6809-488-2570
Fax: 011-6809-488-2570

Pennsylvania
Ms. Cheryl Keenan
Director, Bureau of Adult, Basic and
Literacy Education

Department of Education
333 Market St., 6th Floor
Harrisburg, PA 17126-0333
717-787-5532
Fax: 717-783-5420

Puerto Rico
Ms. Carmen Venlen Rivera
Assistant Secretary for Adult Education
Educational Extension
P.O. Box 759
Hato Rey, PR 00919
809-753-9211
Fax: 809-754-0843

Republic of the Marshall Islands
Ms. Biram Stege
State Director
Republic of the Marshall Islands
College of the Marshall Islands
Majuro, Marshall Islands 96960
011-692-625-3394
Fax: 011-692-625-3538

Rhode Island
Mr. Robert Mason
Adult Education Specialist
Department of Education
22 Hayes St., Room 222
Roger Williams Building
Providence, RI 02908
401-277-2705
Fax: 401-277-6033

South Carolina
Mr. Sam Drew
State Director
Office of Community Education
South Carolina Department of Education
1429 Senate St.
403 Rutledge Office Building
Columbia, SC 29201
803-734-8563
Fax: 803-734-8624

South Dakota
Mr. Gene K. Dickson
Adult Education
Office of Adult, Vocational and Technical
Education
700 Governors Dr.
Pierre, SD 57501-2291
605-773-4716
Fax: 605-773-6139

Money For Classes, Degrees or PhDs

Tennessee

Mr. Phil White
Executive Director
Division of Adult and Community
Education
Department of Education
1130 Menzler Rd.
Nashville, TN 37210
615-741-7054
Fax: 615-741-6236

Texas

Dr. Pavlos Roussos
Program Director
Adult Education
Division of A.E./Employment
Training, Funding and Compliance
Texas Education Agency
1701 North Congress Ave.
Austin, TX 78701
512-463-9294
Fax: 512-475-3575

Utah

Dr. Brent Gubler
Specialist
Adult Education Services
Office of Education
250 East 500 South St.
Salt Lake City, UT 84111
801-538-7844
Fax: 801-538-7521

Vermont

Ms. Sandra Robinson
Chief, Adult Education Unit
Department of Education
State Office Building
Montpelier, VT 05602
802-828-3131
Fax: 802-828-3140

Virginia

Dr. Lennox L. McLendon
Associate Director, A.E.
Department of Education
Commonwealth of Virginia
P.O. Box 6Q
Richmond, VA 23216
804-225-2075
Fax: 804-371-8593

Virgin Islands

Ms. Anna C. Lewis
Director, ABE
Department of Education
P.O. Box 6640
St. Thomas, VI 00801
809-774-5394
Fax: 809-774-4679

Washington

Dr. Patricia Green
Director
Office of Adult Literacy
State Board for Community and Technical
Colleges
P.O. Box 42495
Olympia, WA 98504-2495
206-664-9402
Fax: 206-664-8808

West Virginia

Ms. Kathi Polis
Assistant Director, A.E.
Department of Education
Building 6, Room 230
Capitol Complex
1900 Kanawha Blvd., East
Charleston, WV 25305
304-558-6318
Fax: 304-558-0048

Wisconsin

Mr. Dwight A. York
State Director, Vocational, Technical and
Adult Education
Board of Vocational, Technical and Adult
State and Adult Education
310 Price Place
P.O. Box 7874
Madison, WI 53707
608-266-1207

Wyoming

Mr. Lloyd Kjornes
Coordinator, Adult Education
Hathaway Building
Cheyenne, WY 82002
307-777-6228
Fax: 307-777-6234

How To Make A High School Diploma Worth More

The School-to-Work program provides money to states and local partnerships of business, labor, government, education, and community organizations to develop school-to-work systems. School-to-Work is based on the concept that education works best and is most useful for future careers when students apply what they learn to real life, real work situations. School-to-Work has three core elements: School-based learning, Work-based learning, and Connecting activities. School-to-Work looks different in each state and locality.

Contact your state information operator listed in the Appendix, and ask for your state office to learn more. You can also contact National School-To-Work Learning and Information Center, 400 Virginia Ave., SW, Room 210, Washington, DC 20024; 800-251-7236; {www.stw.ed.gov}.

Money To Write A Book

Yes, you can make money writing a book. Sometimes you can even make a <u>lot</u> of money. I've made a bundle, and I even got a D in college English. So, if I can do it, there is no reason why you can't.

There are a number of ways you can make money writing a book:

1. You can get a grant from the government or a nonprofit organization
2. You can go directly to publishers
3. You can find a literary agent who will contact publishers for you
4. You can publish the book yourself

What Kind Of Money Is Available

The government money that's available is in the form of a grant. That's money you don't have to pay back, so of course, there's no better money than that. The money you might get from a publisher will usually be in the form of an advance towards future royalties. That means they will give you a certain amount of money when you sign the contract. Sometimes this money will be spread out in payments, some you could receive at the signing and some when you turn in the manuscript. This advance will be deducted from the royalties you earn when the book sells. If the book sells more than what the publisher gave you in the advance, you will receive more money. If the book sells less than the advance figure, the publisher loses.

Using the government or a publisher will usually mean **you get money up front**. Publishing yourself means **you put up your own money**. There is more risk, but it can also mean more reward. I've published about 12 books with New York publishers, but in the last five years I've been publishing myself. And to tell you the truth, I'm a lot happier now.

What You Need To Start

So many people believe that you have to have the entire book completed in order to get anyone interested in your project. Not so. All you usually need to have completed is a chapter or two along with an outline to get someone interested. I believe that it is important not to write the entire book, especially for the commercial market. If your idea is of any value, people are going to give you ideas on how to make it better. More importantly, they will tell you what they want to see in the book in order for them to publish it. And a bigger issue today is that no one has time to read a complete manuscript. They are more likely to review your book if you give them as little to do as possible. Most people want to see the basic concept of a book in progress, and nothing more.

Government Grants To Publish Your Books

This can be the most difficult way to get published mainly because so few books are published this way each year. Approximately 50,000 books are published annually by commercial publishers, while the government only publishes a few hundred titles. However, the odds of getting a grant from the government are probably a lot better than getting money from private sources. You have about a one in eight chance of getting a government grant for your book, which as odds go, isn't bad at all. Many of the government programs have now stopped giving money directly to individuals and only give money to organizations who in turn pass it on to the individuals who have applied for it.

The point is to ignore what I just said, because if you want to change your life you have to try everything, and I mean **everything!** Listed below are the sources of government grants for writers. When you call the organizations listed below, be thorough in your questioning of the person on the other end of the line — have they told you about every program available that might be able to give you some money? Also look in the *Free Money To Be A Freelancer* chapter to learn how to get a job writing for the government.

National Endowment for the Arts
1100 Pennsylvania Ave., NW
Washington, DC 20506
202-682-5400

National Endowment for the Humanities
1100 Pennsylvania Ave., NW
Washington, DC 20506
202-606-8438

Going Directly To Publishers

This seems to be the most obvious method and it works for many people. The world of publishing is very big and there is probably an editor at some publishing house who would be interested in your idea. Life, like so many things, is a numbers game. So the more publishers you call, the more editors you talk with, and the more likely you are to find someone interested in your book idea.

Listed below are the sources that identify publishers in the United States. You can find these sources in most local libraries.

Literary Marketplace, Reed Reference Publishing Co., New
    Providence, NJ
Literary Agents of North America, The Associates, New York, NY

Insider's Guide to Book Editors, Publishers, and Literary Agents,
Prima Publishing, Rocklin, GA
Literary Agents: A Writer's Guide, Adam Begley, Penguin, New
York, NY

Publishing Your Own Book

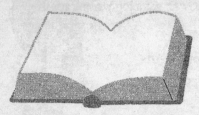

With a successful book, you'll
make a lot more money
publishing it yourself. What
profits a publishing company
would have made will end up
being yours to keep. But you'll
need money up front to publish your own book. How much? That
depends on the kind of book.

There are three major issues involved in publishing your own
book: printing, distribution and marketing. The most expensive
part of it can be printing. There are ways of getting the other two
necessities for free, but you need to have books to sell first. The
first book is the most expensive to produce. If you print 5,000 to
10,000 copies of a 300 page book you may be able to have them
printed for about $2 each. But printing only 300 books can cost
you $30 each. If you are going to sell your book for $20, you're in
big trouble if you only print 300 copies. But if you print 5000
copies, it's going to cost you $10,000 before you make even one
sale. A $10,000 advance from a publisher may start to look a lot
better after adding up these numbers.

If you are publishing a self help book, you can consider other
alternatives. You can make single copies of books at a local copy
store, or your home computer and put it into a three ring binder.
You can also charge more for the book in this kind of format. This
could work well for books like: *How To Fix Your Credit*, *How To*

Get Free Legal Advice, How To Travel Cheap, Make Money On The Internet, etc.

Distribution is an important element in anything you produce in this country. Getting your book in bookstores can be a major problem. You can find distributors who will do it for you and charge you a commission for doing so, or you can contact the bookstore chains directly. Either way it's hard, but not impossible. The bigger problem for a self publisher is that bookstores work on consignment. That means if they sell your book, you get the money. If they don't, you get the book back and get no money. And it may take three to six months to find out which of these two events actually occur.

When I first started publishing my own books, I decided that I couldn't afford to be in bookstores. If every bookstore purchased 10 copies of my book, I'd be out of business. If there are 5,000 book stores, that would mean 50,000 books at $2 each. I would have to put up $100,000 to cover printing costs and have no idea if and when I'd get anything back. So I decided on distributing my publications through mail order. If someone sent me the money, I would send them the book.

Nothing happens without successful marketing. You can have production and distribution all figured out, but if you don't know how to sell your book, you're sunk. I use talk shows. I was on talk shows when I was writing for New York publishers, so I knew how the system works (you make hundreds of telephone calls and try to convince the producers you have something interesting to say). But this time when I got on the shows, instead of saying the book was in book stores, I'd say the book was only available by calling 1-800-UNCLE-SAM.

If you want to sell your own book, you'll find the way that works best for you.

Using A Literary Agent

This may be the most productive method for someone trying to get their first book published. Using a middle man, in this case a literary agent, can save you time in finding a publisher. Also, most big publishers would rather deal with an agent who knows the business rather than dealing directly with you. They don't want to spend time explaining contracts and educating you about the process. The agent performs this role for them.

Every literary agent has her area of expertise, and a collection of publishers, and editors within those companies, whom they are close to and know the kinds of books they are looking for. So instead of contacting hundreds of publishers and editors directly, you can now concentrate on just dozens of agents. To contact an agent, write a brief letter describing your work, list any prior publications, and include a self-addressed stamped envelope (SASE) to receive a reply. The cost? They will normally ask you for 10% to 15% of what they get for you from the publisher. Some particularly successful agents are in such demand for their time that they charge a flat fee just to read your book outline or sample chapters.

For additional information on literary agents, contact: Association of Authors' Representatives (AAR), 10 Astor Place, 3rd Floor, New York, NY 10003, 212-353-3709. The AAR will send you a list of 22 suggested questions to ask, the AAR's *Canon of Ethics*, and a listing of agents who are members for $5, plus postage and handling.

Writer's Organizations

Writing can be a lonely and isolating profession. Writer's organizations are there to assist you with networking and to provide you with some added inspiration when you most need it. Membership entitles you to a variety of services such as newsletters, job information, workshops, and other types of support services. Associations

typically focus on a specific genre (i.e. mystery writing, science writing), and membership fees or dues are usually required. The list that follows provides information on a variety of organizations to get you started on finding your place among fellow writers.

Writer's Organizations

American Medical Writers Association (AMWA)
9650 Rockville Pike
Bethesda, MD 20812

301-493-0003
Fax: 301-493-6384
Email: amwa@amwa.org

Since 1940, AMWA has served an interdisciplinary membership of medical writers, editors, public relations specialists, audiovisual experts, and other professionals with varied roles in biocommunications. Benefits of membership in AMWA include: professional identification as a communicator; meetings, workshops, and Core Curriculum program; and professional development. Membership fee is $75.

American Society of Journalists and Authors, Inc. (ASJA)
1501 Broadway, Suite 302
New York, NY 10036

212-997-0947
Fax: 212-768-7414
Email: 75227,1650@compuserve.com

ASJA membership is open only to professional freelance writers of non-fiction for general audiences, produced over a substantial period of time. ASJA provides its members with an array of professional supports including: monthly newsletter, membership directory, and an ongoing survey of payment rates. A $25 application fee will be applied to the $100 initiation fee upon acceptance. Annual membership dues are $165.

Money To Write A Book

American Translators Association (ATA)
1800 Diagonal Rd., Suite 220   703-683-6100
Alexandria, VA 22314   Fax: 703-683-6122

The ATA is the largest professional association of translators and interpreters in the US. Their primary goals include fostering and supporting professional development for translators and interpreters and promoting the translation profession. ATA membership is open to anyone with an interest in translation as a profession or as a scholarly pursuit. Benefits of membership include: networking opportunities, subscription to the ATA Chronicle, job information, and a copy of the ATA Membership Directory. Membership fees are $50 for students, $95 for Associate Member, $120 for Institutional Membership, and $175 for Corporate Membership.

The Associated Writing Programs (AWP)
Tallwood House, Mail Stop 1E3   703-993-4301
George Mason University   Fax: 703-993-4302
Fairfax, VA 22030   Email: awp@gmu.edu

For 29 years, writers and teachers have joined the AWP for community and support, for information and inspiration, for contacts and new ideas. The $50 membership fee includes six issues of AWP Chronicle, seven issues of AWP Job List, a 33% discount to enter Award Series, and an 18% discount on annual conferences.

The Authors Guild, Inc.
330 West 42nd St.   212-563-5904
New York, NY 10036-6902   Fax: 212-564-8363

The Authors Guild is the nation's oldest, largest, and most prestigious professional society of published authors. A few benefits of membership include the quarterly Bulletin; symposia and seminars; online services; business advice on problems that arise with publishers, agents, booksellers, or editors, as well as legal and accounting advice. There is no initiation fee. First year dues are $90. After the first year of membership the dues are based on an individual's annual writing income.

The Dramatists Guild, Inc.
234 West 44th St.
New York, NY 10036-3909   212-398-9366

The Guild works to protect and promote the professional interests and rights of writers of dramatic and musical works. Membership privileges include Dramatists Guild production contracts, business advice, marketing information, royalty collection, publications, free Guild symposia, and access to health and dental insurance programs. Categories of membership and dues are: Active members who have had a theater production, $125; Associate members are all other theater writers, $75; Estate members services are available to the estate of any playwright, composer, bookwriter, or lyricist, $125; Student members must be currently enrolled in an accredited writing degree program, $35.

Editorial Freelancers Association (EFA)
71 West 23rd St., Suite 1504
New York, NY 10010   212-929-5400

Any full or part time freelancer may apply for membership. All EFA members receive: bimonthly newsletter, annual membership directory, Business Practices Survey; admission to all meetings and events; reduced tuition for courses; and eligibility for medical, dental, and disability insurance. Annual membership is $95 for resident members living in the greater New York City metropolitan area, and $75 for non-resident members.

180   *Information USA, Inc.*

Educational Writers Association (EWA)
1331 H St., NW, Suite 307
Washington, DC 20005

202-637-9700
Fax: 202-637-9707
Email: EWAoffice@aol.com
http://www.ewa.org

Members include over 800 education reporters from newspapers, television and radio; and education writers and public information offers from organizations, school districts and colleges. Membership brings free copies of all EWA publications, the bimonthly newsletter Education Reporter, useful referral and source information by phone, Email, and through mailings, and study opportunities. Annual membership fees are $50.

Freelance Editorial Association
P.O. Box 380835
Cambridge, MA 02238-0835

617-643-8626

The Freelance Editorial Association is a nonprofit, volunteer organization. Membership is open to all those with an interest in editorial freelancing, regardless of specialty or experience. Members are self employed editors, proofreaders, indexers, writers, translators, project managers, desktop publishers, illustrators, and other publication specialists. Annual dues are $90.

Horror Writers Association (HWA)
5 Solitaire Court
Gaithersburg, MD 20878

301-926-7687
Fax: 301-990-9395
Email: lawrence@clark.net
http://www.horror.org

The HWA is devoted to helping writers at every point in their career. Whether you're an aspiring writer or trying to make that first sale, or a seasoned novelist with a dozen books to your name, the HWA has something for you. Benefits include publicity information, agent database, networking, regional chapters, Internet connections, grievance committee and worldwide organizations. Annual dues are $55.

International Association of Crime Writers (IACW)
(North American Branch)
JAF Box 1500
New York, NY 10116

Phone/Fax: 212-243-8966
Email: mfrisque@apc.org

IACW is an organization of professional published writers whose primary goal is to promote communication among writers of all nationalities and to promote crime writing as an influential and significant art form. IACW sponsors a number of conferences and an annual celebration. The North American branch publishes a newsletter, sponsors social events, and has created several anthologies of international crime writing. Membership dues are $50.

International Television Association (ITVA)
6311 North O'Connor Rd., Suite 230
Irving, TX 75039

214-869-1112
Fax: 214-869-2980
Email: itvahq@ix.netcom.org
http://www.itva.org

ITVA is the only association dedicated to serving the needs of video professionals in nonbroadcast video production. The association has worked to advance the video profession and to promote the growth and quality of video related media through providing relevant member services. Membership offers you: career advancement, networking, special services, discounts, industry leadership, and periodicals. Annual fee is $150.

Money To Write A Book

The International Women's Writing Guild
Box 810, Gracie Station
New York, NY 10028

212-737-7536
Fax: 212-737-9469
Email: iwwg@iwwg.com
http://www.iwwg.com

The Guild is a worldwide nonprofit organization open to all women, regardless of portfolio, which offers its members services including: annual subscription to NETWORK newsletter, membership listing, list of 35 agents and other writing services, health plans, opportunities to participate in regional and national writing conferences, and various online services. Annual dues are $35.

Mystery Writers of America
17 East 47th St.
New York, NY 10017

212-888-8171
Fax: 212-888-8107

This is a nonprofit professional organization of mystery and crime writers in all categories. Benefits of membership include: mystery writing courses, the Edgar Allan Poe Awards Banquet, monthly meetings, local bulletins, the Third Degree, which is published 10 times a year, and the MWA Anthology, which is published annually. There is no initiation fee and dues for all categories of memberships are $65 per year.

National Association of Science Writers (NASW)
P.O. Box 294
Greenlawn, NY 11740

516-757-5664
Fax: 516-757-0069
Email: 71223,3441@compuserve.com

The NASW sponsors directly or works closely with regional science writing groups and around the country where members gather for workshops, meetings, and field trips. Members receive the newsletter, ScienceWriters, which provides timely, incisive reports on professional issues. To join, you must show evidence of science writing ability and be sponsored by at least two active NASW members. Membership dues are $15 for Student, $60 for Associate, and $60 for Active membership.

The National Association of American Pen Women, Inc.
Pen Arts Building
1300 17th St.
Washington, DC 20036-1973

202-785-1997

The League offers its members association with creative professional women, workshops, discussion groups and lectures. The Pen Woman, the official publication of The League, is published six times a year and features news, accomplishments, and works of its members. Membership requires the submission of at least three sample chapters and proof of sale. Authors who are self published (not vanity published) shall submit copies to be evaluated by the Branch.

The National Writers Association
1450 South Havana, Suite 424
Aurora, CO 80012

303-7551-7844

It doesn't matter if you're a new writer needing to know proper manuscript format, or a professional needing contract suggestions and assistance, the Association offers help with searching out competent and reliable agents, assistance in writing a good synopsis, and professional advice about self publishing. Membership fees are $50 for General member and $60 for Professional member (credits required).

National Writers Union
(East Coast Office)
113 University Place, 6th Floor
New York, NY 10003

212-254-0279
Fax: 212-254-0673

(West Coast Office)
337 17th St., Suite 101   510-839-0110
Oakland, CA 94612   Fax: 510-839-6097

The National Writers Union is an innovative labor union committed to improving the working conditions of freelance writers through the collective strength of its members. The Union welcomes all writers whether you write for money or publication. Dues are based on one's annual writing income. The National Writers unions also has a Supporter's Circle open to individuals who are not writers, but advocate on their behalf.

The PEN American Center
568 Broadway   212-334-1669
New York, NY 10012-3225   Fax: 212-334-2181

PEN American Center, the largest of the 124 centers worldwide that compose International PEN, is a membership association of prominent literary writers and editors. The 2,800 members are poets, playwrights, essayists, editors, and novelists, as well as literary translators and those agents who have made a substantial contribution to the literary community. Among the activities, programs, and services are public literary events, literary awards, outreach projects, and assistance to writers in financial need. Members of American PEN are elected by the Membership Committee. Dues are paid annually.

Poet and Writers, Inc.
72 Spring St.   212-226-3586
New York, NY 10012   Fax: 212-226-3963
                                                   Email: infocenter@pwonline.com

Poets and Writers is a central source of practical information for the Literary community. Their Information Center keeps track of addresses for over 7,000 poets and fiction writers and compiles a Directory of American Poets and Fiction Writers. The Reading/Workshops Program provides matching fees for readings and workshops given by emerging and established writers. The Writers Exchange is a national program that introduces emerging writers to literary communities outside their home state. Poets and Writers is not a membership organization, and therefore, anyone can use their services.

Poets

Poetry Society of America (PSA)
15 Grammercy Park
New York, NY 10003   212-254-9628

The PSA is the nation's oldest poetry organization reaching more people daily with poetry than any other literary organization. Membership is open to everyone. Members are entitled to: enter all PSA contests, discount admission to PSA readings, workshops, the PSA newsletter, program calendars and invitations to readings and events, discounts on book purchases, and vote in PSA elections. Membership fees are tax deductible and range from $25 Student, $40 Member, and can go as high as $1000.

Romance Writers of America (RWA)
13700 Veterans Memorial Dr., Suite 315   713-440-6885
Houston, TX 77014   Fax: 713-440-7510

RWA is dedicated to promoting excellence in romantic fiction. General membership is open to all writers actively pursuing a career in romantic fiction. Associate membership is open to all editors, agents, booksellers, and other industry professionals. Published members are invited to join the Published Authors Network (PAN) for an additional $20 a year. Membership benefits include workshops; networking opportunities with authors, editors, agents and industry professionals; awards; and RWA publications. There is a $10 processing fee for new applicants and annual dues are $60.

Science-Fiction and Fantasy Writers of America, Inc. (SFWA)
5 Winding Brook Dr., #1B
Guilderland, NY 12084-9719   518-869-5361

The SFWA has brought together the most successful and daring writers of speculative fiction throughout the world, and has grown in numbers and influence and is now recognized as one of the most effective nonprofit writers' organizations in existence. Over 1200 SF/Fantasy writers, artists, editors, and allied professionals are members. The SFWA Bulletin, published quarterly, is subscribed to by many non-members. Beginning writers might be particularly interested in its informative market reports and articles about the business of writing and selling science fiction and fantasy. Dues are collected annually.

Society of American Travel Writers
4101 Lake Boone Trail, Suite 201   919-787-5181
Raleigh, NC 27607   Fax: 919-787-4916

The Society of American Travel Writers is a nonprofit, public service organization dedicated to serving the interest of the traveling public, to promote international understanding and good will, and to further promote unbiased, objective reporting of information on travel topics. Membership in the Society is by invitation. Applicants must be sponsored by two members. The initiation fee for Active members is $200 (yearly dues $120), for Associate members $400 (yearly dues $240). A nonrefundable $50 application fee will be applied toward the initiation fee of accepted members.

Society of Children's Book Writers and Illustrators (SCBWI)
22736 Vanowen St., Suite 106
West Hills, CA 91307   818-888-8760

The SCBWI acts as a network for the exchange of knowledge between writers, illustrators, editors, publishers, agents, librarians, educators, bookstore personnel, and others involved with literature for young people. Membership is open to anyone with an active interest in children's literature. Membership dues are $50 per year.

Society of Professional Journalists (SPJ)
16 South Jackson St.
P.O. Box 77   317-653-3333
Greencastle, IN 46135-0077   Fax: 317-653-4631

Society of Professional Journalists (SPJ) membership offers many benefits, including: continuing professional education, career services and support, and journalism advocacy. Membership dues range from $33 to $85.

Washington Independent Writers (WIW)
220 Woodward Building
733 Fifteenth St., N.W.   202-347-4973
Washington, DC 20005   Fax: 202-628-0298

WIW's membership includes recognized writers, writers with a growing number of credits and those who are just beginning their careers in the freelance profession. Membership benefits include: WIW's newsletter , the Independent Writer; the Job Bank; access to Small Groups based on areas of mutual interest; and the availability of a group health insurance plan and a legal services program. Dues are: Students-1yr $55 & 2yr $100; Dual-new members 1yr $160 & 2yr $285; renewing members-1yr $130 & 2yr $240; Full and Associate-new members 1yr $95 & 2yr $1700, current renewing members, 1yr $80 & 2yr $145.

Western Writers of America
1012 Fair St.
Franklin, TN 37064   615-791-1444
                          Internet: http://www.imt.net/-gedison/wwa.html

Western Writers of America (WWA) is an association of professional writers dedicated to preserving and celebrating the heritage of the American West, past and present. For over 40 years, WWA has served both fiction and non-fiction writers recognized for their work in all types of books, periodicals, screenplays, and other media. To be eligible for membership in WWA, you must be published. A subscription to Roundup Magazine is included with membership dues or if you are interested in subscribing to the Roundup Magazine, the cost is six issues a year for $30.

The Writers Alliance
12 Skylark Lane
Stony Brook, NY 11790   516-751-7080

The Writers Alliance is a grass roots support and information network for writers. They have been serving the writing community since 1982, helping writers find publishers, other writers, and learn about specialized programs that will help them reach their goals. With a one year membership ($10) you get a booklet titled The Mini-Guide To Writing for $1. With a two year membership ($17) the Mini-Guide is free and you receive their newsletter, The Backup Street Irregular. For more information, send a self addressed stamped envelope to the address listed above.

Writers Guild of America-East
555 West 57th St.   212-767-7800
New York, NY 10019   Fax: 212-582-1909

Writers Guild Of America-West
700 West 3rd St.
Los Angeles, CA 90048   213-951-4000

Writers Guild of America is a labor union representing professional writers in motion pictures, television, and radio. Membership can be acquired only through the sale of literary material or employment for writing services in one of these areas. There is an initiation fee of $1,500 for new members, basic dues of $100 paid in quarterly installments of $25, and an assessment of 1-11/2 on earnings from the sale of material or from employment as a writer in motion pictures, television, or radio. The Guild also provides a registration service for literary material. Writers are advised to register their material before showing it to a producer or agent.

Money To Be An Artist

Attention Artists!
Over $180,000,000 Available From State Governments

How do most struggling artists perfect their craft? By working alongside masters in their specific craft, and believe it or not, there are money programs administered on the state level to help you do just that. If you are working with an arts group, there are state grants to assist you in organizing special productions, grants that will allow you the resources to travel around the state to represent your art organization, or grants that would allow you to hire people with special capabilities to enhance your productions.

Here's just a sampling of what some states can provide:

- ✦ $2,000 to study music, dance, or storytelling (Alaska)
- ✦ $2,500 for choreographers (California)
- ✦ Money for architects to help school children (Georgia)
- ✦ $5,000 to work with a master artist in their studio (Idaho)
- ✦ $10,000 for creative writers (Idaho)
- ✦ $10,000 for photographers (Illinois)
- ✦ $1,000 for poets (Iowa)
- ✦ $2,000 for art teachers to attend a workshop (Maine)
- ✦ $150 a day for artists who can spend two days a week at a local school (Massachusetts)

- ✦ $10,000 to put on a program of poetry readings (Nebraska)
- ✦ $8,000 for dancers (North Carolina)
- ✦ $500 for writers to attend a workshop (North Carolina)
- ✦ $10,000 for art critics (North Dakota)
- ✦ $2,000 to put on an arts festival (Oklahoma)
- ✦ $5,000 for printmakers (Texas)
- ✦ $500 to writers on a first-come first-served basis (Virginia)

Eligibility Requirements

Almost every state requires that you be a state resident to receive money through these programs. The exceptions to this rule are often found in those programs where the state will pay an artist from another state to come to work with school children within their state. Eligibility requirements for all programs vary greatly. Some states, like Pennsylvania, require that you have lived in the state for two years and have three years of professional experience. States like Rhode Island require that you are at least 18 years of age and have resided in the state for at least one year. With residency requirements being as minimal as one year, it may be worth looking for a state that has some specific programs that interest you, and then establish residency there.

What Are Your Chances?

Remember, you have to play to win, and your chances of winning and receiving these funds will be slightly different for each of the programs listed. For instance, Virginia has a program that gives out money on a first-come first-served basis. So, if your application is the first received, your chances of success are 100 percent. Vermont, on the other hand, has one of the more competitive programs that awards funds to only approximately 5% of their applicants. Whatever your chances, remember that each year the money has to be awarded to someone, and your chances will be just plain zero if you don't apply!

How To Work With Arts Organizations

A lot of the state money programs are awarded to art organizations. Therefore, if you have trouble getting money as an individual, it may be worth your time to find an art organization to collaborate with or perhaps become your own art organization. Your state arts council can help you locate organizations that may be willing (and even eager) to work with you in order to be awarded this grant money. Talk to your local community college, community group, or even your church about joining together to win funding. You might make an arrangement where you share the proceeds of the program if you win, and both you and the community group lose nothing if your efforts are unsuccessful.

Some of the money given to organizations requires matching grants in order to receive the funding. A matching grant requires that the recipient raise funds in some proportion to the amount awarded. This may not be as difficult as it sounds because oftentimes, in-kind goods and services may be used as matching grants. An in-kind contribution of goods is an offering of any tangible, useable item that the organization would have otherwise had to purchase. An in-kind contribution of a service includes intangible contributions such as donations of volunteer time, or the use of facilities or equipment.

For more information, contact your State Arts Council located in your state capitol. Your state information operator listed in the Appendix can help you.

Money To Travel

If your dream is to become an international jet setter, don't let a little problem like money stand in your way. The Federal government has over 60 programs devoted to travel within the U.S. and abroad, spending over 65 million dollars a year to send you packing. They will even pay to have foreign relatives come and study here. No matter if you are 16 or 65, there is something in these programs for everyone.

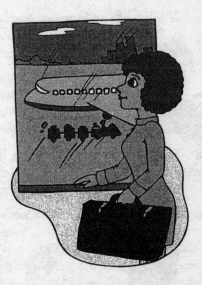

You can be like:

- Cowboy artists from the Western Folklife Center of Elko, NV who shared their lore at a festival in Melbourne, Australia with a grant from the National Endowment for the Arts.

- Nancy Friese of Cranston, RI who went to Japan for six months to explore relationships between natural and man-made environments in Japanese landscape gardens through the United States/Japan Artist Exchange Program at the Japan/US Friendship Commission.

- Carl A. Chase, a steel drum maker and tuner from Brooksville, MA who was able to visit Trinidad and Tobago for a residency with one of the islands' foremost steel drum makers through the Travel Grants Program at the National Endowment for the Arts.

- ♣ William Ulfelder who spent a year studying the rain forest in Costa Rica as a Fulbright Scholar.

- ♣ A police officer from Los Angeles who helped in the creation of D.A.R.E. (Drug Awareness Resistance Education) in several Latin American countries through the U.S. Thematic Programs.

- ♣ Piano/violin duo Susan Keith and Laura Kobayashi who toured Latin America and the Caribbean together as Artistic Ambassadors for the U.S. Information Agency.

- ♣ Tamara Astor from Northfield, IL who spent a year teaching grades 1-3 in London, England through the Fulbright Teacher Exchange Program at the U.S. Information Agency.

- ♣ Central Washington University who sent thirteen K-12

teachers from the state of Washington to Chile for a four-week seminar on the country through the Fulbright-Hays Group Projects Abroad through the U.S. Department of Education.

- ♣ Columbia University in New York City acting as the host of seven different humanities seminars for college teachers with grants from the National Endowment for the Humanities.

- ♣ Maria Marotti from Santa Barbara, CA who was awarded a $3,000 grant from the National Endowment for the Humanities to study Italian feminism.

Money To Travel Abroad And Share Your Expertise
(U.S. Thematic Programs)

U.S. Thematic Programs
U.S. Information Agency
301 4th St., SW
Washington, DC 20547
202-619-4764
http://www.usia.gov
In response to requests from posts overseas, USIA sends approximately 600
Americans abroad annually for short-term speaking programs. The U.S.
Thematic Program is one of the principal vehicles for fostering discussion on
major issues with overseas audiences. Experts are usually in the fields of
economics, international affairs, U.S. political and social processes, sports, or
science and technology. A U.S. Speaker's tour generally includes informal
lectures or discussions, followed by questions and answers with a small group
of experts. The total amount of money available is $1.1 million. Contact the
office listed above for an informational brochure.

HIGH SCHOOL STUDENTS AND TEACHERS CAN VISIT RUSSIA
(Secondary School Exchange Initiative)

U.S. Information Agency
E/PY Room 320
301 4th St., SW
Washington, DC 20547
202-619-6299
Fax: 202-619-5331
http://www.usia.gov
Email: exchanges@usia.gov

The program objective is to sponsor
the exchange of high school students
and teachers between the U.S. and the
former Soviet Union through grants to
private not-for-profit organizations and public institutions. Grants are awarded
to fund projects in four program areas: academic year in the U.S.; semester in

the U.S. and in the NIS; short-term exchanges of groups of students and teachers between linked schools; and short-term thematic projects. The total amount of money available is $31.5 million. Contact the office listed above for information on organizations to which you need to apply or for more information on the programs available.

Spend A Year In Europe On A Mid-Career Break
(Hubert Humphrey Fellowship)

Hubert H. Humphrey Fellowship Program
Institute of International Education
1400 K St., NW, Suite 650
Washington, DC 20005-2403
202-619-5289
202-898-0600
Fax: 202-401-1433
Fax: 202-842-1219

FOREIGN HIGH SCHOOL TEACHERS CAN SPEND SIX WEEKS IN THE U.S.
(Study Of The United States)

Study of the US Division
U.S. Information Agency
301 4th St., SW, Room 252
Washington, DC 20547
202-619-4557
http://www.usia.gov
Email: exchanges@usia.gov

This program provides grants to foreign secondary school educators for a 4 to 6 week program of academic workshops in U.S. history, culture, and institutions to enhance and update the content of what is taught about the United States abroad. The total amount of money available is $1.6 million. Contact the office listed above for guidelines and application information.

The program provides opportunities for accomplished mid-career professionals from developing countries, East and Central Europe, and the former Soviet Union to come to the United States for a year of study and related practical professional experiences. The program provides a basis for establishing lasting ties between citizens of the United States and their professional counterparts in other countries, fostering an exchange of knowledge and mutual understanding throughout the world. Fellows are placed in groups at selected U.S. universities and designed individualized programs of academic coursework and professional development activities. The total amount of money available is $5 million. Applications must be submitted in the candidates' home countries to the United States Information Service Posts or Fulbright Commissions. Applicants must have an undergraduate degree, five years of substantial professional experience, demonstrated leadership qualities, and fluency in English. Contact the office listed above for more information on the application process.

Money For Artists, Filmmakers, Playwrights, And Museum Professionals To Go Overseas
(Creative Arts Exchanges)

Creative Arts Exchanges Division (E/DE)
Office of Arts America
U.S. Information Agency
301 4th St., SW
Washington, DC 20547
202-205-8362
http://www.usia.gov
Email: jdorsey@usia.gov

The program supports projects by U.S. nonprofit organizations for exchanges of professionals in the arts and museum fields. Priority is given to institutionally-based projects involving artists in the creation of their particular art forms and projects which will lead to institutional linkages. Two way exchanges are encouraged and cost sharing is required. This exchange program is designed to introduce American and foreign participants to each other's cultural and artistic life and traditions. It also supports international projects in the United States or overseas involving composers, choreographers, filmmakers, playwrights, theater designers, writers and poets, visual artists, museum professionals, and more. The program operates through biannual

Federal Register requests for proposals. For more information on the application process and program eligibility, contact the office listed above.

Money For Students, Teachers, Bankers, Lawyers, And Journalists To Travel Overseas
(Fulbright Scholar Program)

Council for International Exchange of Scholars
3007 Tilden St., NW, Suite 5M
Box GBRO
Washington, DC 20008-3009
202-686-4000
Fax: 202-362-3442
Email: cies1@ciesnet.cies.org
The program provides grants to U.S. students, teachers, and scholars to study, teach, lecture, and conduct research overseas, and to foreign nationals to engage in similar activities in the United States to increase mutual understanding and peaceful relations between the people of the United States and the people of other countries. Fields of study and subjects taught include the arts and humanities, social sciences, and physical sciences. In addition to the exchange of students and scholars, the program includes professional exchanges in journalism, law, management, banking, and public administration. Participants take part in degree programs, nondegree and self-study courses, internships, and professional seminars. The total amount of money available is $108 million. Contact the office listed above for application information.

Librarians Can Spend A Year Abroad Checking Out Foreign Books
(Library Fellows Program)

American Library Association
Attn. Carol Erickson
50 E. Huron St.
Chicago, IL 60611
312-280-3200

Fax: 312-280-3256
http://www.ala.org
The program places U.S. library professionals in institutions overseas for periods of four months to a year to: increase international understanding through the establishment of professional and personal relationships and the accomplishment of mutual goals; promote international sharing of resources; and increase access to U.S. materials in the host country. Individual grants are approximately $34,000 per year. The program is administered by the American Library Association. For more information on the application process, contact the office listed above.

TEACH SCHOOL OVERSEAS
(Dependent Schools)

U.S. Department of Defense
Teacher Recruitment Section
4040 N. Fairfax Dr.
Arlington, VA 22203-1634
703-696-3058
Fax: 703-696-2695
The U.S. Department of Defense is responsible for providing schooling to dependent children of military personnel. There are employment positions for elementary and secondary teachers, as well as those that can provide support services. The schools are located in 19 countries around the world, with an enrollment of approximately 100,000 students, and are staffed with 13,000 employees. Contact the office listed above for an application and program information.

Money For English, Law, And Journalism Teachers To Go Abroad
(Academic Specialist)

Office of Academic Programs
U.S. Information Agency
301 4th St., SW, Room 238
Washington, DC 20547
202-205-0525
http://www.usia.gov
Email: exchanges@usia.gov
This program sends American academics overseas in response to requests relayed by USIA posts from foreign institutions seeking professional assistance

in such academic disciplines as English teaching, law, and journalism. Experts on the United States can consult with academic and professionals at foreign educational or other relevant institutions about special issues, or to conduct seminars/workshops for professional personnel. The total amount of money available is $1.3 million. Contact the office listed above for guidelines and application information.

EXCHANGE PROGRAM FOR ENGLISH TEACHERS
(English Teaching Fellow)

English Teaching Program Division
U.S. Information Agency (USIA)
301 4th St., SW, Room 304
Washington, DC 20547
202-619-5869
Fax: 202-401-1250
http://www.usia.gov

$20,000 TO STUDY FARMING INTERNATIONALLY
(International Collaborative Research Program)

U.S. Department of Agriculture
International Collaborative Research Program
USDA/OICD/RSED
Ag Box 4314
Room 3230 South Building
14th and Independence Ave., SW
Washington, DC 20250
202-720-7481
Fax: 202-690-1955

This program enables American scientists to work with foreign researchers on projects aimed at potential threats to U.S. agriculture, technology development, and opportunities to enhance trade in foreign markets. Up to $20,000 a year for one to three years is available for each researcher. Contact the office listed above for an application form. U.S. researchers from USDA agencies, universities, and private nonprofit agricultural research institutions are eligible.

Email: exchanges@usia.gov
The program promotes the study and teaching of English abroad, in host country institutions, and through American educational and binational centers in 100 countries. USIA English teaching programs concentrate on training teachers through seminars, exchanges of foreign and American English specialists, and the development and distribution of curricula and materials for teaching the English language and American culture. The total amount of money available is $915,000. Contact the office listed above for application information.

Volunteer In The U.S.
(Corporation for National Service)

(AMERICORPS - 94.006)
Corporation for National Service
1201 New York Ave. NW
Washington, DC 20525
800-942-2677
202-606-5000
http://www.cns.gov
The objective of this program is to supplement efforts of private, nonprofit organizations and federal, state, and local government agencies to eliminate poverty and poverty-related problems by enabling persons from all walks of life and all age groups to perform meaningful and constructive service as volunteers throughout the U.S. Americorps volunteers receive a modest subsistence allowance, an end-of-service stipend, health insurance, and money for college. The total amount of money available is $32,250,000. Applications are available through Americorps State Offices, or contact the office listed above for additional information.

Money to Study Agriculture in Israel
(U.S. - Israel Binational Agriculture Research and Development Fund (BARD)

U.S. Department of Agriculture, Barc-West
Binational Agriculture Research and Development Fund (BARD),
Lynn Gipe
Agriculture Research Service

Building 005, Room 102
Beltsville, MD 20705
301-504-5605
Fax: 301-504-5298
The Binational Agriculture Research and Development Fund promotes
cooperative agriculture research between postdoctoral fellows from the U.S.
and Israel to provide BARD with input into new research areas and to enhance
scientific competence in these areas. The money available is $3,000 per month
and one roundtrip air ticket. To learn more about the program or application
process, contact the office listed above.

Your Friends In The Ukraine Can Come To The U.S. To Learn Free Enterprise
(Special American Business Internship Training Program (SABIT))

U.S. Department of Commerce
International Trade Administration
Special American Business Internship Training Program
Room 3319
Washington, DC 20230
202-482-0073
http://www.doc.gov
This program awards internships in U.S. firms to business managers and
scientific workers from the newly
independent states of the former Soviet
Union. SABIT provides the intern with a
hands-on training program in the
business skills necessary to operate
in a market economy. A counselor is
provided to help with cultural
adjustments. Companies provide
medical insurance, housing, and any
other living expenses beyond those
covered by the daily stipend
provided by the U.S. The amount of money available varies. Apply to the
program through the U.S. Department of Commerce which considers
applications through a competitive process. A SABIT fact sheet is also
available.

Money For Students And Teachers To Travel Together Overseas
(Fulbright-Hays Group Projects Abroad - 84.021)

Office of International Studies Branch
Center for International Education
U.S. Department of Education
600 Independence Ave. SW
Washington, DC 20202-5332
202-401-9798
Fax: 202-205-9489
http://www.ed.gov
This program is designed to contribute to the development and improvement of
the study of modern foreign languages and area studies in the United States,
and provide opportunities for American teachers, advanced students, and
faculty to study in foreign countries. Grants allow groups to conduct overseas
group projects in research, training, and curriculum development. Money can
be used for international travel, maintenance allowances, rent of instructional

$4,000 To Study Overseas
(Scientific Cooperation Program - 10.963)

Ms. Helen Neil
USDA/FAS/ICD/RSED
Room 3230, South Building
14th St. and Independence Ave. SW
Washington, DC 20250
202-690-1955
Fax: 202-720-3282
Email: hneil@ag.gov
This program promotes international cooperation in agriculture and
forestry to attain mutual benefit through short-term (one to four
week) exchange visits of U.S. scientists. Proposals should involve the
collection of unique resources, acquisition of special research,
conservation or production techniques, field work on problems facing
U.S. agriculture, or development of future, long-term research.
Contact the office listed above for guidelines and an application
packet.

materials in the country of study, and more. The total amount of money available is $2.1 million. Contact the office listed above for application information.

Finish Your Doctorate Research Abroad
(Fulbright-Hays Doctoral Dissertation Research Abroad - 84.002)

Advanced Training and Research Branch
Center for International Education
Office of Assistant Secretary for Postsecondary Education
U.S. Department of Education
600 Independence Ave. SW
Washington, DC 20202-5332
202-401-9774
Fax: 202-205-9489
http://www.ed.gov
This program is designed to provide opportunities for graduate students to engage in full-time dissertation research abroad in modern foreign language and area studies with the exception of Western Europe. This program is designed to develop research knowledge and capability in world areas not widely included in American curricula. Money can be used for a basic stipend, round trip air fare, baggage allowance, tuition payments, local travel, and more. The total amount of money available is $1.8 million. Candidates apply directly to the institutions at which they are enrolled in a Ph.D. program.

Money For College Teachers To Do Research Overseas
(Fulbright-Hays Faculty Research Abroad - 84.019)

Advanced Training and Research Branch
Center for International Education
Office of Assistant Secretary for Postsecondary Education
U.S. Department of Education
600 Independence Ave., SW

Washington, DC 20202-5331
202-401-9777
Fax: 202-205-9489
http://www.ed.gov
This program is designed to help develop modern foreign language and area studies in U.S. higher educational institutions. This program enables faculty members to maintain expertise in specialized fields through support of research in the non-Western areas of the world. Fellowships of 3 to 12 months are available. The total amount of money available is $810,000. Candidates should apply directly to their institution. More information is available on this program through the office listed above.

Money For Teachers To Take A Sabbatical Overseas
(Fulbright-Hays Seminars Abroad - 84.018)

International Studies Branch
Center for International Education
Office of Assistant Secretary for Postsecondary Education
U.S. Department of Education
600 Independence Ave., SW
Washington, DC 20202-5332
202-401-9798
Fax: 202-205-9489
http://www.ed.gov
This program is designed to improve modern foreign language and area studies by providing 3 to 8 week summer seminars abroad for high school and elementary school teachers in foreign languages, social sciences and humanities, administrators, and curriculum specialists of state and local education agencies, and college faculty who are primarily responsible for teaching undergraduates in the social sciences, humanities, and international affairs. The total amount  of money available is $940,000. Contact the office listed above for application information, as well as a listing of the seminars available.

Grants To College Teachers Who Want To Create Programs In International Business
(Business And International Education - 84.153)

International Studies Branch
Center for International Education
U.S. Department of Education
600 Independence Ave., SW
Washington, DC 20202-5332
202-401-9778
Fax: 202-205-9489
http://www.ed.gov

This program is designed to promote innovation and improvement in international business education curricula at institutions of higher education and promote linkages between these institutions and the business community. Institutions must enter into an agreement with a business enterprise, trade organization, or association engaged in international economic activity, or a combination or consortium of the named entities. The total amount of money available is $3,329,000. Contact the office listed above for application information.

Conduct Health Research In Eastern Europe
(U.S.-Central and Eastern European Scientist Exchanges)

Program Officer
U.S.-Central and Eastern European Scientist Exchanges
Fogarty International Center
Building 31C, Room B2C35
National Institutes of Health
Bethesda, MD 20892
301-496-4784
Fax: 301-480-3414
http://www.nih.gov

This program is designed to promote contacts and cooperation between well-qualified health professionals and biomedical scientists in the United States and participating countries, and to stimulate relations that show a promise of becoming long-term and self-supporting. The programs provide support for visits to conduct short-term collaborative research or to develop collaborative research activities. Exchanges are with the countries of Bulgaria, Hungary, Poland, Romania, Russia, and Mongolia with most requiring an advanced degree in the health sciences or a related field. Contact the office listed above for application forms, including instructions and other requirements.

Visit The U.S. To Do Health Research
(NIH Visiting Program)

Public Inquiries
Office of Communications
National Institutes of Health (NIH)
Building 31, Room 2B03
Bethesda, MD 20892
301-496-4335
http://www.nih.gov

This program provides talented scientists throughout the world with the opportunity to participate in the varied research activities of the National Institutes of Health. There are three categories of Visiting Program participants: Visiting Fellows, Visiting Associates, and Visiting Scientists. Each participant works closely with a senior NIH investigator who serves as supervisor or sponsor during the period of award or appointment. The Visiting Fellow award is for obtaining research training experience. Fellows must have a doctoral degree, not more than 3 years of relevant postdoctoral research experience, and cannot be U.S. citizens. Visiting Associates and Visiting Scientists are appointed to conduct health-related research and are considered employees of NIH, and receive a salary and benefits. Individuals interested in a Visiting Program fellowship award or appointment should write to NIH senior scientists working in the same research field, enclosing a resume and brief description of his/her particular research area. Information about the research being conducted by NIH scientists and their names may be obtained from the NIH's Scientific Directory and Annual Bibliography, which can be obtained from the office listed above.

Get An Invitation To Do Research Overseas
(Foreign Funded Fellowships For U.S. Scientists)

International Research and Awards Branch
Fogarty International Center
National Institutes of Health
Building 31, Room B2C39
Bethesda, MD 20892
301-496-1653
Fax: 301-402-0779
http://www.nih.gov
Email: m3p@cu.nih.gov

This program provides for international opportunities for research experience and exchange of information in the biomedical and behavioral science. Under these programs, U.S. scientists are invited by foreign host scientists to participate in research projects of mutual interest. Support for U.S. scientists is offered by 10 countries to conduct research in their laboratories. Information and application instructions are available from the office listed above.

New Researchers Abroad Can Use U.S. Facilities
(International Research Fellowships)

International Research Fellowship Program
Fogarty International Center
Building 31, Room B2C39
National Institutes of Health
9000 Rockville Pike
Bethesda, MD 20892
301-496-1653
Fax: 301-402-0779
http://www.nih.gov
Email: m3p@cu.nih.gov

This program provides opportunities for foreign postdoctoral biomedical or behavioral scientists who are in the formative stages of their career to extend their research experience in a laboratory in the United States. The total amount of money available is $4.4 million. To learn more about the requirements and application process, contact the office listed above.

SENIOR SCIENTISTS CAN STUDY ABROAD
(Senior International Fellowship Program)

Senior International Fellowship Program
Fogarty International Center
Building 31, Room B2C39
National Institutes of Health
Bethesda, MD 20892
301-496-1653
Fax: 301-402-2056
http://www.nih.gov
This program provides opportunities for study or research in a foreign
institution to biomedical, behavioral, or health scientists who have established
themselves in their chosen careers in the United States. The Fellowship
enhances the exchange of ideas and information about the latest advances in the
health sciences, including basic, clinical and public health sciences; permits
U.S. scientists to participate abroad in ongoing study or research in the health
sciences; and improves the research, education, and clinical potential of the
fellow's institution. The total amount of money available is $1.2 million.
Information and special application kits can be requested from the office listed
above.

Research Internationally
(International Opportunities In The Health Sciences and Biomedical Research Through The National Institutes Of Health)

International Research and Awards Branch
Fogarty International Center
Building 31, Room B2C39
National Institutes of Health
Bethesda, MD 20892
301-496-1653
Fax: 301-402-0779
Internet: http://www.nih.gov
Email: m3p@cu.nih.gov

This program provides for a variety of exchange and collaboration programs with specific countries. Length of exchange varies, with each program focusing on a specific area of research such as AIDS, neurology, genome research, and more. Many programs focus on bringing foreign researchers to the U.S. to collaborate with scientists. Contact the office listed above to learn about specific exchanges and fellowships available in your area of expertise and the application procedure. NIH also publishes a *Directory Of International Grants And Fellowships In The Health Sciences* book.

A CARIBBEAN WORKING VACATION
(Field Research Program at the Master's and Doctoral Level)

IAF Fellowship Programs
901 North Stuart St., 10th Floor
Arlington, VA 22203
703-841-3830
Fax: 703-527-3529
This program supports dissertation field research in Latin America and the Caribbean on grassroots development topics by doctoral students enrolled in U.S. universities. The total amount of money available is $14,000-16,000 each for doctoral candidates, and $2,000-3,000 each for Master's level students. Contact the office listed above for more information on program eligibility and application requirements.

$30,000 To Study In The U.S. For Latin American and Caribbean Citizens
(U.S. Graduate Study Program for Latin American and Caribbean Citizens)

IAF Fellowship Programs
901 North Stuart St., 10th Floor
Arlington, VA 22203
703-841-3800
Fax: 703-527-3529

This program assists development practitioners and applied researchers from these regions to pursue graduate studies in the United States. Each fellow may receive up to $30,000 for a maximum of two years. Contact the office listed above for more information on program eligibility and application requirements.

MONEY TO STUDY IN JAPAN
(Japan-U.S. Friendship Commission Grants)

Japan-U.S. Friendship Commission
1120 Vermont Ave., NW, Suite 925
Washington, DC 20005
202-275-7712
Fax: 202-275-7413
Email: 72133.2433@
compuserve.com
This program provides grants to institutions and associations to support American studies in Japan, Japanese studies in the United States, exchange programs in the arts, policy-oriented research, and public affairs, and education. In addition, the Commission is interested in sponsoring research on Japan-US economic relations and activities in Asia, with priority given to Japanese investment in Asia and its effect on Japan-US economic, trade and political relations. The total amount of money available is $2.7 million. Contact the office listed above for more information about the various grant programs, as well as a biennial report which lists previous grants recipients and their projects.

$50,000 To Latin American Leaders
(Dante B. Fascell Inter-American Fellowship Program)

IAF Fellowship Programs
901 North Stuart St., 10th Floor
Arlington, VA 22203
703-841-3800
Fax: 703-527-3529
This program supports development dissemination by distinguished Latin American and Caribbean leaders. Fellowships provide outstanding men and women with financial support for reflection upon, analysis, and dissemination of their successful experiences to wide audiences across the hemisphere. The total amount of money available is $50,000. Contact the office listed above for more information on program eligibility and application requirements.

MONEY FOR ARTISTS AND PERFORMERS TO TRAVEL OVERSEAS
(Fund For U.S. Artists at International Festival and Exhibits)

International Program USIA-E/DV
301 4th St., SW
Washington, DC 20547
202-619-4808
http://www.usia.gov
This program provides grants to assist individual U.S. performers of U.S. performing arts groups who have been invited to international festivals abroad, and who need additional support to make their performances possible. Travel, per diem, international communications, shipping, and salary expense related to participation in the international festival are among eligible costs supported through the Fund. The Fund is particularly interested in receiving proposals which reflect the cultural and regional diversity of the United States and which involve events in areas of the world where U.S. work is rarely performed. The total amount of money available is $437,000. Contact the office listed above for guidelines and an application packet.

Money For Artists To Work With the Newly Independent States
(Artslink)

CEC International Partners
12 West 31st St.
New York, NY 10001-4415
212-643-1985
Fax: 212-643-1996
http://arts.endow.gov
Email: cecny@igc.apc.org
Artslink encourages artistic exchange with the newly independent states in Central and Eastern Europe, the former Soviet Union, and the Baltics by offering two categories of support: Artslink Collaborative Projects, which provides funding to U.S. artists to work on mutually beneficial projects with counterparts abroad, and Artslink Residencies, which supports U.S. arts

organizations wishing to host a visiting artist or arts manager for a five-week residency. The total amount of money available varies. Contact the office listed above for guidelines and an application packet.

Artists Can Travel To Improve Their Art
(Travel Grants Fund For Artists)

Arts International
Institute of International Education
809 United Nations Plaza
New York, NY 10017
212-984-5370
Fax: 212-984-5574
http://www.iie.org.ai
Email: ainternational@iie.org

This program is designed to enable U.S. artists to pursue opportunities abroad that further their artistic development. Grant decisions will be based on artistic excellence, the applicant's reasons for wanting to travel to a particular country, as well as his or her sensitivity to the culture and country to which he or she

Go To Japan For 6 Months
(United States/Japan Creative Artists' Program)

Japan-U.S. Friendship Commission
1120 Vermont Ave., NW, Suite 925
Washington, DC 20005
202-275-7712
Fax: 202-275-7413
Email: 72133.2433@compuserve.com

The program is designed to allow artists who create original work to pursue their individual artistic goals and interests by living in Japan for six months, observing developments in their field, and meeting with their professional counterparts in Japan. The total amount of money available is $200,000. Contact the office listed above for guidelines and an application packet.

wants to travel. The grants will support artists pursuing a wide variety of activities abroad including the development or expansion of relationships with artists and arts organizations and the exploration of significant developments in their field. The total amount of money available is $100,000. Contact the office listed above for guidelines and an application packet.

Link Up With The Arts Community From Behind The Old Iron Curtain
(ArtsLink)

Citizen Exchange Council
12 West 31st St.
New York, NY 10001
212-643-1985
Fax: 212-643-1996
Arts Link enables U.S. artists and arts organizations to work collaboratively with their counterparts, both in this country and in the former bloc countries of Central Europe, Eastern Europe, the former Soviet Union, and the Baltics. The Program has two primary components: ArtsLink Collaborative Projects supports U.S. artists working in the former bloc countries on collaborative projects. ArtsLink Residencies provides matching funds to U.S. organizations interested in hosting an artist or arts administrator from the former bloc countries for a five-week residency in the United States. Contact the office listed above for guidelines and an application packet.

Artists Can Get Money To Go International
(Fund for U.S. Artists at International Festivals and Exhibitions)

Institute of International Education
International Partnerships
Office of the National Endowment for the Arts
809 United National Plaza
New York, NY 10017
212-984-5370

Fax: 212-984-5774
http://arts.endow.gov
Email: the fund@iie.org
The Funds for U.S. Artists at International Festivals and Exhibitions support performing artists who have been invited to an international festival and to support U.S. representation at major international contemporary visual arts exhibitions. Through grants to curators or visual arts organizations, the Fund supports the U.S. presence at the major visual arts biennials in Venice, Sao Paulo, and Sydney. It also funds American participation in contemporary arts exhibitions in venues where U.S. work is rarely seen, such as Cairo, Egypt; Cuenca, Ecuador; Istanbul, Turkey and Dakar, Senegal. The total amount of money available is $321,000. Contact the office listed above for guidelines and an application packet.

HUMANITIES RESEARCH
(Interpretive Research - 45.140)

Division of Research Programs
National Endowment for the Humanities
1100 Pennsylvania Ave., NW
Room 318
Washington, DC 20506
202-606-8210
Fax: 202-606-8204
http://www.neh.fed.us
Email: research@neh.fed.us
Grants provide support for scholarly research and interpretation that will advance knowledge and enhance the understanding of humanities. Multi-year collaborative projects entail the close cooperation of two or more scholars investigating topics of broad-ranging significance to the humanities. Archaeology projects that promise to enhance understanding of history and culture are eligible. Grants can be for periods of up to three years. Awards normally range from $10,000 to $250,000 over a maximum grant period of three years. Contact the office listed above for guidelines and applications information.

SUMMER SEMINARS FOR TEACHERS
(Summer Seminars For Teachers - 45.151)

Division of Fellowships and Seminars
National Endowment for the Humanities
1100 Pennsylvania Ave., NW, Room 316
Washington, DC 20506
202-606-8463
Fax: 202-606-8204
http://www.neh.fed.us
Email: research@neh.fed.us
Schoolteachers, principals, and other educators from kindergarten through 12th grade, along with selected foreign secondary teachers, can engage in intensive study of basic humanities texts and documents and work closely with outstanding scholars for 4 to 6 weeks at colleges, universities, and other appropriate sites, some of which may be located in a foreign country. Contact the office listed above for a list of seminar offerings, as well as an application packet.

Travel Abroad To Study History
(International Research - 45.148)

Division of Research Programs
National Endowment for the Humanities
1100 Pennsylvania Ave., NW, Room 318
Washington, DC 20506
202-606-8210
Fax: 202-606-8204
http://www.neh.fed.us
Email: research@neh.fed.us
This program provides grants to national organizations and learned societies that have expertise in the promotion of research on foreign cultures. Grants made by these centers and organizations with the Endowment's assistance enable American scholars to pursue research in the United States and abroad on foreign cultures and to collaborate with foreign colleagues. Individuals apply directly to sponsoring organizations. To find out more information regarding this program and the organizations involved, contact the office listed above.

Money For Teachers To Study
(Summer Stipends - 45.121)

Division of Fellowships and Seminars
National Endowment for the Humanities
1100 Pennsylvania Ave., NW, Room 316
Washington, DC 20506
202-606-8466
Fax: 202-606-8204
http://www.neh.fed.us
Email: research@neh.fed.us
Grants provide support for college and university teachers; individuals
employed by schools, museums, libraries, etc.; and others to undertake full-
time independent study and research in the humanities for two consecutive
summer months. Applicants whose projects require significant travel to
libraries, archives, or other collections may also apply for a travel supplement
to the stipend. Contact the office listed above for guidelines and an application
packet.

Grants For Humanities Teachers To Travel In The Summer
(Summer Seminars For College Teachers - 45.116)

Division of Fellowships and Seminars
National Endowment for the Humanities
1100 Pennsylvania Ave., NW, Room 321
Washington, DC 20506
202-606-8463
Fax: 202-606-8204
http://www.neh.fed.us
Email: research@neh.fed.us
This program provides teachers at undergraduate colleges and universities and
other qualified individuals not affiliated with an academic institution the
opportunity to study at major research institutions with eminent scholars in
their own or related fields. Contact the office listed above for guidelines and an
application packet. They can also provide you with a list of seminar offerings.

$30,000 To Study And Conduct Research
(Fellowships for College Teachers and Independent Scholars)

Division of Fellowships and Seminars
National Endowment for the Humanities
1100 Pennsylvania Ave., NW, Room 316
Washington, DC 20506
202-606-8466
Fax: 202-606-8204
http://www.neh.fed.us
Email: research@neh.fed.us

Grants provide support for teachers in two-year, four-year, and five-year colleges and universities that do not grant the Ph.D.; for individuals employed by schools, museums, libraries, etc.; and also for independent scholars and writers to undertake full-time independent study and research in the humanities. The maximum amount of stipend is $30,000 each. Contact the office listed above for guidelines and an application packet.

media projects
(Humanities Projects In The Media)

Division of Public Programs
National Endowment for the Humanities
1100 Pennsylvania Ave., NW
Washington, DC 20506
202-606-8267
Fax: 202-606-8557
http://www.neh.fed.us
Email: publicpgms@neh.fed.us

Grants support the planning, writing, or production of television and radio programs in the humanities intended for general audiences. The collaboration of scholars in the humanities with experienced producers, writers, and directors is required. The Endowment is particularly interested in applications for television and radio projects on the lives of historically significant Americans. Travel is included in the grant. Contact the office listed above for guidelines and an application packet.

Become A Humanities Fellow
(Fellowships At Centers for Advanced Study)

Division of Research Programs
National Endowment for the Humanities
1100 Pennsylvania Ave., NW
Room 318
Washington, DC 20506
202-606-8210
Fax: 202-606-8204
http://www.neh.fed.us
Email: research@neh.fed.us
Grants support postdoctoral fellowship programs at independent centers for advanced study which offer scholars opportunities to pursue independent research in the humanities while benefiting from collegial association with scholars in other areas or disciplines of study. Fellowships in this program are awarded and administered by the centers themselves. Tenure of the fellowships may run from six to twelve consecutive months, and stipends vary at the different centers. Eligibility also varies from center to center, but neither candidates for degrees nor persons seeking support for work toward degrees are eligible to apply. Contact the office listed above for more information on theses programs, as well as a list of centers which accept applications.

Foreign Language Study For K-12 Teachers
(NEH Fellowship Program For Foreign Language Teachers K-12)

NEH Fellowship Program for FL Teachers K-12
Connecticut College
270 Mohegan Ave.
New London, CT 06320
860-439-2282
Fax: 860-469-5341

This program is designed to support elementary and secondary school foreign language teachers by providing fellowships. Fellowships of $3,750 are intended to support six weeks of summer study abroad, designed to enhance teacher knowledge and confidence in the classroom. Contact the office listed above for application information.

Fellowships For University Teachers
(Fellowship for University Teachers)

Division of Fellowships and Seminars
National Endowment for the Humanities
1100 Pennsylvania Ave., NW, Room 316
Washington, DC 20506
202-606-8467
Fax: 202-606-8204
http://www.neh.fed.us
Email: research@neh.fed.us
This program offers faculty members (and retirees) of Ph.D.-granting

Money For K-12 Teachers To Travel During The Summer To Study The Humanities
(Independent Study In The Humanities - 45.151)

Independent Study In The Humanities
P.O. Box 135
Ashton, MD 20861
202-347-4171
Fax: 202-347-5047
This program offers teachers, librarians, and principals a summer in which to engage in sustained scholarly independent study of humanities topics of their own choosing. This program provides teachers an opportunity for intellectual and professional growth. Fellowships are from 4-6 weeks. Fellows can choose to study anything within the field of humanities, and can study where they find the most sources — libraries, universities, museums, or in their own home. Stipends range from $2,100-$3,200. Contact the office listed above for application information.

universities the opportunity to undertake 6 to 12 months of full-time independent study and research in the humanities. Fellowships provide opportunities for individuals to pursue advanced work that will enhance their capacities as teachers, scholars, or interpreters of the humanities. Fellowships are intended for a range of individuals, from those who stand at the beginning of their careers to those who have made significant contributions to the humanities. The maximum stipend is $30,000. Contact the office listed above for guidelines and application information.

Scientific Collaboration
(Research Collaboration Between U.S. and Foreign Scientists and Engineers)

International Programs Division
National Science Foundation
4201 Wilson Blvd., Room 935
Arlington, VA 22230
703-306-1710
Fax: 703-306-0476
http://www.nsf.gov
Email: info@nsf.gov
This program is designed to advance and benefit U.S. interests by enabling U.S. scientists and engineers to avail themselves of research opportunities in other countries. The Division of International Programs supports efforts to initiate international cooperation involving new foreign collaborators, or new types of activities with established partners. Contact the office listed above for guidelines and application information.

Spend Your Summer In Japan
(Summer Institute In Japan)

International Programs Division
National Science Foundation
4201 Wilson Blvd., Room 935
Arlington, VA 22230
703-306-1701
Fax: 703-306-0474
http://www.nsf.gov

Email: intpubs@nsf.gov
The objective of this program is to introduce U.S. graduate students to
Japanese science and engineering in the context of a research laboratory and to
initiate personal relationships that will better enable the students to collaborate
with Japanese partners in the future. The total amount of money available is
$231,000. Contact the office listed above for application procedures and
requirements.

Teachers Can Study The Classics In Italy
(Fulbright Teacher Exchange Program)

Research In The Tropics
(Short-Term Fellowships)

Office of Education
Smithsonian Tropical Research
Institute
Unit 0948
APO AA 34002-0948
507-227-4918
Fax: 507-227-6022
Email: stri.tivoli.dealbag@ic.si.edu
The objective of this program is to
enable selected candidates to work
in the tropics and explore research
possibilities at the Smithsonian
Tropical Research Institute.
Fellowships are primarily for
graduate students, but awards are
made occasionally to
undergraduate and postdoctoral
candidates. Contact the office listed
above for guidelines and
application procedures.

Fulbright Teacher Exchange
Program
ATTN: NSL
600 Maryland Ave., SW
Room 142
Washington, DC 20224-2520
800-726-0479
202-401-9418
Fax: 202-401-1433
The program is designed to
promote mutual understanding
between citizens of the United
States and other countries through
educational and cultural
exchanges. It is open to teachers
and administrators from the
elementary through the
postsecondary levels, allowing for
classroom-to-classroom exchange
of teaching assignments between
U.S. teachers and counterpart
teachers from selected countries
worldwide. Exchange grants may
include full or partial travel grants
and cost of living supplements,
depending on the country. The
Program also offers an eight week

seminar in Italy for college faculty and teachers (grades 9-12) of Latin, Greek, of the Classics. The total amount of money available is $527,000. Contact the office listed above for guidelines and an application packet.

Scientific Exchange With India
(United States-India Cooperative Science Program)

U.S.-India Cooperative Science Program
Room 935
Division of International Programs
National Science Foundation
4201 Wilson Blvd.
Arlington, VA 22230
703-306-1707
Fax: 703-306-0473
http://www.nsf.gov/sbe/int/intfund.htm
This program supports short-term cooperative research projects, international travel, conferences and workshops, and more. All of these activities are designed to promote cooperation and understanding between the United States and India, and to encourage the formation of enduring relationships. The total amount of money available is $162,000. Contact the office listed above for application and eligibility information.

Money To Attend
Workshops Overseas
(Citizens Exchanges)

Office of Citizen Exchanges
U.S. Information Agency (USIA)
E/P-Room 216
301 Fourth St., SW
Washington, DC 20547
202-619-5348
Fax: 202-619-4350
http://www.usia.gov
Email: exchanges@usia.gov
This program awards grants to U.S. nonprofit organizations for projects that link their international exchange interests with counterpart institutions/groups

in other countries. Subject areas include environmental protection, trade unionism, education administration and curriculum reform, civil and human rights protection, legislative reform, small business development and management training, and more. Programs are normally multi-phase and extend over more than one fiscal year. Programs usually consist of sending American specialists on 2-3 week visits to a country for workshops and meetings, followed by a visit to the U.S. by foreign counterparts. The total amount of money available is $21 million. The Office of Citizen Exchanges develops a series of Requests for Proposals (RFPs) during the course of the fiscal year. Specific application and review guidelines are available upon written request to the office listed above. RFPs are also published in the *Federal Register*.

Money For Artists To Visit U.S. Embassies Abroad
(Arts America Program)

Arts America
Bureau of Educational and Cultural Affairs
U.S. Information Agency (USIA)
301 4th St., SW, Room 568
Washington, DC 20547
202-619-4779
Fax: 202-619-6315
http://www.usia.gov
Email: exchanges@usia.gov
This program develops projects in response to requests from U.S. embassies abroad, selecting artists, performers and exhibitions on the basis of artistic evaluations by expert panels drawn from the U.S. arts community. It also supports privately-funded arts initiatives abroad by providing information, referrals, contacts, and other facilitative assistance. The total amount of money available is $845,000. This is not organized as a grant application program from which individuals or institutions can request financial assistance for overseas projects, but is in response to a specific request from embassies overseas. Individuals or groups that wish to tour for USIA must go through a screening process where their work is reviewed. Contact the office listed above for information about when the peer review panels meet, the work samples that are required, and more. A brochure describing the program is available from the office listed above.

Money For Musicians, Dancers And Actors To Perform Overseas
(Performing Arts)

Arts America
Bureau of Educational and
Cultural Affairs
U.S. Information Agency (USIA)
301 4th St., SW, Room 567
Washington, DC 20547
202-619-4783
Fax: 202-619-6315
http://www.usia.gov
Email: exchanges@usia.gov

This program sends abroad a small number of fully-funded performing arts
presentations in music, dance, and theater. Only those performing artists and
groups receiving a "highly recommended" evaluation from the appropriate Arts
America panel are selected for these tours. In addition to performances,
overseas tours usually involve workshops or master classes, interviews with
foreign media, and representational events such as dinners or receptions. The
total amount of money available is $465,000. This is not organized as a grant
application program from which individuals or institutions can request
financial assistance for overseas projects, but is in response to a specific request
from embassies overseas. Individuals or groups that wish to tour for USIA must
go through a screening process where their work is reviewed. Contact the office
listed above for information about when the peer review panels meet, the work
samples that are required, and more.

MONEY TO GIVE TALKS ABOUT ART IN FOREIGN COUNTRIES
(Arts America Speakers)

Arts America
Bureau of Educational and Cultural Affairs
U.S. Information Agency (USIA)
301 4th St., SW, Room 567
202-619-4779
Washington, DC 20547

Fax: 202-619-6315
http://www.usia.gov
Email: exchanges@usia.gov
This program is designed to encourage the exchange of ideas in the areas of creative and performing arts. Arts America recruits experts, mostly practitioners of the arts, in response to requests made to U.S. embassies by foreign cultural institutions, schools, or associations. Arts America speakers usually spend two weeks giving lectures or participating in seminars or conferences of a few days' duration in one or more countries. The total amount of money available is $90,000. For information on how to have your name placed on the Arts America Speaker roster, contact the office listed above.

Spend Six Weeks In A Foreign Country Working With Art Colleagues
(American Cultural Specialists)

Arts America
Bureau of Educational and Cultural Affairs
U.S. Information Agency (USIA)
301 4th St., SW, Room 567

$10,000 For Eastern Europeans and Russians To Study In U.S.
(Russia/Eurasia Awards Program)

Russia/Eurasia Awards Program
1875 Connecticut Ave., NW
Suite 1000
Washington, DC 20009
202-939-3111
Fax: 202-667-3419
The program provides grants up to $10,000 to U.S. institutions for graduate and undergraduate students from Russia and Eurasia. Funds may be used for students' transportation, room, board, and other expenses not covered by the institution's aid package. Fields of study include public administration, public policy, political science, urban planning, economics, business, marketing, law, education, journalism, and more. The hard sciences and engineering are not eligible fields of study. To learn more about the program or application process, contact the office listed above.

Washington, DC 20547
202-619-4779
Fax: 202-619-6315
http://www.usia.gov
Email: exchanges@usia.gov
Participants in this program spend two to six weeks in one country working
with foreign colleagues. Among other activities, they may conduct workshops
or master classes, direct a play, rehearse a ballet, or advise on arts management.
The total amount of money available is $380,000. This is not a grant program
from which individuals can request financial assistance for overseas projects,
but as a response to a specific request from embassies abroad. To learn more on
how to have your resume reviewed so your name can be placed on the Cultural
Specialist roster, contact the office listed above.

Eight Week Foreign Tours For Musicians And Bands
(Artistic Ambassador Program)

Arts America
Bureau of Educational and Cultural Affairs
U.S. Information Agency (USIA)
301 4th St., SW, Room 567
Washington, DC 20547
202-619-4779
Fax: 202-619-6315
http://www.usia.gov
Email: exchanges@usia.gov
This program is designed to use the wealth
of often undiscovered musical talent in the U.S. to enhance USIA's mission of
promoting cross-cultural understanding. Artistic Ambassadors travel to four or
five countries for a period of four to eight weeks. In addition to public
performances, they may conduct workshops and master classes. The total
amount of money available is $169,000. Nominations of classical musicians in
various categories are sought from music schools, conservatories, colleges and
universities throughout the U.S. Artistic Ambassadors may not be under
management and are selected through live auditions on the basis of their
musical ability and suitability as "goodwill ambassadors." To learn more about
the application process, contact the office listed above.

FOREIGN LEADERS CAN STUDY IN THE U.S.
(International Visitors Program)

Office of International Visitors
U.S. Information Agency (USIA)
301 4th St., SW, Room 255
Washington, DC 20547
202-619-5217
Fax: 202-205-0792
http://www.usia.gov
Email: exchanges@usia.gov
USIA arranges programs for foreign leaders and potential leaders designed to develop and foster professional contacts with their colleagues in the United States and provide a broader exposure to American social, cultural, and political institutions. Areas of expertise government, politics, media, education, science, labor relations, the arts, and other fields. The total amount of money available is $40 million. Participants are nominated by U.S. embassies. For more information on the program, contact the office listed above.

Money For Engineering Students To Travel The Country Visiting DOE Laboratories
(University-Laboratory Cooperative Program - 81.004)

Cindy Music
Postsecondary Programs Division
Office of University and Science Education Programs
Office of Science and Technology
U.S. Department of Energy
Washington, DC 20585
202-586-0987
Fax: 202-586-0019
The program objective is to provide college and university science and engineering faculty and students with energy-related training and research experience in areas of energy research at Department of Energy research facilities. Funds can be used to conduct energy research at one of the DOE research facilities, and students will also receive a stipend and a small travel allowance. Students can also participate in energy-related workshops and conferences. The total amount of money available is $5,525,000. Students must

apply to a participating laboratory or university. Contact the office listed above for information on laboratories and universities which take part in this program.

Money For Minority Students To Go To Energy-Related Conferences
(Minority Educational Institution Research Travel Fund)

Annie Whatley
Office of Minority Economic IMPACT, MI-1
U.S. Department of Energy
Forrestal Building, Room 5B-110
Washington, DC 20585
202-586-0281

The program objective is to provide travel funds to faculty members and students of minority postsecondary educational institutions to encourage and

Do Your Part To Help The World
(Peace Corps)

Peace Corps
1990 K St., NW
Washington, DC 20526
800-424-8580
Fax: 202-606-9410
http://www.peacecorps.gov

The program objective is to promote world peace and friendship, to help other countries in meeting their needs for trained manpower, and to help promote understanding between the American people and other peoples served by the Peace Corps. Volunteers serve for a period of 2 years, living among the people with whom they work. Volunteers are expected to become a part of the community and to demonstrate, through their voluntary service, that people can be an important impetus for change. Volunteers receive a stipend and health insurance. Contact the office listed above for information on how to become a Peace Corps volunteer.

assist in initiating, improving, renewing and expanding energy-related research. Funds can be used to reimburse students for travel expenses, including travel related tickets and per diem cost, so that they may attend energy-related conferences, workshops, and symposia. The total amount of money available is $50,000. Application forms can be requested by contacting Oak Ridge Associated Universities, Minority Institution Research Travel, University Programs, P.O. Box 117, Oak Ridge, TN 37830, 615-586-8158.

Grants To Junior and Senior College Science And Engineering Students To Visit Energy Laboratories
(Science and Engineering Research Semester - 81.097)

Donna Prokop
Postsecondary Programs
Office of University and Science Education Programs
Office of Energy Research
U.S. Department of Energy
Washington, DC 20585
202-586-8949
202-488-2426
Fax: 202-586-0019

The objective of this program is to give juniors and seniors the opportunity to

participate in hands-on research at the cutting edge of science at the Department of Energy Laboratories, and to provide training and experience in the operation of sophisticated state-of-the-art equipment and instruments. College juniors and seniors who are majoring in an energy-related field can spend a semester using some of the Federal government's equipment and instruments at many of the Department of Energy's labs. The

energy research must be in an area of the laboratory's ongoing research. Students receive a weekly stipend of $225, complimentary housing or a housing allowance, and a round-trip ticket to the lab. The total amount of money available is $2,500,000. Applications may be obtained by writing to

Science and Engineering Research Semester, Office of Science and Technology (ST-50), Room 3F-061, U.S. Department of Energy, 1000 Independence Avenue, SW, Washington, DC 20585.

The Military Could Be Your Ticket Overseas
(U.S. Department of Defense)

U.S. Air Force Recruiting Service
550 D St., W, Suite 1
Randolph Air Force Base, TX 78150-4527
210-652-5993
www.airforce.com/

Commander
Naval Recruiting Command
801 N. Randolph St.
Arlington, VA 22203
800-USA-NAVY
www.navyjobs.com/

Commanding General
Marine Corps Recruiting Command
2 Navy Annex
Washington, DC 20380-1775
703-614-2901
www.usmc.mil/wwwmcpc.htm

Army Opportunities
P.O. Box 3219
Warminster, PA 18974-9845
800-USA-ARMY
www.goarmy.com/

U.S. Coast Guard Information Center
14180 Dallas Parkway
Suite 626
Dallas, TX 75240-9795
800-689-0816

The Army, Navy, Marine Corps, Air Force, and the Coast Guard (part of U.S. Department of Transportation) are responsible for protecting the security of the U.S. There are 2.1 million men and women on active duty, with 518,000 serving outside the United States. Length of service does vary, as does pay and types of jobs available. You can even earn the chance to go to college. The military has bases all around the country and the world, and your local recruiter can answer all your questions about the opportunities they have to offer.

join the foreign service
(Foreign Service with the Department of State)

Recruitment Branch
Employment Division
U.S. Department of State
P.O. Box 9317
Arlington, VA 22219
703-875-7490
http://www.state.gov

Money To Invest In Companies Overseas
(Foreign Investment Guaranties - 70.002)

Information Center
Overseas Private Investment Corporation
1100 New York Ave., NW
Washington, DC 20527
202-336-8799
Fax: 202-336-8700
The program objective is to guarantee loans and other investments made by eligible U.S. investors in friendly developing countries and emerging economies throughout the world, thereby assisting development goals and improving U.S. global competitiveness, creating American jobs and increasing U.S. exports. Eligible investors must be U.S. citizens; corporations, partnerships, or other associations created under the laws of the U.S. or any State or territory, and substantially owned by U.S. citizens; or 95 percent owned foreign subsidiary of such entity or combination of such entities. The total amount of money available is $106,000,000. Contact the office listed above for a free copy of Investment Finance Handbook and more information.

Information USA, Inc.

Professionals in the Foreign Service advance and protect the national interests and security of the United States, both overseas and at home. Foreign Service Officers are generalists who perform administrative, consular, economic and political functions. Foreign Service Specialists perform vital technical, support, and administrative services overseas and in the United States. You must be a U.S. citizen, between the ages of 21 and 59, a high school graduate, and be available for assignment anywhere in the world. Contact the office listed above for information and application procedures.

Thousands Of Government Jobs In Foreign Countries
(Office of Personnel Management)

Federal Job Information Center
Office of Personnel Management
1900 E St., NW
Washington, DC 20415
202-606-2700
Fax: 202-606-2329
Telnet: fjob.mail.opm.gov
FTP: ftp.fjob.mail.opm.gov
Email: info@fjob.mail.opm.gov
The Federal government hires personnel to do everything from typing to spying, and there are posts all around the world. Those interested in jobs overseas can contact the Office of Personnel Management to learn current job openings and the skills required. Other government agencies also hire for jobs abroad, and you could contact them directly for information on employment opportunities. Contact the office listed above for more information, or you may contact the Career America Connection at 912-757-3000. Other agencies that hire for overseas employment include:

Agency For International Development
Recruitment Division
320 21st St., NW
Washington, DC 20523
202-647-7284
http://www.info.usaid.gov

U.S. Information Agency (USIA)
Office of Personnel
301 4th St., SW

Washington, DC 20547
202-619-4539
Fax: 202-401-0557
www.usia.gov

U.S. Customs Service
1301 Constitution Ave., NW
Washington, DC 20229
202-634-2040

Central Intelligence Agency
Personnel Representative
P.O. Box 12727
Arlington, VA 22209-8727
703-482-1100
800-562-7242
Fax: 703-482-7814

U.S. Department of Commerce
U.S. and Foreign Commercial Service
Office of Foreign Service Personnel
14th and Constitution Ave., NW

Room H-3813
Washington, DC 20230
202-482-4701
Fax: 202-482-1629

U.S. Department of Agriculture
Foreign Agricultural Service
Susan Brown
Personnel Division - Room 5627
14th St. and Independence Ave., SW
Washington, DC 20250
202-254-8337

Sell Your Goods Overseas
(U.S. Department of Commerce)

Trade Information Center
U.S. Department of Commerce
Washington, DC 20230
800-USA-TRADE
http://www.doc.gov
The Trade Information Center is a comprehensive "one-stop-shop" for
information on U.S. government programs and activities that support exporting
efforts. This hotline is staffed by trade specialists who can provide information
on seminars and conferences, overseas buyers and representatives, overseas
events, export financing, technical assistance, and export counseling. They also
have access to the National Trade Data Bank. They offer trade missions to help
you find local agents, representatives, distributors, or direct sales. Their Trade
Shows promote U.S. products with high export potential. The Agent/
Distributor Service will locate, screen, and assess agents, distributors,
representatives, and other foreign partners for your business. Matchmaker
Trade Delegations prescreen prospects interested in your product and assist
with meetings. If you cannot afford the cost of traveling overseas, the Trade
Information Center can refer you to several programs which offer loans to help
you start exporting. You can also receive assistance from your own state's
Department of Economic Development. Contact the office listed above for
more information on exporting in general, and for more specific information on
your product or service.

Money For Your
Invention

If you have a great idea and
want to turn it into reality,
don't rush out and spend
what could be thousands of
dollars for a private
invention company and a
patent attorney. You can get
a lot of this help for free or
at a fraction of the cost.
There is a lot of help out
there; university-sponsored

programs, not-for-profit groups, state affiliated programs, profit-
making companies, etc. Depending on the assistance and the
organization, some services are free, others have reasonable fees.

Many of the inventors' organizations hold regular meetings where
speakers share their expertise on topics such as licensing, financing and marketing. These groups are a good place for inventors to
meet other inventors, patent attorneys, manufacturers, and others
with whom they can talk and from whom they can get help.

You can contact one of the following organizations for help.

1. ***Small Business Development Center***
    Washington State University
    Parkplace Building
    1200 6th Ave., Suite 1700   206-553-7328
    Seattle, WA 98101   Fax: 206-553-7044
    www.sbdc.wsu.edu/franz.htm

This service will evaluate your idea for a fee. They also provide counseling
services and can assist you with your patent search.

2. ***Wisconsin Innovation Service Center/Technology***
   Small Business Development Center
   Ms. Debra Malewicki, Director
   University of Wisconsin - Whitewater
   402 McCutchan Hall   414-472-3217
   Whitewater, WI 53190   Fax: 414-472-1600

The only service that is guaranteed is the evaluation. However, efforts are made to match inventors with exceptional high evaluation scores with manufacturers seeking new product ideas. (They do not offer direct invention development or marketing services). WISC charges a $495 flat fee for an evaluation. The goal is to keep research as affordable as possible to the average independent inventor. Most evaluations are completed within 30 - 45 days. Inventions from specialized fields may require more time. WISC also provides preliminary patent searches via online databases to client.

3. ***Drake University***
   Small Business Development Center
   Mr. Benjamin C. Swartz, Director
   Drake Business Center   515-271-2655
   2507 University   1-800-532-1216
   Des Moines, IA 50311-4505   Fax: 515-271-1899
   www.iabusnet.org

INVENTURE is a program of the Drake University Business Development and

Research Institute designed to encourage the development of valid ideas through the various steps to becoming marketable items. INVENTURE has no paid staff. The entire panel is made up of volunteers. The administration of the program is handled by existing staff from the Small Business Development Center and the College of Business and Public Administration. They will review items from **any person** regardless of their place of residence. They will review a product idea and check it for market feasibility. INVENTURE may link individuals with business and/or financial partners.

INVENTURE screens every product submitted, but will not consider toy/game or food items. Products are evaluated on 33 different criteria, (factors related to legality, safety, business risk, and demand analysis, to market acceptance/competition). It normally takes up to 6 weeks to receive results of the evaluation. Evaluators are experienced in manufacturing, marketing, accounting, production, finance and investments.

Money For Your Invention

INVENTURE acts in a responsible manner to maintain confidence of an idea, but cannot guarantee confidentiality. For assistance with business plans, financial projections, and marketing help, you're encouraged to contact your Small Business Development Center (SBDC).

4. ***U.S. Department of Energy***
    Mail Stop EE-24
    1000 Independence Ave., SW   202-586-1478
    Washington, DC 20585   Fax: 202-586-7114
    www.oit.doe.gov/inventions/

Financial assistance is available at 2 levels: up to $40,000 and up to $200,000 by the Inventions and Innovations program as stated by the Office of Industrial Technologies (OIT) Department of Energy (DOE) for ideas that significantly impact energy savings and future commercial market potential. Successful applicants will find technical guidance and commercialization support in addition to financial assistance.

DOE has given financial support to more than 500 inventions with nearly 25% of these reaching the marketplace bringing in nearly $710 million in cumulative sales.

5. ***U.S. Environmental Protection Agency***
    Center for Environmental Research Information
    Cincinnati, OH 45260   513-569-7562
    www.epa.gov

Directory Description: Environmental Protection Agency, Office of Research and Development, 401 M Street, SW, Washington, DC 20460; 202-260-7676, Fax: 202-260-9761

The Office of Research and Development conducts an Agency wide integrated program of research and development relevant to pollution sources and control, transport and fate processes, health/ ecological effects, measurement/ monitoring, and risk assessment. The office provides technical reviews, expert consultations, technical assistance, and advice to environmental decision-makers in federal, state, local, and foreign governments.

Center for Environmental Research Information
26 W. ML King Drive, Cincinnati, OH 45268, Calvin O. Lawrence, Director; 513-569-7562; Fax: 513-569-7566.
A focal point for the exchange of scientific/ technical information both within the federal government and to the public.

Office of Research and Development

Is responsible for working with laboratories, program offices, regions to produce information products that summarize research, technical, regulatory enforcement information that will assist non-technical audiences in understanding environmental issues. Contact Office of Research and Development, U.S. Environmental Protection Agency, 401 M St., SW, Washington, DC 20460; 202-260-5767.

Office of Exploratory Research

Robert Menzer, Acting Director, 401 M Street, SW, Washington, DC 20460; 202-564-6849, Fax: 202-260-0450.

The Office of Exploratory Research (OER) plans, administers, manages, and evaluates the Environmental Protection Agency's (EPA) extramural grant research. It supports research in developing a better understanding of the environment and its problems. Main goals are: to support the academic community in environmental research; maintain scientific/technical personnel in environmental science/ technology; to support research for the identification/solution of emerging environmental problems.

Goals are accomplished through four core programs:

1. **The Research Grants Program:**
    Supports research initiated by individual investigators in areas of interest to the agency.

2. **The Environmental Research Centers Program:**
    Has two components: The Academic Research Center Program (ARC) and the Hazardous Substance Research Centers Program (HSRC).

3. **The Small Business Innovation Research (SBIR) Program:**
    Program supports small businesses for the development of ideas relevant to EPA's mission. Focuses on projects in pollution control development. Also receives 1.5% of the Agency's resources devoted to extramural Superfund research.

4. **The Visiting Scientists Program:**
    Components are an Environmental Science and Engineering Fellows Program and a Resident Research Associateship Program. The Fellows Program supports ten mid-career post-doctoral scientists and engineers at EPA headquarters & regional offices. The Research Associateship Program attracts national and international scientists and engineers at EPA research laboratories for up to 3 years to collaborate with Agency researchers on important environmental issues.

Other programs available are:
A Minority Fellowship Program
A Minority Summer Intern Program
The Agency's Senior Environmental Employment Program (SEE)
The Federal Workforce Training Program
An Experimental Program to Stimulate Competitive Research (EPSCoR).

To learn more, contact Grants Administration, U.S. Environmental Protection Agency, 401 M St., SW, 3903E, Washington, DC 20460; 202-564-5315. The best way, though, is to search for the word "grant" at the EPA's website, {www.epa.gov}.

State Sources for Inventors

Don't call 1-800-IDEA or some other invention company to get help on your invention. Every state has local government and nonprofit supported organizations that are there to help you for free. There organizations are usually found at local colleges and universities. They can help you protect your idea, develop prototypes, find money or even manufacturers or distributors for your end product.

To find out what organizations are near you, see page 292 for your local Small Business Development Center, or contact the main office at: The Small Business Development Center, 409 Third Street, SW, Suite 4600, Washington, DC 20416, 202-205-6766, {www.sbaonline.sba.gov/SBDC/mission.html}.

$1 BILLION
TO WORK ON IDEAS

The Small Business Innovation Research (SBIR) Program is a highly competitive program that encourages small businesses to explore their technological potential and provides the incentive to profit from its commercialization.

Each year, ten federal departments and agencies are required to reserve a portion of their research and development funds to award to small businesses. SBIR funds the critical start-up and development stages and it encourages the commercialization of the technology, product, or service. There are three phases to the program: start-up, development, and marketplace.

To learn more about how to apply and about the various agencies involved, contact Office of Technology, U.S. Small Business Administration, 409 Third St., SW, Washington, DC 20416; 202-205-6450; {www.sba.gov/SBIR/ sbir.html}.

Invention Assistance

Do you have a plan to develop a company based on your energy-saving invention or innovation? Have you been searching for financial and technical support to bring your idea to market? The U.S. Department of Energy's Inventions and Innovation Program can help.

236   *Information USA, Inc.*

Money For Your Invention

This program provides financial assistance for establishing technical performance and conducting early development of innovative ideas and inventions. Ideas that have a significant energy savings impact and future commercial market potential are chosen for financial support through a competitive solicitation process. In addition to financial assistance, this program offers technical guidance and commercialization support to successful applicants.

For more information, contact U.S. Department of Energy, Golden Field Office, Inventions and Innovation Program, 1617 Cole Blvd., 17-3, Golden, CO 80401; 303-275-4744; {www.oit.doe.gov/Access/inventions/inventions.html}.

Money To Start A
Nonprofit

You say you're committed to a particular social issue, and would like to set up a nonprofit to further your cause? But you're afraid that the paperwork involved makes it much too complicated and time consuming? Contrary to popular belief, you don't have to hire a lawyer and have thousands of dollars in the bank to consider starting your own nonprofit. With as little as $35 and 30 minutes of paperwork that you can complete sitting at your kitchen table, you can be well on your way to raising funds and raising the consciousness of the country.

Try The Easy, Cheap Way — First!

Dan Meeks of Columbus, Ohio had a dream of starting his own nonprofit that could be staffed by Vietnam veterans who would help local kids tackle various personal and community-related problems. He called a lawyer to investigate the costs associated with becoming a nonprofit. He was astounded to hear that it would cost $800, and that it would take several months to complete the lengthy process. Since theirs was a new and fledgling organization, Dan and the other interested participants didn't have that kind of money. Through a friend, Dan heard of a special IRS office that does nothing but assist people in starting nonprofits. They sent Dan the necessary forms and instructions which were easily completed in a few hours, after clarifying a few points over the telephone with the IRS office. A letter soon followed notifying Dan that his organization had qualified as a nonprofit, and the entire process cost him less than $20! Within a few months, Dan had raised $5,000 through a fundraiser and donated the money to several other nonprofit organizations, including the local Ronald McDonald House. Success stories like Dan's don't necessarily take lots of time and effort — just the right information.

Tamara Gates is another individual determined to make a difference. She wanted to start a chapter of V-COPS (Veteran-Civilian Observation Patrol) in Cleveland, to tackle the dual problem of a high crime rate coupled with a high number of homeless veterans residing on the city's streets. The V-COPS program offers shelter for homeless veterans in exchange for their services patrolling the streets at night, acting as the eyes and ears of the police. Ms. Gates contacted the special IRS office to find out how to apply for nonprofit status, and was sent the appropriate forms. It took her a little over a week to complete the forms, and several months later she received her confirmation as a nonprofit. Because of the budget for her organization, Ms. Gates was required to pay a fee of several hundred dollars, but it was still much less than the $50,000 that a consultant estimated that she would be required to pay. Thanks to her commitment to forge ahead and get the right information, Ms. Gates can point to the very tangible shelter services that her V-COPS program offers to Cleveland's homeless veterans, in exchange for the valuable services that they provide to the local community.

If you are thinking about establishing a nonprofit, check out this FREE source of valuable information before you decide that the obstacles are too great. Just like Dan and Tamara, you may find yourself pleasantly surprised and able to achieve your goal, without handing over a ton of your hard earned money to someone just to figure it out for you!

How To Become A Nonprofit

Filing With The IRS

Internal Revenue Service Forms Line
800-829-3676
www.irs.ustreas.gov/forms_pubs/forms.html
   or
Your Local IRS Office
Listed in the government section of your telephone book

To help you determine if your organization may qualify for tax exempt status or to find out what you will need to do to qualify, request Publication 557, *Tax-Exempt Status For Your Organization*. This publication takes you step-by-step through the filing process, and contains instructions and checklists to help you provide all of the necessary information required to process your application correctly the first time around.

Most organizations seeking tax exempt status from the Federal government must use either: Form 1023, *Application for Recognition of Exemption Under Section 501(c)(3) of the Internal Revenue Code*, or Form 1024, *Application for*

Filing With The State Government

You will also be required to file as a nonprofit organization with your state government. This is normally done at the same time that you file with the IRS. Although it is the IRS who gives you the authority to raise money as a tax-exempt organization, your state government will also want to know about the proposed activities of your organization. Relevant information that they will be interested in includes:

★   the name and address of registrant,
★   the purpose of the nonprofit,
★   any articles of incorporation,
★   the names and addresses of any Board of Directors.

The charge for filing this information with the state is minimal, usually from $30 to $50. To obtain the necessary forms, Contact your state information operator listed in the Appendix and ask for your state Department of Revenue.

Recognition of Exemption Under Section 501(a) or for Determination Under Section 120. The forms will ask you to provide:

- ♠ a description of the purposes and the activities of your organization,
- ♠ financial information, and if you have not yet begun operation, a proposed budget, along with a statement of assets and liabilities (if you have any),
- ♠ information on how you intend to finance your activities, through fundraisers, grants, etc.

Examples of who qualifies under each of the laws and samples of forms are provided in these publications. If the necessary forms have been properly completed and all goes well, a ruling or determination letter should be on its way to you in no time.

GETTING HELP FROM THE IRS

Internal Revenue Service Info-Line
800-829-1040
    or
Your local IRS Office
Listed in the government section of your telephone book
    or
Exempt Organizations Technical Division
Internal Revenue Service
U.S. Department of the Treasury
1111 Constitution Ave., NW, Room 6411
Washington, DC 20224
202-622-8100
www.irs.ustreas.gov/bus_info/eo/

The first two offices listed above can provide you with the answers to any questions that might arise in filling out the necessary forms. If the first person that you speak with in that office cannot answer your question completely, they can put you in touch with a specialist who will discuss your question in detail. The Exempt Organization Technical Division is not set up to handle every question that might arise in  completing forms, but it can serve as a good backup when all else fails. This is the office that will actually process your application.

How To Raise Money For Your Nonprofit

Catalogue Of Federal Grant Programs

Federal Domestic Assistance Catalogue Staff
General Services Administration
Ground Floor, 300 7th St., SW
Washington, DC 20407
202-708-5126
800-669-8331

Everything you will need to get you started in searching for grants is found in this concise government publication. The *Catalog of Federal Domestic Assistance* is available in most libraries and describes Federal government programs providing funds or other non-financial assistance to organizations. Included in the publication are various programs' eligibility requirements, application procedures, information contacts, and more. This manual of more than 1,000 pages provides the most comprehensive information on federal funds currently available. Many congressional offices have access to this information on two databases known as PREaward Grants and POSTaward Grants on the House Information System. The Catalog costs $77 and is available by check or credit card from the Superintendent of Documents, U.S. Government Printing Office, Washington, DC 20402; 202-512-1800; {www.access.gpo.gov/}.

GRANTS AND FOUNDATION SUPPORT RESOURCE LIST

Your Local Representative's or Senator's Office
or
Your Representative or Senator, U.S. Capitol
Washington, DC 20515
202-224-3121

A free report called *Grants And Foundation Support* (IP50G), describes sources of funding (both government and private), as well as information regarding grant proposal development. It is available from your congressman's office.

The Center For Foundation Support

The Foundation Center
79 Fifth Ave/16th St.
New York, NY 10003-3076
800-424-9836
http://fndcenter.org

The Foundation Center is a nonprofit organization which gathers and
disseminates factual information on foundations. The Center's libraries contain
copies of foundations' tax returns, collections of books, documents, and reports
about the foundation field, and related material. They also publish funding
directories specific to certain fields, and offer programs to assist individuals in
information searches. You may also request a list of cooperating libraries in each
state where Center publications containing foundation information may be
consulted. The Center has the following regional offices:

The Foundation Center
1001 Connecticut Ave., NW
Suite 938
Washington, DC 20036
202-331-1400
Fax: 202-331-1739

The Foundation Center
312 Sutter St.
San Francisco, CA 94108
415-397-0902
Fax: 415-397-7670

The Foundation Center
1422 Euclid Ave., Suite 1356
Cleveland, OH 44115
216-861-1933
Fax: 216-861-1926

The Foundation Center
50 Hurt Plaza
Atlanta, GA 30303
404-880-0094
Fax: 404-880-0097

How Someone Can Give You Money And Make It Tax Deductible

Internal Revenue Service Forms Line
800-829-3676
www.irs.ustreas.gov/forms_pubs/pubs.html
or
Your Local IRS Office
Listed in the government section of your telephone book

Obtain a free copy of Publication 526 entitled *Charitable Contributions*. It will explain the kinds of charitable contributions that are tax deductible and the types of organizations that can qualify for this deduction.

Information About Existing Nonprofits

The One Book of Nonprofits

Exempt Organizations Technical Division
Internal Revenue Service
U.S. Department of the Treasury
1111 Constitution Ave., NW
Room 6411
Washington, DC 20224
202-622-8100

To find out about other nonprofits that have filed with the Internal Revenue Service, subscribe to the *Cumulative List of Organizations* (Publication #78), which includes a complete listing of names and addresses of exempt organizations. The subscription is $45 annually by check or credit card, and can be obtained by contacting the Superintendent of Documents, U.S. Government Printing Office, Washington, DC 20402; 202-512-1800.

MAILING LISTS OF NONPROFITS

Internal Revenue Service
P.O. Box 2608
Washington, DC 20013-2608
202-874-0700
Fax: 202-874-0964
www.irs.ustreas.gov/prod/tax_stats/index.html

A database of over 1,000 tax-exempt organizations is maintained by the Internal Revenue Service from which you can access a wealth of priceless information. You may access this database through the website given above. In order to understand the codes in these files, you will also have to download the *Instructions Booklet*, which is available on the same link. This information is also available on CD-ROM and includes more financial information per organization than the Internet data. Ask for Statistics of Income (SOI) samples of Forms 990 and 990-EZ. Years 1993-1996 are available. Years 1993 and 1994 are available for $100 and years 1995 and 1996 for $300.

Freebies and Cheapies For Nonprofits

Americorp And You

Corporation for National Service
1201 New York Ave., NW
Washington, DC 20525
202-606-5090
www.cns.gov

Does your nonprofit work to eliminate poverty or poverty-related problems? Americorp provides full-time, full-year volunteers to local organizations, with participants working to improve the community's ability to solve its own problems. Americorp has assisted in setting up drug abuse action centers, literacy programs, food distribution efforts, and shelters for runaway youth and the homeless. The benefits for the Americorp Volunteer include college loan deferment or cancellation, a modest subsistence allowance, an education

Art For Sale

National Gallery of Art
Office of Visual Services
Washington, DC 20565
202-842-6231
Fax: 202-842-2356
www.nga.gov/resources/divsdesc.htm

You don't have to sell cheap candy or ugly wrapping paper for your next fundraiser when you can sell works of real art. It's no joke — the National Gallery of Art in Washington rents color transparencies of various works of art to nonprofits at half the commercial rate price. Although some restrictions apply to their use, you can produce wall calendars, address books, or cards as a money making project for your school or youth organization.

award of $4,725, health insurance, training, and travel. Contact the office listed above to learn how your organization can apply for Americorp volunteers.

Local Community Service

Corporation for National Service
Learn and Serve Program
1201 New York Ave., NW
Washington, DC 20525
202-606-5090
www.cns.gov

If your nonprofit needs help addressing the needs of the poor, you can get some
energetic help from high school and college students who take part in Student
Community Service projects. Student Community Service Volunteers have
assisted in a variety of programs including Headstart, drug abuse prevention,
runaway youth, and elderly assistance. The volunteers receive no stipend, but
projects utilizing the services of these students are awarded grants for staff
salaries, project support expenses, and much more. For information on how your
organization can take advantage of this wonderful volunteer program, contact
Corporation for National and Community Service.

Tons Of Free Books

Surplus Books Section
Anglo-American Acquisitions Division
Library of Congress
Madison Building
101 Independence Ave., SE
Washington, DC 20540
202-707-9514
Fax: 202-707-0380
Email: rov@loc.gov

Need to raise a little cash? Why not appeal to the intellectual side of most folks
and hold a book sale? Thousands of surplus books from the Copyright Division
and private gifts in a variety of subject areas are available to nonprofit
organizations from the Library of Congress. All you need is a letter from your
nonprofit which includes the names of the person or persons coming to select
books and your organization's name. The only cost to you will be shipping and
handling charges for the publications that your representatives select. Your
organization may also be eligible to have the shipping and handling charges due
on these books paid for by your Congressman's office through the use of franks
(the means by which a Congressional office pays postage expenses).

Information USA, Inc.

Cheap Postage

U.S. Postal Service
Consumer Information and Product Support
475 L'Enfant Plaza West, SW
Room 5092
Washington, DC 20260
www.usps.gov

Bulk mailings are easier with Uncle Sam
picking up part of the tab. Your
organization can send its mail for
almost half of the regular rate
just by filing an application for
nonprofit status. Contact your
local post office for information on
application procedures and request
publications entitled *Special Bulk
Third-Class Rates* (Publication 417) and
Customer Guide To Cooperative Mailings
(Publication 417A).

Conserve And Improve Your Part Of The World

Natural Resource Conservation Service
U.S. Department of Agriculture
Room 6121-S
Washington, DC 20013
www.nrcs.usda.gov/NRCstate.html

Why not raise money for a new park or save a crumbling edifice in your area?
Resource Conservation and Development (RC&D) Councils may be able to help
you do this, as each council identifies priorities and sets goals to achieve them.
The Resource Conservation and Development Councils may be able to provide
some funding and necessary technical assistance. For more information on
RC&D and the location of a council near you, contact your local Soil
Conservation Representative listed in the blue pages of your phone book under
U.S. Government Agriculture.

Strike Up The Band

Blue Angel Public Affairs Office
Navy Flight Demonstration Squadron
390 San Carlos Road, Suite A
Pensacola, FL 32508-5508
850-452-4784
Fax: 850-452-2681
www.blueangels.navy.mil

RE: Golden Knights
Department of the Army
Office of the Chief of Public Affairs
Attn: SAPA POPD
1500 Army Pentagon
Washington DC 20310-1500
703-695-9368
Fax: 703-695-4323

USAFADS Thunderbirds
4445 Tyndall Avenue
Nellis AFB, NV 89191
www.nellis.af.mil/thunderbirds

Your parade can get a little noisier and a lot more colorful with a band and color
guard supplied by local Defense Department installations. Most installations
have community relations officers who handle requests from nonprofit
organizations for these and other little-known services, so contact them for
information on availability and restrictions. If you would like an aerial flyover
from the Blue Angels or the Thunderbirds, or a parachute show from the Golden
Knights, you must put your request in writing. There are obviously some costs
involved in providing some of these highly specialized services, but some are
actually free.

Free Food For
Nonprofits And The Homeless

Food Distribution Division
Food and Nutrition Service
U.S. Department of Agriculture

3101 Park Center Dr., Room 510
Alexandria, VA 22302
703-305-2882
Fax: 703-305-2420
www.fns.usda.gov/fdd

Does your nonprofit offer meals or bulk foods to those in need? Through the
Food Distribution Program, the U.S. Department of Agriculture (USDA)
distributes foods to state agencies for use by eligible local agencies. The foods
go to schools and institutions participating in child and elderly nutrition
programs, to needy families on Indian reservations, and to food banks, soup
kitchens, hospitals, and prisons. The foods are also used to assist victims of
natural disasters and in situations of distress. For a free copy of *Food
Distribution - State Distributing Agencies Directory*, contact the address listed
above.

A Home For The Homeless

Division of Health Facilities Planning
Public Health Service
U.S. Department of Health and Human Services
Room 17A-10, Parklawn Building
5600 Fishers Lane
Rockville, MD 20857
800-927-7588

If you are part of a nonprofit organization
ministering to the homeless, the government is
now taking applications for eligible groups to
receive excess or unused federal buildings or
land for homeless people. Homeless
organizations pay operating and repair costs
on the surplus properties that are leased
rent-free and in "as is" condition. The program
is administered by a combination of the
Department of Housing and Urban
Development (HUD), which screens applications, the General Services
Administration (GSA), which makes the properties available, and the
Department of Health and Human Services (HHS), which reviews applications.
In accordance with Title V of the McKinney Homeless Assistance Act, HUD
publishes a list of properties available in the *Federal Register*. Additional
information regarding the properties (as well as the Title V process) can be

obtained by calling 800-927-7588, a toll-free number established by HUD. After a property is published, homeless providers must submit expressions of interest by providing a written notice to the Division of Health Facilities Planning at HHS within 60 days of publication. You will then receive an application packet containing complete instructions on how to apply for the property. You can also request the following helpful publications:

- *How To Acquire Federal Surplus Real Property for Public Health Purposes*
- *Obtaining Federal Property for the Homeless*
- *Questions and Answers About Federal Property Programs*
- *HHS/HUD/GSA joint regulation covering specific information on Title V process*

Government Property And Land If You Use It For Education Or Training

Federal Real Property Assistance Program
Office of the Administrator for Management Services
U.S. Department of Education
400 Maryland Ave., SW., Room 1175
Washington, DC 20202
202-260-4558
www.ed.gov
Application: {http://aspe.os.dhhs.gov/cfdg/P84145.htm#;38}

No need to put a bond issue on the ballot. The Federal government is giving away surplus buildings and properties for educational use, including higher education, elementary and secondary education, libraries, educational television and radio, and more. The buildings are free, but recipients must cover all expenses for improvement, renovation, repair, maintenance, and operation of the program and facilities. Some of the properties range from improved or unimproved land in rural and urban settings (such as former Nike missile sites), to complete military bases (such as former Air Force stations). For information on properties available, contact the Federal Real Property Assistance Program.

Donations Or Loan Of Military Equipment For Museums And Towns

Office of Public Affairs
Federal Center
74 N. Washington
Battle Creek, MI 49017
616-961-7015
888-352-9333
Fax: 616-961-7410
Email: pubaff@drms.dla.mil
www.drms.dla.mil

Veterans' groups and museums should take note: the Federal government donates or lends obsolete combat materials to veterans' organizations, libraries, museums, and municipalities. Items include books, manuscripts, works of art, drawings, plans, models, and other specified items to be used only for historical, ceremonial or display purposes. It's no joke — you can even get a Navy vessel! Contact your nearest military installation for general information on this program, or write to the office listed above.

Money For Nonprofit Radio and TV Stations

Office of Telecommunications and Information Applications
National Telecommunications and Information Administration
U.S. Department of Commerce
14th and Constitution Ave., NW, Room 4096
Washington, DC 20230
202-482-5802
Fax: 202-501-8009
www.ntia.doc.gov/otiahome/otiahome.html

If you always wanted to operate or appear on public or noncommercial television or radio, the Federal government can help you get started or improve your existing facilities. There are grants for planning and construction of facilities, and matching grants for equipment necessary for production. For information on application procedures, contact the office listed above.

Tools For Schools

Attn: Sue Ellen Walbridge
Office of Science
Used Energy Related Equipment
U.S. Department of Energy
1000 Independence Ave., SW
Washington, DC 20585
202-586-7231
http://erle.osti.gov/erle/

Is the equipment in your college's laboratories broken, outdated, or just worn out? The U.S. Department of Energy (DOE) will send your school energy-related lab equipment that they no longer need, for no charge other than shipping and handling. The following free publications explain the program and outline the equipment available: *Energy-Related Laboratory Equipment Catalog*, and *Instruction and Information On Used Energy-Related Equipment Grants for Educational Institutions of Higher Learning*. This information is also accessible on the Federal Information Exchange (FEDIX) online database of government information, and is entitled Eligible Equipment Grant Access Data System (EEGADS).

Change An Outdated Military Base Into A New Public Park

National Park Service
Rivers, Trails and Conservation Service
U.S. Department of the Interior
1849 C St., NW
Washington, DC 20240
202-565-1190

States or local governments can apply to receive surplus property (even closed military bases) from the Federal government to be used for public parks and recreation and historic monument purposes. Properties must be converted to nature study areas, play areas, state and regional parks, arts and crafts centers, or senior citizen areas. For information regarding properties available and the necessary application procedures, contact the office listed above.

ḣelp Ṫhe Ṅeedy Buy A ḣome

Frances Bush
Office of Affordable Housing
451 7th St., SW, Room 7218
Washington, DC 20410
202-708-3226

To request Fact Sheet: Hope for Homeownership of Single Family Homes
800-998-9999
www.hud.gov/progdesc/hope3fin.html

Help those in your community become homeowners through the HOPE 3
Program. The U.S. Department of Housing and Urban Development (HUD)
administers the HOPE 3 Program which provides federal grant funds to eligible
organizations that, in turn,
select eligible families to
purchase single-family
properties at affordable
prices. All single-family
properties used in the
program were previously
owned by federal, state, or
local governments. The
funds can be used for
financial assistance in
mortgage financing,
reductions in the sale price
of homes, counseling in

Homeownership of
Single Family Homes
800-998-9999
www.hud.gov/
progdesc/hope3fin.html

personal financial management, home maintenance training, or job training. For
information on how your nonprofit organization can compete for HOPE 3 funds,
contact the number listed above.

$50,000 For Local Community Groups To Fight Area Polluters

Office of Emergency and Remedial Response
U.S. Environmental Protection Agency
401 M St., SW
Washington, DC 20460

800-424-9346
www.epa.gov/epaoswer/hotline

The Superfund Technical Assistance Grants (TAG) provide $50,000 for community groups to hire technical advisors to assist them in interpreting technical information about potential hazards and the selection and design of appropriate remedies to clean up sites under the Superfund program. The program is designed to benefit homeowners, land/property owners, as well as other individuals living near a site or otherwise affected by a site. You can be referred to your regional TAG officer, who will explain the application procedure, by contacting RCRA/Superfund Hotline, U.S. Environmental Protection Agency, 401 M St., SW, Washington, DC 20460; 800-424-9346.

Free Art Films And Videos From The National Gallery Of Art

Department of Education Resources
Extension Programs Section
National Gallery of Art
Washington, DC 20565
202-842-6263
www.nga.gov/resources/derdesc.htm

Impress your women's group or art organization by borrowing free slide programs, videocassettes, and films from the National Gallery of Art. The available materials might cover specific artists, time periods for a particular art form, or present an overview of the Gallery's extensive collection. To receive a complete catalogue and ordering information, contact the Extension Programs Office.

Government Real Estate To Nonprofits

Office of Property Disposal
Federal Property Resources Service
General Services Administration
1800 F St., NW
Washington, DC 20408

Information USA, Inc.

202-501-0084
Fax: 202-208-1714
http://propertydisposal.gsa.gov/property

The government has surplus property that they want to lease, sell, exchange, or donate. These properties can be used for public parks or other recreational uses, public health or educational purposes, public airports, wildlife conservation areas, correctional facilities, replacement housing, and for historic monument purposes. State and local government agencies are eligible to apply for any of the above reasons, and tax-supported and nonprofit medical and educational institutions can apply for property to be used for health, educational, and homeless uses. For more information regarding the application process, as well as appropriate use and restrictions of the properties, contact the office listed above.

Government Goods To Nonprofits

GSA/FSS
Property Management Division
1941 Jefferson Davis Highway
Crystal Mall 4
Room 812
Arlington, VA 22202
703-305-7240
http://pub.fss.gsa.gov

Need some desks, chairs, or even hospital beds for your nonprofit? Here's how you can get them. Nonprofits (which include medical institutions, clinics, schools, museums, libraries and others), can receive free furniture, clothing, and equipment from Uncle Sam through their state surplus property agency which receives items for distribution from the Federal government. To find out about the office nearest you, request the brochure *Federal Surplus Personal Property Donation Programs* from the address listed above, or contact your state information operator listed in the Appendix and ask for your state General Services Agency.

Free Accounting Services For Nonprofits and Small Businesses

There are a number of organizations around the country that provide free accounting services to help nonprofits, small businesses, and even needy individuals get the accounting help they need. They can help with bookkeeping instruction, system analysis, preparation of 990 forms, preparation for audits and free publications. A minimal one-time cost may be required.

Community Accountants in Philadelphia provides volunteers to assist nonprofits with one-on-one help to:

1) Establish a bookkeeping system
2) Set up an easy payroll system

ACCESS $200 MILLION PRODUCTS

Gifts In Kind International
333 North Fairfax St.
Alexandria, VA 22314
703-836-2121
Fax: 703-549-1481
www.giftsinkind.org

Nonprofits now have a way to tap into the resources and donations from companies across the country. Through Gifts In Kind America, nonprofits can register for The Agency Partnership program. This program entitles you to receive monthly catalogues of donated goods including computers, office equipment, software, children's items, personal care items, building materials, and clothing. Each year over 200 million dollars worth of products become available. Your nonprofit can then apply to receive these goods. Gifts In Kind America also has a Transportation and Logistics Center to help reduce the costs of shipping and handling. There is a minimal registration fee based upon the revenue of the nonprofit (under $1 million costs $125; over $1 million costs $250). Some states require State Charitable Solicitation Registration. Contact Gifts in Kind America to learn if your state requires certification and where you need to apply.

3) Help provide the financial information needed for IRS Application for
    Tax Exempt Status
4) Free Hotline and Email service for accounting questions

To find free accounting help in your area, contact Accountants for the Public
Interest, University of Baltimore, Thurnel Business Center, Room 155, 1420
North Charles Street, Baltimore, MD 21201; 410-837-6533; Fax: 410-837-
6532; {www.accountingnet.com/asso/api/index.html}.

If this source doesn't work, contact your state association of Certified Public
Accountants (CPA). Many of these associations should be able to identify a
volunteer CPA who would be willing to help. Contact your state capitol
operator listed in the Appendix or call your local public library.

Make Money As A
Volunteer

Volunteers are the backbone of almost every community service or public organization. Without volunteers, meals would not be

delivered to seniors; children would not have scout masters; our parks would not be maintained. Volunteerism is also a great way to get the experience you may need to get a job. You can even try out a profession before you spend four years in college pursuing that career. You can meet people whose life experiences are different from yours and from whom you may learn a new way to look at an old problem.

Being a volunteer also gets your foot in the door with potential new employers. They can see how you could fit into their organization and learn your work habits, skills, and abilities (at no real risk to them) before they employ you on a full time basis. The Federal government has also provided an added bonus for those who join the AmeriCorp program. Every volunteer earns $4,250 which is targeted for college or job training tuition. While you are an AmeriCorp volunteer, you also receive child care funds and health care coverage. Now, who says it doesn't pay to be a volunteer?

Make Money As A Volunteer

Below are some programs sponsored by the Federal government, but let these be a starting point for you. Your church, school, library, and other service organizations can provide you with other examples and opportunities to dedicate your free time towards helping to improve your own little corner of the world.

AmeriCorps*VISTA

Corporation for National
   Service
AmeriCorp Programs
1201 New York Ave., NW
Washington, DC 20525
800-942-2677
202-606-5000
www.cns.gov

For more than 30 years,
AmeriCorps*VISTA members
have been serving
disadvantaged communities.
The program increases the
capability of people to improve

America Reads

Corporation for National Service
1201 New York Ave., NW
Washington, DC 20525
202-606-5000
800-USA-LEARN

America Reads is looking for
programs and individuals who want
to help kids learn to read.

their lives. Members of AmeriCorps*VISTA work and live in the communities
they serve, creating programs that can continue after they complete their
service. Members must be at least 18 years old, and there is no upper age limit.

Community Based Programs

Corporation for National Service
Learn and Serve Programs
1201 New York Ave., NW
Washington, DC 20525
202-606-5000, ext. 117

In Learn and Serve's Community Based Programs, state offices and nonprofit
organizations implement, expand, and replicate service learning programs in
local communities. Participants are between the ages of 5 and 17 and include
students and youth who are not in school.

FISH AND WILDLIFE SERVICE

U.S. Fish and Wildlife Service
4401 N. Fairfax Dr.
Arlington, VA 22203
703-358-1730
www.fws.gov/who/careers.html

Would you like to spend some time banding birds at a national wildlife refuge, feeding fish at a national fish hatchery, or doing research in a laboratory? Then consider volunteering with the U.S. Fish and Wildlife Service. There are no age requirements; however, anyone under 18 must have written parental approval. Young people under 16 years of age are encouraged to volunteer as part of a supervised group, such as a Boy Scout troop, Girl Scout troop, or 4H Club. Contact one of the U.S. Fish and Wildlife regional offices for possible volunteer programs in your area.

Forest Service Volunteers

Public Affairs Office
Forest Service
U.S. Department of Agriculture
P.O. Box 96090
Washington, DC 20090-6090
202-205-1760
Fax: 202-205-0885
www.fs.fed.us/people/programs

The Forest Service has a volunteer program for almost everyone — retirees, professionals, housewives, students, teenagers, and youngsters. Typical jobs include working with specialists in resource protection and management, cooperative forestry, or research. You may also work at a Visitor Information Center by conducting interpretive natural history walks.

Information USA, Inc.

Health Research Volunteers

National Institutes of Health
Warren Grant Magnuson Clinical Center
Bethesda, MD 20892
800-411-1222
Fax: 301-480-9793
www.nimh.nih.gov/studies

Many of the research programs at National Institutes of Health require normal
volunteers who can provide clinicians with indices of normal body functions.
There is a small compensation for their participation.

Higher Education

Corporation for National Service
Learn and Serve Programs
1201 New York Ave., NW
Washington, DC 20525
202-606-5000, ext. 117
www.cns.gov

Learn and Serve America: Higher Education helps create and strengthen
community service and service learning initiatives at colleges and universities,
which involve a wide array of students and organizations working together to
address community needs. Grants also support technical assistance for
expanding the field of service learning.

School Based Programs

Corporation for National Service
Learn and Serve America Programs
1201 New York Ave., NW
Washington, DC 20525
202-606-5000, ext. 117

In Learn and Serve's School Based Programs, schools plan,
implement, and expand service activities for elementary and
secondary students. Schools also use Learn and Serve grants for adult
volunteer programs and teacher training.

National Civilian Community Corp.

Corporation for National Service
AmeriCorp Programs
1201 New York Ave., NW
Washington, DC 20525
800-942-2677
www.cns.gov

A full time residential service program, AmeriCorps*NCCC (the National
Civilian Community Corps) combines the best practices of civilian service with
the best aspects of military service, including leadership and team building.
Men and women, ages 18-24, serve full time and are based at one of the four
AmeriCorps*NCCC campuses — in Perry Point, MD; Charleston, SC; Denver,
CO, and San Diego, CA.

National Park Service

National Park Service
1100 Spring St., SW, Suite 1130
Atlanta, GA 30303
404-331-5711
www.nps.gov/volunteer

The National Park Service provides many opportunities for volunteers to help at
their many parks and historic sites. Contact the National Park nearest you for
more information.

SMITHSONIAN MUSEUMS TOUR GUIDES

Visitor Information and Associates' Reception Center
Smithsonian Institution
SI Building, Room 153
Washington, DC 20560
202-357-2700

Volunteers are needed and welcomed at the Smithsonian Institution to serve as
information volunteers or tour guides at many of the museums and Smithsonian
programs and activities.

Smithsonian Curatorial-Aides

Visitor Information and Associates' Reception Center
Smithsonian Institution
SI Building, Room 153
Washington, DC 20560
202-357-2700
www.si.edu/resource/faq/volunteer

Volunteers can participate in an independent program in which their educational
and professional backgrounds are matched with curatorial or research requests
from within the Smithsonian Institution.

Speakers for Community Groups

Every federal department and many government agencies have a speakers'
bureau to inform interested organizations and citizen groups about many of the
major community concerns. Many resources are available on medical issues
such as health fairs and cholesterol screening. Public education, space programs,
housing programs, weapons systems are some of the other areas where federal
experts might be available to come to speak to your community group.

NATIONAL ARCHIVES AND GENEALOGY

Volunteer and Visitor Services
The National Archives and Records Administration
Washington, DC 20408
202-501-5205
Fax: 202-501-5248
www.nara.gov/professional/volunteer/naravol

**Volunteers are needed to lead tours, welcome visitors at the
information desk, assist staff with information and administrative
services, and to become genealogical staff aides to assist new
genealogical researchers. Positions are available in the Washington,
DC area, regional facilities, and Presidential libraries.**

Senior Volunteer Opportunities

Shuffleboard, dominoes, bridge, and golf...Excited yet? Wouldn't you rather improve your neighborhood, lead nature walks or teach children to read? Being retired doesn't have to mean spending your afternoons idling, chasing a little white ball. And just because now you might find yourself on a fixed income, it doesn't mean that you can't take that trip to Africa that you've always dreamed about. The government has hundreds of ways to help you get excited about your newfound free time. Some of these can even pay you a small stipend. Read on to learn more about these opportunities to give a part of yourself to help others. What a satisfying way to spend some of your retirement time and give something back to your community?

Make Money Helping Out Other Seniors

(Senior Companion Program - 94.016)
National Senior Service Corps
1201 New York Ave., NW
Washington, DC 20525
800-424-8867

Nursing homes have got to be among the last places people want to spend the remaining years of their lives. Through the Senior Companion Program, you can be matched up with someone who needs just a little help to stay in the comfortable surroundings of their own home, and you can gain a friend in the bargain. As a participant, you will give individual care to other seniors who need help with transportation and shopping, or just sharing their reminiscences with someone that shows interest.

Volunteers must be 60 years of age or older and have a low income. Volunteers usually provide 20 hours a week of service and receive a small paycheck and other benefits. Nearly 14,000 Senior Companions provide 13 million hours of service annually to help more than 36,000 frail elderly stay independent. The federal budget for the program is $43,090,000. For more information, contact the office listed above.

$3,000 To Help The Kids

(Foster Grandparent Program -
94.011)
National Senior Service Corps
1201 New York Ave., NW
Washington, DC 20525
800-424-8867

The Foster Grandparent Program
matches low income seniors with
young people who need various kinds
of special help. Volunteers serve as mentors, tutors, and caregivers for children and young kids with special needs, and can also work in schools, hospitals, and recreation centers in their communities.

To be eligible, Foster Grandparents must be 60 years of age or over, with a low income, and interested in serving infants, children, and youth with special or exceptional needs. Volunteers work twenty hours per week, and receive a small paycheck and other benefits such as transportation costs or uniforms. 80,000 children, teenagers and their families are supported by the services of nearly 24,000 Foster Grandparents each year. The funds allocated from the federal budget for this program is $78,810,000. For more information, contact the office listed above.

Volunteer As A Consultant

(Retired Senior Volunteer Program (RSVP) - 94.002)
National Senior Service Corps
1201 New York Ave., NW
Washington, DC 20525
800-424-8867

You've got 40 years of business experience out there with you on the golf course during your retirement. There are hundreds of businesses and even nonprofit groups starting up each day, run by people who have the energy, but not the experience that you possess. You can lend your expertise to those who need your help the most. The Retired Senior Volunteer Program (RSVP) gives retired people a chance to continue using their professional experience by working with local service organizations doing such things as conducting employment workshops and acting as consultants to nonprofit organizations. You can even work in schools, libraries, hospitals, and other community service centers. RSVP participants serve from one to forty hours a week, providing assistance to hundreds of services and organizations. Participants are not restricted in income and are not compensated for their service.

450,000 RSVP members serve through more than 60,000 public and nonprofit community agencies. RSVP's annual budget is $44,500,000. For more information, contact the office listed above.

Volunteer To Help Entrepreneurs

(Service Corps of Retired Executives - 59.026)
SCORE
409 Third St., SW, Fourth Floor
Washington, DC 20024
800-634-0245
www.score.org

Your spouse may want you to slow down now that you're retired, but every time you walk into a business, you have this sudden urge to help. Instead of getting kicked out of every place you shop, try volunteering with SCORE, Service Corps of Retired Executives. SCORE volunteers are usually retired business professionals who want to share their expertise with the next generation of business owners. You won't get paid as a volunteer, although you may get reimbursed for certain out-of-pocket expenses. SCORE even conducts seminars and workshops covering major considerations for running a business.

Since it began, SCORE has responded to over 3 million requests for assistance and has an annual budget of $3,250,000. If you are interested in becoming one of over 13,000 SCORE members nationwide, contact SCORE at the office listed above.

travel the world at government expense

(Peace Corps)
Peace Corps
1990 K St., NW
Washington, DC 20526
800-424-8580

The average roundtrip ticket to Nepal will cost you $2,800, Poland is $1,800, and Sudan is $2,100. Who can afford those prices on a fixed income? Become one of the senior Peace Corps volunteers and see the world.

As a volunteer, you will serve for two years, living among the native people, and becoming part of the local community. The Peace Corps sends volunteers throughout Latin America, Africa, the Near East, Asia, the Pacific, and Eastern Europe to share their expertise in education, agriculture, health, economic development, urban development, and the environment. Volunteers receive a stipend and health benefits. Currently over 6,500 volunteers are serving with an annual budget of $231,300,000. For more information, contact the office listed above.

Dig Up Dinosaur Bones In The Original Jurassic Park

This is a once in a lifetime opportunity. Get off your couch and volunteer with the Forest Service. You can join in on projects like historic preservation activities, archaeological excavations, rock art recording, and building restoration. You learn history and archaeology, while helping to preserve some of the nation's most significant heritage sites. For two summers in a row, my wife, two teenage boys and myself had wonderful experiences. One was in upstate Minnesota where we repaired historic cabins in the wilderness, and the other was on the coast of Maine where we learned marine biology.

Come on. Help the country and learn great stuff at the same time. There's no fee and you may receive a small fee to offset expenses. For a list of projects, contact Passports in Time Clearinghouse, P.O. Box 31315, Tucson, AZ 85751; 800-281-9176; {http://www.fs.fed.us/recreation/heritage/pit_netscape.shtml}.

Money To Fix Up Your
Community

Federal money programs
exist that are designed to
help communities solve
many of today's difficult
problems — economic
development opportunities
such as job training funds,
community improvement
programs for emergency
shelters, rural housing,
senior centers, and mass
transit services, as well as airport modernization loans and grants.
You can discover various services such as school lunch and
nutrition programs, runaway halfway houses and health clinics.

The best single resource for leads on federal funding programs is
published by the federal government and is called the *Catalog
of Federal Domestic Assistance*. This manual of more
than 1,000 pages provides the most comprehensive information
on federal funds, cross-indexed by agency, program type,
applicant eligibility, and subject. The Catalog is available in
many libraries, and describes federal government programs that
provide funds or non-financial assistance to state and local
governments, public agencies, organizations, institutions, and
individuals. Included are the program's legislative authority,
explanations of each program, types of assistance provided,
restrictions, eligibility requirements, financial information,
application and award procedures, information contacts, and
related programs.

You can purchase a copy of the *Catalog of Federal Domestic Assistance* for $87 by contacting the Superintendent of Documents, U.S. Government Printing Office, P.O. Box 371954, Pittsburgh, PA 15250; 202-512-1800. You can also find the *Catalog* in many libraries and you can search it online at {www.cfda.gov}. In addition, you may purchase a copy of the *Catalog* on CD-ROM or on floppy diskette. The CD-ROM also contains the Federal Assistance Award Data System (FAADS) database. With this feature, you can check out a specific program to see who received the program funds in the past. This is an incredible feature, as it may help you tailor your proposal accordingly. You can search by program number, keyword, or location. The CD-ROM and diskette are available for $50 each by contacting the Federal Domestic Assistance Catalog Staff (MVS), 300 7th St., SW, Reporters Building, Room 101, Washington, DC 20407; 202-708-5126; Fax: 202-401-8233; {www.cfda.gov}.

Private Foundations

If you can't find what you need through the government, then you can turn to other sources for funds. Private foundations are nonprofit entities that are managed by a board of trustees and directors. When you think of these foundations, you usually think of the Ford or Rockefeller Foundations. These were established by wealthy families, and are designed to support a variety of humanitarian causes. They receive their monies from a principle fund or endowment. More than two-thirds of foundations are *Family Foundations* that are influenced or managed by the founding donor or donor's family. Another type of foundation, called a *Community Foundation*, receives their monies from a variety of donors in a specific area and the focus is to support charitable activities in their area. In 1998, foundations made nearly $19.5 billion in charitable grants.

Before approaching these foundations as your funding source, there are many issues to consider. Primarily these foundations provide grants to other nonprofits, not to individuals. Some foundations fund a specific focus area, such as the arts, children, or housing. Other considerations have to do with the geographic area. Foundations may fund projects nationally or internationally, but some only support projects in a particular state or region. It is generally a good to identify state or local foundations, as they may have a greater interest in local problems. Also, the type of support varies. Foundations may supply grants for scholarships, building funds, or seed money. Foundations often have specific funding cycles to consider and strict eligibility requirements. Planning ahead is the key.

The Foundation Center

The Foundation Center is a nonprofit organization which gathers and disseminates factual information on foundations. The

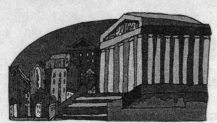

Center's libraries in New York City, Atlanta, San Francisco, Cleveland, and Washington, DC, contain copies of foundations' tax returns, extensive collections of books, documents, and reports about the foundation field, and current files on the activities and programs of about 50,000 U.S. foundations, plus knowledgeable staff to assist users in locating appropriate information.

The Foundation Center also publishes funding directories specific to certain fields, such as: aging; arts and culture; children, youth, and families; health; higher education; international programs; libraries and information services; religion; women and girls; and elementary and secondary education.

In addition, the Center has established cooperating reference collections in each state, where Center publications and information on foundations in the immediate state or region can be consulted. A list of cooperating libraries housing these regional collections appears in most of the Center's publications.

It is a good idea to look for foundations close to home; they are more likely to have a greater interest in local problems than would larger foundations with a national focus. Foundation Center resources are a good starting point for identifying likely funding sources. The next step is to learn more about these foundations by obtaining copies of their annual reports and/or grants guidelines. Some may be available at the Foundation Center's cooperating libraries. Grantseekers will need to find out whether their projected proposals match the foundation's areas of interest and geographic guidelines, whether the proposal is within the foundation's budgetary constraints, and whether the foundation normally funds the type of project being considered. For further information, contact the Foundation Center, 79 Fifth Avenue, New York, NY 10003; 800-424-9836; 212-620-4230; {http://fdncenter.org}.

Free Money To Be A
Freelancer

The Joys of Freelancing:
Starting a Business Without Money

More and more people are realizing that there are many benefits to freelancing. In fact, every day more data show that the demand for freelancing is growing. Some analysts estimate that 25% of the nation's workforce is now working on a freelance basis, which includes part time, temporary, and contractual workers[1]. In the last five years, the number of temporary agencies that supply these kinds of workers increased from 3,500 to 7,000[2]. Manpower, one of these temporary agencies, now employs more than General Motors or IBM[3]. Other experts predict that less than 50% of the workforce will be in standard full time jobs by the year 2000[3].

We've heard the terms in recent years: downsizing, rightsizing, restructuring, streamlining, reinventing, and now outsourcing. All this boils down to more and more companies becoming less and less interested in providing for the long term wellbeing of its employees. It's a trend that's likely to continue at an even greater pace. In 1994, corporations experienced record profits, but the number of jobs that were cut was equal to the number they eliminated at the height of the last recession. So, even in good times most corporations are not taking care of employees[4].

Free Money To Be A Freelancer

Companies want to be lean and mean. They want to be flexible and don't want to take on the responsibility and financial burden of full time employees. This may be bad for employees, but it's great for the world of freelancing. And don't think of freelancing as losing benefits: think of it as an exchange of benefits. Your personal freedom and control over your life are worth more than your health and retirement benefits and the security of your job, all of which are disappearing fast anyway. The new status symbol of the 90's won't be doing your own thing, it will be controlling your own time.[5]

Here are some advantages to being a freelancer:

* You can be still looking for a full time job while you are pretending to look for freelancing or consulting work.
* You can give yourself a title while you are out of work, such as an independent consultant, freelance wordprocessor, etc.
* You can take more tax deductions around the home and at play, such as the part of your house and car you use for business. Even some of your meals and entertainment expenses may fall into this category.
* You can have more control over your hours, take vacations when you want, or only work certain days.
* It's ideal for a household member that is only interested in a part time job while staying at home with the kids. A freelance artist can easily work 20 hours a week at home and still be with the children.

And here are some advantages from the employer's eyes. You may even want to include some of these points in your sales letter:

* They don't have to commit to you forever, and then worry about firing you when they want to downsize.
* They don't have to pay you benefits, overhead, supplies, etc.
* They can show their bosses that they are getting more work

done with less people because freelancers are not counted as employees, and are often paid from a different budget than that of full time employees.

* They can get a project done and not worry about keeping those people busy once the project is completed.
* They can get more value for their money by hiring more qualified people for a shorter period of time.
* They have less liability from the potential harmful effects of employee protection laws like Equal Employment Opportunity Laws.

What Do You Need To Be A Freelancer?

The only thing you really need is a customer. And this is basically true for any business. If you have a customer or a client, you're in business. The tools that will make getting a customer easier are a phone, a desk, and business cards. And the next level of tools you will find helpful are a resume, a brochure, or samples of your work.

If you think you need a lot of expensive equipment, you may want to rethink being a freelancer. The beauty of freelancing is that you can start a business without any money. All your money should be invested in getting business, not in equipment.

Even if you think you need to buy a lot of equipment to do the work you want to do, for heaven's sake, don't go out and buy it. Nothing can put you out of business faster than having a lot of equipment around that is not being used because you don't have a lot of business. Rent the equipment only when you need it, or use someone else's equipment at night.

Free Money To Be A Freelancer

Believe me, all your resources should be spent in getting customers. Once you have a steady flow of customers, then you should look into buying your own equipment. Sure it would be nice to have all the fancy equipment you need, right in your house, but in the beginning that can be a ticket to failure. The most important part of being a successful freelancer is staying in business long enough to reap the rewards of all the seeding that you are planting in your "garden of opportunity." What you plant today will come back to you next year, and what you plant next year will come back to you the year after. The trick is to be around a few years from now so that you can enjoy the benefits of what you planted today. Buying all the equipment you need will just run you out of money faster, so that you will have less of a chance of being around and in business next year. It's a game of beat the clock. You have to figure out how to get all the customers you need before you run out of money.

How To Get Free Legal, Marketing, and Tax Advice

What stops many people from starting their own freelancing career is misinformation. Here's the kind of thinking that can go through your head when you think about freelancing. "Gee. I'm going to start a business at home. If something goes wrong, somebody will sue me and I'll lose my house. I wonder if incorporating as a business will protect me?"

Now that the "what ifs" got you, you're smart enough to know that this sounds like a legal question and you'd better talk to an attorney. So you call a friend of a friend who is an attorney and they tell you it will cost you $500 to $1000 to help you solve this problem. You don't have an extra $500 to $1000, so you figure you will put off starting your new career until you get the extra money. **You don't have to do that.** You can get free legal advice on this or any other subject if you just contact one of the local Small Business Development Centers that are located in almost

Information USA, Inc. 275

every city in the country. (See the chapter entitled "Money For A Big or Small Business" for a state-by-state listing of Small Business Development Centers.)

These centers will sit down with you for free and help you figure out any kind of legal, management, financial, or even tax problem you are having in trying to start and develop a business. They will even help you get the business you need. They can help you identify potential clients and will work with you to devise a plan for getting development money. You just can't beat that.

The Government Will Buy Your Freelancing Services

The government buys more freelancing services than anyone else in the world. They buy typing services, legal services, accounting services, and landscaping services, to name just a few. One year the government even spent $30,000 for the services of a freelance priest. And you don't have to be living in Washington, DC to get the work. Only about 20% of all government business is done in Washington, DC. The rest is done all over the country and all over the world.

Freelancing can be your first step to a multimillion dollar business. The time is right and you can do it without any money of your own.

To find out how you can get a freelancing government contact your local Small Business Development Center listed on page 292, or contact the main office at: The Small Business Development Center, 409 Third Street, SW, Suite 4600, Washington, DC 20416, 202-205-6766, {www.sbaonline. sba.gov/SBDC/mission.html}.

The Department of Defense also sponsors a number of Federal Procurement Assistance Offices around the country that offer free help to those who want to sell their goods and services to any government agency. For an office near you, contact The Defense Logistics Agency, Office of Small and Disadvantaged Utilization, Bldg.4, Cameron Station, Room 4B110, Alexandria, VA 22304- 703-767-1661, {www.dla.mil/ddas/}.

Sources:

[1] When Workers Lives Are Contingent On Employers' Whims, Sue Shellenbager, The Wall Street Journal, Page B1, February 1, 1995.

[2] The Network Society, Peter Drucker, The Wall Street Journal, Page A12, March 29, 1995.

[3] Job Shift, William Ridges, Addison-Wesley Publishing Company, Reading, Massachusetts.

[4] Amid Record Profits, Companies Continue To Lay Off Employees, The Wall Street Journal, Page 1, May 4, 1995.

[5] Job Shock, Harry S. Dent, Jr., St. Martin's Press, New York, NY.

Free Local Help:
The Best Place To Start To Sell
To The Government

Within each state there are offices that can help you get started in the federal procurement process. As stated previously, your local Small Business Administration (SBA) office is a good resource. In addition to their other services, the SBA can provide you with a list of Federal Procurement Offices based in your state, so you can visit them in person to gather valuable information. Another place to turn is your local Small Business Development Center (see page 292). These offices are funded jointly by federal and state governments, and are usually associated with the state university system in your area. They are aware of the federal procurement process, and can help you draw up a sensible business plan that will be successful.

Some states have established programs to assist businesses in the federal procurement process for all departments in the government. These programs are designed to help businesses learn about the bidding process, the resources available, and provide information on how the procurement system operates. They can match the product or service you are selling with the appropriate agency, and then help you market your product. Several programs have online bid matching services, whereby if a solicitation appears in the *Commerce Business Daily* that matches what your company markets, then the program will automatically contact you to start the bid process. The program office can then request the appropriate documents, and assist you in achieving your goal. These Procurement Assistance Offices (PAOs) are partially funded by the Department of Defense to assist businesses with Defense Procurement. For a current listing of PAOs contact:

> *Defense Logistics Agency*
> Office of Small and Disadvantaged Utilization
> Bldg. 4, Cameron Station, Room 4B110
> Alexandria, VA 22304-6100
> 703-767-1661
> {www.dla.mil}, then go to the small business site

Let Your Congressman Help You

Are you trying to market a new product to a department of the Federal government? Need to know where to try to sell your wares? Is there some problem with your bid? Your Congressman can be of assistance.

Because they want business in their state to boom, most Congressmen will make an effort to assist companies in obtaining federal contracts. Frequently they will write a letter to accompany your bid, or if you are trying to market a new product, they will write a letter to the procurement office requesting that they review your product.

Your Congressman can also be your personal troubleshooter. If there is some problem with your bid, your Congressman can assist you in determining and resolving the problem, and can provide you with information on the status of your bid. Look in the blue pages of your phone book for your Senators' or Representatives' phone numbers, or call them in Washington at 202-224-3121.

Small Business Set-Asides

The Small Business Administration (SBA) encourages
government purchasing agencies to set aside suitable government
purchases for exclusive small business competition. A purchase
which is restricted to small business bidders is identified by a set
aside clause in the invitation for bids or request for proposals.
There is no overall listing of procurements which are, or have
been, set aside for small business. A small business learns which
purchases are reserved for small business by getting listed on
bidders' lists. It also can help keep itself informed of set aside
opportunities by referring to the *Commerce Business Daily*. Your
local SBA office can provide you with more information on set
asides. To locate your nearest SBA office, call 1-800-827-5722 or
{www.sba.gov}.

Veterans Assistance

Each Small Business Administration District Office has a
Veterans Affairs Officer which can assist veteran-owned
businesses in obtaining government contracts. Although there is
no such thing as veterans set aside contracts, the Veterans
Administration does make an effort to fill its contracts using
veteran-owned businesses whenever possible. Contact your local
SBA office for more information.

Woman-Owned Business Assistance

There are over 3.7 million women-owned businesses in the United
States, and the number is growing each year. Current government
policy requires federal contracting officers to increase their
purchases from women-owned businesses. Although the women-
owned firms will receive more opportunities to bid, they still must
be the lowest responsive and responsible bidder to win the
contract. To assist these businesses, each SBA district office has a

Women's Business Representative, who can provide you with
information regarding government programs. Most of the offices
hold a *Selling to the Federal
Government* seminar, which is
designed to educate the business
owner on the ins and outs of
government procurement. There is
also a helpful publication, *Women
Business Owners: Selling to the Fed-
eral Government*, which provides information on procurement
opportunities available. Contact your local SBA office or your
Procurement Assistance Office (listed below) for more
information.

**SELLING TO THE
FEDERAL
GOVERNMENT**

Minority and Labor Surplus Area Assistance

Are you a socially or economically disadvantaged person who has
a business? This group includes, but is not limited to, Black
Americans, Hispanic Americans, Native Americans, Asian Pacific
Americans, and Subcontinent Asian Americans. Socially and
economically disadvantaged individuals represent a significant
percentage of U.S. citizens, yet account for a disproportionately
small percentage of total U.S. business revenues. The 8(a)
program assists firms to participate in the business sector and to
become independently competitive in the marketplace. SBA may
provide participating firms with procurement, marketing,
financial, management, or other technical assistance. A Business
Opportunity Specialist will be assigned to each firm that
participates, and is responsible for providing that company with
access to assistance that can help it fulfill its business goals.

Some areas of the country have been determined to be labor
surplus areas, which means there is a high rate of unemployment.
Your local SBA office can tell you if you live in such an area, as
some contracts are set asides for labor surplus areas. For more

information, contact your local Small Business Administration office (call 1-800-827-5722 for the SBA office nearest you; or online at {www.sba.gov}), or contact your local Procurement Assistance Office from the Defense Logistics Agency listed on page 279.

State Procurement Assistance

Have you ever wondered where the government buys all of the products that it works with each day? You might be surprised to learn that they buy from small businesses just like yours that produce products such as:

- work clothing
- office supplies
- cleaning equipment
- miscellaneous vehicles
- medical supplies and equipment

Imagine what your bottom line could look like each year if you won just ONE lucrative government contract that would provide your business with a secure income! It might even buy you the freedom to pursue other clients that you wouldn't have the time or money to go after otherwise. If your business performs well and completes a government contract satisfactorily, chances are you'll have a shot at more and maybe even bigger contracts.

The offices listed below are starting places for finding out who in the state government will purchase your products or services.

State Procurement Offices

Alabama
Finance Department
Purchasing Division
100 N. Union
Suite 192
Montgomery, AL 36104
334-242-7250

Fax: 334-242-4419
www.purchasing.state.al.us

Alaska
State of Alaska
Department of Administration
Division of General Services

P.O. Box 110210
Juneau, AK 99811-0210
907-465-2250
Fax: 907-465-2189
www.state.ak.us/local/akpages/
ADMIN/dgs/home.htm

Arizona
State Procurement Office
15 S. 15th Ave., Suite 103
Phoenix, AZ 85007
602-542-5511
Fax: 602-542-5508
http://sporas.ad.state.az.us

Arkansas
Office of State Purchasing
P.O. Box 2940
Little Rock, AR 72203
501-324-9316
Fax: 501-324-9311

California
Office of Procurement
Department of General Services
1823 14th St.
Sacramento, CA 95814
916-445-6942
Fax: 916-323-4609
www.td.dgs.ca.gov/

Colorado
Division of Purchasing
225 E. 16th Ave., Suite 900
Denver, CO 80203
303-866-6100
Fax: 303-894-7444
www.gssa.state.co.us

Connecticut
State of Connecticut
Department of Administrative
Services

Bureau of Purchases
165 Capitol Ave.
Hartford, CT 06106
860-713-5095
Fax: 860-713-7484
www.das.state.ct.us/busopp.htm

Delaware
Purchasing Division
Purchasing Bldg.
P.O. Box 299
Delaware City, DE 19706
302-834-4550
Fax: 302-836-7642
www.state.de.us/purchase

District of Columbia
Office of Contracts and
Procurement
441 4th St. NW, Suite 800
Washington, DC 20001
202-727-0252
Fax: 202-724-5673
www.ci.washington.dc.us

Florida
General Service Department
Division of Purchasing
4050 Esplanade Way
Tallahassee, FL 32399-0950
850-488-5498
http://purchasing.state.us/

Georgia
Administrative Services
Department
200 Piedmont Ave.
Room 1308 SE
Atlanta, GA 30334
404-656-3240
Fax: 404-651-6963
www.doas.state.ga.us

Free Money To Be A Freelancer

Hawaii
Purchasing Branch
Purchasing and Supply Division
Department of Accounting and
General Services
Room 416, 1151 Punch Bowl St.
Honolulu, HI 96813
808-586-0575
Fax: 808-586-0570
www.state.hi.us/icsd/dags/
spo.html

Idaho
Division of Purchasing
Administration Department
5569 Kendall St.
State House Mall
Boise, ID 83720
208-327-7465
Fax: 208-327-7320
www2.state.id.us/adm/purchasing

Illinois
Department of Central
Management Services
Procurement Services
801 Stratton Bldg.
Springfield, IL 62706
217-782-2301
Fax: 217-782-5187
www.state.il.us/cms

Indiana
Department of Administration
Procurement Division
402 W. Washington St.
Room W-468
Indianapolis, IN 46204
317-232-3032
Fax: 317-232-7213
www.state.in.us/idoa/proc

Iowa
State of Iowa
Department of General Services
Purchasing Division
Hoover State Office Building
Des Moines, IA 50319
515-281-3089
Fax: 515-242-5974
www.state.ia.us/government/dgs/
csap/purhome/business.htm

Kansas
Division of Purchasing
Room 102 North
Landon State Office Bldg.
900 SW Jackson St.
Topeka, KS 66612
785-296-2376
Fax: 785-296-7240
http://da.state.ks.us/purch

Kentucky
Purchases, Department of Finance
Room 367, Capital Annex
Frankfort, KY 40601
502-564-4510
Fax: 502-564-7209
http://purch.state.ky.us

Louisiana
State Purchasing Office
Division of Administration
P.O. Box 94095
Baton Rouge, LA 70804-9095
225-342-8010
Fax: 225-342-8688
www.doa.state.la.us/osp/osp.htm

Maine
Bureau of Purchases
State House Station #9
Augusta, ME 04333

207-287-3521
Fax: 207-287-6578
http://janus.state.me.us/purchase

Maryland
Purchasing Bureau
301 W. Preston St.
Mezzanine, Room M8
Baltimore, MD 21201
410-767-4600
Fax: 410-333-5482
www.dgs.state.md.us

Massachusetts
Purchasing Agent Division
One Ashburton Place
Room 1017
Boston, MA 02108
617-727-7500
Fax: 617-727-4527
www.comm-pass.com

Michigan
Office of Purchasing
Mason Bldg.
P.O. Box 30026
Lansing, MI 48909
or 530 W. Ellegan, 48933
517-373-0330
Fax: 517-335-0046
www.state.mi.us/dmd/oop

Minnesota
State of Minnesota
Department of Administration
Suite 112, Administration
Building
50 Sherburne Ave.
St. Paul, MN 55155
651-296-6152
Fax: 651-297-3996
www.mmd.admin.state.mn.us

Mississippi
Office of Purchasing and Travel
1504 Sillers Bldg.
550 High St., Suite 1504
Jackson, MS 39201
601-359-3409
Fax: 601-359-3910
www.dfa.state.ms.us

Missouri
State of Missouri
Division of Purchasing
P.O. Box 809
Jefferson City, MO 65102
573-751-2387
Fax: 573-751-2387
www.oa.state.mo.us/purch/
bids.htm

Montana
Department of Administration
Procurement Division
165 Mitchell Bldg.
Helena, MT 59620-0135
406-444-2575
Fax: 406-444-2529
www.state.mt.us/doa/ppd

Nebraska
State Purchasing Division
301 Centennial Mall S.
P.O. Box 94847
Lincoln, NE 68509
402-471-2401
Fax: 402-471-2089
www.nol.org/home/DASMAT

Nevada
Nevada State Purchasing Division
209 E. Musser St., Room 304
Blasdel Bldg.
Carson City, NV 89710
702-684-0170
Fax: 702-684-0188
www.state.nv.us/purchasing/

New Hampshire
State Purchasing Department
25 Capitol St.
State House Annex, Room 102
Concord, NH 03301
603-271-2201
Fax: 603-271-2700
www.state.nh.us/das/purchasing/
index.html

New Jersey
Division of Purchase and Property
P.O. Box 039
Trenton, NJ 08625
609-292-4886
Fax: 609-984-2575
www.state.nj.us/treasury/purchase

New Mexico
State Purchasing Division
1100 St. Frances Dr.
Room 2016
Joseph Montoya Bldg.
Santa Fe, NM 87503
505-827-0472
Fax: 505-827-2484
www.state.nm.us/spd

New York
Division of Purchasing
Corning Tower
Empire State Plaza, 38th Floor
Albany, NY 12242
518-474-3695
Fax: 518-486-6099
www.ogs.state.ny.us

North Carolina
Department of Administration
Division of Purchase and Contract
116 W. Jones St.
Raleigh, NC 27603-8002
919-733-3581
Fax: 919-733-4782
www.state.nc.us/pandc/

North Dakota
Central Services Division of State
Purchasing
Purchasing
600 E Boulevard, I Wing
Bismarck, ND 58505-0420
701-328-2683
Fax: 701-328-1615
www.state.nd.us/centserv

Ohio
State Purchasing
4200 Surface Rd.
Columbus, OH 43228-1395
614-466-4635
Fax: 614-466-2059
www.gsa.ohio.gov/gsa/ods/
pur/pur.html

Oklahoma
Office of Public Affairs
Central Purchasing Division
Suite 116, Rogers Bldg.
2401 N. Lincoln
Oklahoma City, OK 73105
405-521-2110
Fax: 405-521-4475
www.dcs.state.ok.us

Oregon
General Services
Purchasing and Print Services
Division
1225 Ferry St.
Salem, OR 97310
503-378-4643
Fax: 503-373-1626
tpps.das.state.or.us/purchasing

Pennsylvania
Procurement Department
Secretary
N. Office Bldg., Room 414
Commonwealth and North St.
Harrisburg, PA 17125
717-787-5733
Fax: 717-783-6241
www.dgs.state.pa.us

Rhode Island
Department of Administration
Purchases Office
One Capital Hill
Providence, RI 02908-5855
401-222-2317
Fax: 401-222-6387
www.purchasing.state.ri.us

South Carolina
Materials Management Office
General Service Budget and
Control Board
1201 Main St., Suite 600
Columbia, SC 29201
803-737-0600
Fax: 803-737-0639
www.state.sc.us/mmo/mmo/

South Dakota
Division of Purchasing
523 E. Capitol Ave.

Pierre, SD 57501
605-773-3405
Fax: 605-773-4840
www.state.sd.us/boa

Tennessee
Department of General Services
Division of Purchasing
Third Floor, Tennessee Towers
312 8th Ave. North
Nashville, TN 37243-0557
615-741-1035
Fax: 615-741-0684
www.state.tn.us/generalser/
purchasing

Texas
State Purchasing and General
Services Commission
P.O. Box 13047
Austin, TX 78711
512-463-3445
Fax: 512-463-7073
www.gsc.state.tx.us

Utah
Purchasing Division
Dept. of Administrative Services
State Office Bldg., Room 3150
Salt Lake City, UT 84114
801-538-3026
Fax: 801-538-3882
www.purchasing.state.ut.us

Vermont
Purchasing and Contract
Admiistration Division
128 State St., Drawer 33
Montpelier, VT 05633-7501
802-828-2211
Fax: 802-828-2222
www.bgf.state.vt.us/pca

Free Money To Be A Freelancer

Virginia
Department of General Services
Purchasing Division
P.O. Box 1199
Richmond, VA 23209
804-786-3842
Fax: 804-371-8936
www.dgs.state.va.us/dps

Washington
Office of State Procurement
Suite 201, General Admin Bldg.
210 11th Ave. SW
Olympia, WA 98504-1017
360-902-7400
Fax: 360-586-2426
www.ga.wa.gov/proc.htm

West Virginia
Department of Administration
Purchasing Section
Building 15
2019 Washington St. East
Charleston, WV 25305-0110
304-558-2306
Fax: 304-558-6026
www.state.wv.us/admin/purchase

Wisconsin
Division of State Agency Services
Bureau of Procurement
101 E. Wilson, 6th Floor
P.O. Box 7867
Madison, WI 53707-7867
608-266-2605
Fax: 608-267-0600
http://vendornet.state.wi.us

Wyoming
Department of Administration
Procurement Services
2001 Capitol Ave.
Cheyenne, WY 82002
307-777-7253
Fax: 307-777-5852
www.state.wy.us

Money For A Big Or Small
Business

The Best Starting Places
For Starting A Business

Small Business Development Centers (SBDCs) could be the best
deal the government has to offer to entrepreneurs and inventors,
and a lot of people don't even know about them! Where else in the
world can you have access to a $150 an hour consultant for free?
There are over 700 of these offices all over the
country and they offer free (or very low cost)
consulting services on most aspects of
business including:

* how to write a business plan
* how to get financing
* how to protect your invention
* how to sell your idea
* how to license your product
* how to comply with the laws
* how to write a contract
* how to sell overseas
* how to get government contracts
* how to help you buy the right equipment

You don't even have to know how to spell ENTREPRENEUR to
contact these offices. They cater to both the dreamer, who doesn't
even know where to start, as well as to the experienced small
business that is trying to grow to the next stage of development. In
other words, the complete novice or the experienced professional
can find help through these centers.

Information USA, Inc.

Why spend money on a consultant, a lawyer, an accountant, or one of those invention companies when you can get it all for free at your local SBDC?

Recently, I spoke with some entrepreneurs who used a California SBDC and each of them had nothing but praise for the services. A young man who dropped out of college to start an executive cleaning business said he received over $8,000 worth of free legal advice from the center and said it was instrumental in getting his business off the ground. A woman who worked in a bank started her gourmet cookie business by using the SBDC to help her get the money and technical assistance needed to get her venture up and running. And a man who was a gymnast raved about how the SBDC helped him get his personal trainer business off the ground. All kinds of businesses being started, and all kinds of compliments for the SBDC's role in assisting these entrepreneurs, in whatever they are attempting. It sounds like a solid recommendation to me.

Money and Technical Assistance

Can something that is free be so good? Of course it can. Because most of the people who work there are not volunteers, they are paid for by tax dollars. So it's really not free to us as a country, but it is free to you as an entrepreneur. And if you don't believe me that the SBDCs are so good, would you take the word of Professor James J. Chrisman from the University of Calgary in Calgary, Alberta, Canada? He was commissioned to do an independent study of SBDCs and found that 82% of the people who used their services found them beneficial. And the businesses who used SBDCs had average growth rates of up to 400% greater than all the other businesses in their area. Not bad. Compare this to the Fortune 500 companies who use the most expensive consulting firms in the country and only experience growth rates of 5% or less. So, who says you get what you pay for?

Small Business Development Centers

Alabama

Lead Center:
Office of State Director
Alabama Small Business Development
Consortium
University of Alabama at Birmingham
1717 11th Ave. S.
Suite 419
Birmingham, AL 35294-7645
205-934-7260
Fax: 205-934-7645

Auburn University
Small Business Development Center
108 College of Business
Auburn, AL 36849-5243
334-844-4220
Fax: 334-844-4268

University of Alabama at Birmingham
Small Business Development Center
1601 11th Ave. S.
Birmingham, AL 35294-2180
205-934-6760
Fax: 205-934-0538

Alabama Small Business Procurement
System
University of Alabama at Birmingham
Small Business Development Center
1717 11th Ave. S., Suite 419
Birmingham, AL 35294-4410
205-934-7260
Fax: 205-934-7645

University of North Alabama
Small Business Development Center
P.O. Box 5248
Keller Hall, School of Business
Florence, AL 35632-0001
205-760-4629
Fax: 205-760-4813

North East Alabama Regional Small
Business Development Center
Alabama A&M University and University of
Alabama in Huntsville
225 Church St., NW
Huntsville, AL 35804-0168

205-535-2061
Fax: 205-535-2050

Jacksonville State University
Small Business Development Center
114 Merrill Hall
Jacksonville, AL 36265
205-782-5271
Fax: 205-782-5179

Livingston University
Small Business Development Center
212 Wallace Hall
Livingston, AL 35470
205-652-9661, ext. 439
Fax: 205-652-9318

University of South Alabama
Small Business Development Center
8 College of Business
Mobile, AL 36688
334-460-6004
Fax: 334-460-6246

Alabama State University
Small Business Development Center
915 S. Jackson St.
Montgomery, AL 36195
334-229-4138
Fax: 334-269-1102

Troy State University
Small Business Development Center
102 Bibb Graves
Troy, AL 36082-0001
205-670-3771
Fax: 205-670-3636

Alabama International Trade Center
University of Alabama
250 Bidgood Hall
Tuscaloosa, AL 35487-0396
205-348-7621
Fax: 205-348-6974

University of Alabama
Small Business Development Center
250 Bidgood Hall
Tuscaloosa, AL 35487-0397

Information USA, Inc.

205-348-7011
Fax: 205-348-9644

Alaska
Lead Center:
Jan Fredericks
University of Alaska
Small Business Development Center
430 West 7th Ave., Suite 110
Anchorage, AK 99501
907-274-7232
Fax: 907-274-9524
Outside Anchorage: 800-478-7232

University of Alaska-Anchorage Small
Business Development Center
430 West 7th Ave., Suite 110
Anchorage, AK 99501
907-274-7232
Fax: 907-274-9524
outside Anchorage: 800-478-7232.

University of Alaska-Fairbanks
Small Business Development Center
510 Fifth Ave., Suite 101
Fairbanks, AK 99701
907-456-1701
Fax: 907-456-1873
outside Fairbanks: 800-478-1701

Southeast Alaska Small Business
Development Center
400 Willoughby St., Suite 211
Juneau, AK 99801
907-463-3789
Fax: 907-463-3929

Matanuska-Susitna Borough
Small Business Development Center
1801 Parks Highway, #C-18
Wasilla, AK 99654
907-373-7232
Fax: 907-373-2560

Kenai Peninsula
Small Business Development Center
110 S. Willow St., Suite 106
Kenai, AK 99611-7744
907-283-3335
Fax: 907-283-3913

Arizona
Lead Center:
Arizona Small Business Development Ctr.
9215 N. Black Canyon Highway
Phoenix, AZ 85021
602-943-9818
Fax: 602-943-3716

Coconino County Community College
Small Business Development Center
3000 N. 4th St., Suite 25
Flagstaff, AZ 86004
520-526-5072
Fax: 520-526-8693
1-800-350-7122

Northland Pioneer College
Small Business Development Center
P.O. Box 610
Holbrook, AZ 86025
520-537-2976
Fax: 520-524-2227

Mojave Community College
Small Business Development Center
1971 Jagerson Ave.
Kingman, AZ 86401
520-757-0894
Fax: 520-787-0836

Rio Salado Community College
Small Business Development Center
301 West Roosevelt, Suite B
Phoenix, AZ 85003
602-238-9603
Fax: 602-340-1627

Gateway Community College
Small Business Development Center
108 N. 40th St.
Phoenix, AZ 85034
602-392-5223
Fax: 602-392-5329

Yavapal College
Small Business Development Center
117 E. Gurley St., Suite 206
Prescott, AZ 86301
602-778-3088
Fax: 602-778-3109

Cochise College
Small Business Development Center
901 N. Colombo, Room 411
Sierra Vista, AZ 85635
602-459-9778
Fax: 602-459-9737
1-800-966-7943, ext. 778

Eastern Arizona College
Small Business Development Center
622 College Ave.
Thatcher, AZ 85552-0769
602-428-8590
Fax: 602-428-8462

Pima Community College
Small Business Development Center
4903 E. Broadway, Suite 101
Tucson, AZ 85709-1260
602-748-4906
Fax: 602-748-4585

Arizona Western College
Small Business Development Center
281 W. 24th St.
#152 Century Plaza
Yuma, AZ 85364
520-341-1650
Fax: 520-726-2636

Arkansas
Lead Center:
Arkansas Small Business Development
Center
University of Arkansas at Little Rock
Little Rock Technology Center Building
100 S. Main, Suite 401
Little Rock, AR 72201
501-324-9043
Fax: 501-324-9049

Henderson State University
Small Business Development Center
P.O. Box 7624
Arkadelphia, AR 71923
501-230-5224
Fax: 501-230-5236

University of Arkansas at Fayetteville
Small Business Development Center
College of Business - BA 117

Fayetteville, AR 72701
501-575-5148
Fax: 501-575-4013

Arkansas State University
Small Business Development Center
P.O. Box 1403
Jonesboro, AR 72467
501-932-3957
Fax:-501-932-0135

Genesis Technology Incubator--Small
Business Development Center (SBDC)
University of Arkansas Engineering
Research Center
Fayetteville, AR 72701-1201
501-575-7446
Fax: 501-575-7446

W. Arkansas Regional Office
Small Business Development Center
1109 S. 16th St.
P.O. Box 2067
Fort Smith, AR 72901
501-785-1376
Fax: 501-785-1964

NW Arkansas Regional Office--SBDC
818 Highway 62-65-412 N.
P.O. Box 190
Harrison, AR 72601
501-741-8009
Fax: 501-741-1905

W. Central Arkansas Regional Office
Small Business Development Center
835 Central Ave., Box 402-D
Hot Springs, AR 71901
501-624-5448
Fax: 501-624-6632

NE Arkansas Regional Office--SBDC
100 S. Main, Suite 401
Little Rock, AR 72201
501-324-9043
Fax: 501-324-9079

SW Arkansas Regional Office
Small Business Development Center
600 Bessie, P.O. Box 767
Magnolia, AR 71753
501-234-4030
Fax: 501-234-0135

SE Arkansas Regional Office--SBDC
Enterprise Center III
400 Main, Suite 117
Pine Bluff, AR 71601
501-536-0654
Fax: 501-536-7713

Arkansas State University--SBDC
Drawer 1650
State University, AR 72467
501-972-3517
Fax: 501-972-3868

Stuttgart Regional Office--SBDC
301 S. Grand, Suite 101
P.O. Box 289
Stuttgart, AR 72160
501-673-8707
Fax: 501-673-8707

California
Lead Center:
California Small Business Development
Center
California Department of Commerce
Office of Small Business
801 K St., Suite 1700
Sacramento, CA 95814
916-322-3502
Fax: 916-322-5084

Central Coast Small Business Assistance
Center
6500 Soquel Dr.
Aptos, CA 95003
408-479-6136
Fax: 408-479-6166

Sierra College
Small Business Development Center
560 Wall St., Suite J
Auburn, CA 95603
916-885-5488
Fax: 916-823-4142

Weill Institute
Small Business Development Center
1330 22nd St., Suite B
Bakersfield, CA 93301
805-322-5881
Fax: 805-322-5663

Butte College
Tri-County Small Business Development
Center
260 Cohasset Ave., Suite A
Chico, CA 95926
916-895-9017
Fax: 916-895-9099

Southwestern College
Small Business Development Center and
International Trade Center
900 Otay Lakes Rd.
Building 1600
Chula Vista, CA 91910
619-482-6393
Fax: 619-482-6402

Satellite Operation
Small Business Development Center
Hilltop Professional Center
Suite 205, Box 4550
Clearlake, CA 95422-4550
707-996-3440
Fax: 707-995-3605

North Coast Small Business Development
Center
207 Price Mall
Crescent City, CA 95531
707-464-2168
Fax: 707-445-9652

North Coast Satellite Center
529 E. St.
Eureka, CA 95501
707-465-6008
Fax: 707-445-9652

Central California Small Business
Development Center
1999 Tuolumine St., Suite 650
Fresno, CA 93721
209-275-1223
Fax: 209-275-1499

Money For A Big Or Small Business

Gavilan College
Small Business Development Center
7436 Monterey St.
Gilroy, CA 95020
408-847-0373
Fax: 408-847-0393

Accelerate Technology Small Business
Development Center
Graduate School of Management
Room 230, University of California
Irvine, CA 92717-3125
714-509-2990
Fax: 714-509-2997

Greater San Diego Chamber of Commerce
Small Business Development Center
4275 Executive Square, Suite 920
La Jolla, CA 92037
619-453-9388
Fax: 619-450-1997

Export Small Business Development Center
of Southern California
110 E. 9th, Suite 669
Los Angeles, CA 90079
213-892-1111
Fax: 213-892-8232

Satellite Operation
Small Business Development Center
1632 N. St.
Merced, CA 95340
209-385-7312
Fax: 209-383-4959

Valley Sierra SBDC
1012 11th St., Suite 300
Modesto, CA 95354
209-521-6177
Fax: 209-521-9373

Napa Valley College
Small Business Development Center
1556 First St., Suite 103
Napa, CA 94559
707-253-3210
Fax: 707-253-3068

East Bay Small Business Development
Center
519 17th St., Suite 210

Oakland, CA 94612
510-893-4114
Fax: 510-893-5532

Satellite Operation
Small Business Development Center
300 Esplanade Dr., Suite 1010
Oxnard, CA 93030
805-981-4633
Fax: 805-988-1862

Eastern Los Angeles County Small Business
Development Center
363 Main St., Suite 101
Pomona, CA 91766
909-629-2247
Fax: 909-629-8310

Inland Empire Small Business Development
Center
2002 Iowa Ave., Suite 110
Riverside, CA 92507
909-781-2345
Fax: 909-781-2345

Greater Sacramento Small Business
Development Center
1410 Ethan Way
Sacramento, CA 95815
916-563-3210
Fax: 916-563-3264

Silicon Valley - San Mateo County
Small Business Development Center
111 N. Market St., #150
San Jose, CA 95113
408-298-7694
Fax: 408-971-0680

San Mateo County Satellite Center
Bayshore Corporate Center
1730 S. Amphlett Blvd., Suite 208
San Mateo, CA 94402
415-358-0271
Fax: 415-358-9450

Rancho Santiago Small Business
Development Center
901 East Santa Ana Blvd., Suite 101
Santa Ana, CA 92701
714-647-1172
Fax: 714-835-9008

Money For A Big Or Small Business

Redwood Empire
Small Business Development Center
520 Mendocino Ave., Suite 210
Santa Rosa, CA 95401
707-524-1770
Fax: 707-524-1772

San Joaquin Delta College
Small Business Development Center
814 N. Hunter
Stockton, CA 95202
209-474-5089
Fax: 209-474-5605

Solano County Small Business Development
Center
320 Campus Lane
Suisun, CA 94585
707-864-3382
Fax: 707-864-3386

Southwest Los Angeles County Small
Business Development Center
21221 Western Ave., Suite 110
Torrance, CA 90501
310-782-6466
Fax: 310-782-8607

Northern Los Angeles Small Business
Development Center
14540 Victory Blvd., Suite #206
Van Nuys, CA 91411
818-373-7092
Fax: 818-373-7740

Satellite Operation
Central California Small Business
Development Center
430 W. Caldwell, Suite D
Visalia, CA 93277
209-625-3051/3052
Fax: 209-625-3053

Colorado
Lead Center:
Colorado Small Business Development
Center
Office of Economic Development
1625 Broadway, Suite 1710
Denver, CO 80202
303-892-3809
Fax: 303-892-3848

Adams State College
Small Business Development Center
Alamosa, CO 81102
719-589-7372
Fax: 719-589-7522

Canon City (Satellite)
402 Valley Rd.
Canon City, CO 81212
719-275-5335
Fax: 719-275-4400

Pikes Peak Community College/
Colorado Springs Chamber of Commerce
Small Business Development Center
P.O. Drawer B
Colorado Springs, CO 80901-3002
303-471-4836
Fax: 303-635-1571

Colorado Northwestern Community College
Small Business Development Center
50 College Dr.
Craig, CO 81625
970-824-7078
Fax: 970-824-3527

Delta Montrose Vocational School
Small Business Development Center
1765 U.S. Highway 50
Delta, CO 81416
970-874-8772
Fax: 970-874-8796

Community College of Denver/
Denver Chamber of Commerce
Small Business Development Center
1445 Market St.
Denver, CO 80202
303-620-8076
Fax: 303-534-3200

Fort Lewis College
Small Business Development Center
Miller Student Center, Room 108
Durango, CO 81301
970-247-9634
Fax: 970-247-7620

Morgan Community College
Small Business Development Center
300 Main St.

Fort Morgan, CO 80701
970-867-3351
Fax: 970-867-3352

State Colleges

Mesa State College
Small Business Development Center
304 W. Main St.
Grand Junction, CO 81505-1606
970-243-5242
Fax: 970-241-0771

Aims Community College/Greeley and Weld
Chamber of Commerce
Small Business Development Center
902 7th Ave.
Greeley, CO 80631
970-352-3661
Fax: 970-352-3572

Red Rocks Community College
Small Business Development Center
777 S. Wadsworth Blvd.
Lakewood CO 80226
303-987-0710
Fax: 303-987-1331

Lamar Community College
Small Business Development Center
2400 S. Main
Lamar, CO 81052
719-336-8141
Fax: 719-336-2448

Arapaho Community College/
South Metro Chamber of Commerce
Small Business Development Center
7901 S. Park Plaza, Suite 110
Littleton, CO 80120
303-795-5855
Fax: 303-795-7520

Pueblo Community College
Small Business Development Center

900 West Orman Ave.
Pueblo, CO 81004
719-549-3224
Fax: 719-546-2413

Stratton (Satellite)
P.O. Box 28
Stratton, CO 80836
719-348-5596
Fax: 719-348-5887

Trinidad State Junior College
Small Business Development Center
136 W. Main St.
Trinidad, CO 81082
719-846-5645
Fax: 719-846-4550

Front Range Community College
Small Business Development Center
3645 West 112th Ave.
Westminster, CO 80030
303-460-1032
Fax: 303-469-7143

Connecticut
Lead Center:
Connecticut Small Business Development
Center
University of Connecticut
School of Business Administration
2 Bourn Place, U-94
Storrs, CT 06269
806-486-4135
Fax: 806-486-1576

Business Regional B.C.
Small Business Development Center
10 Middle St., 14th Floor
Bridgeport, CT 06604-4229
203-330-4813
Fax: 203-366-0105

Quinebaug Valley Community College
Small Business Development Center
742 Upper Maple St.
Danielson, CT 06239-1440
203-774-1133
Fax: 203-774-7768

University of Connecticut/MBA
Small Business Development Center
1800 Asylum Ave.
West Hartford, CT 06117
860-241-4986
Fax: 860-241-4907

University of Connecticut
Small Business Development Center
Administration Building, Room 300
1084 Shennecossett Rd.
Groton, CT 06340-6097
860-449-1188
Fax: 860-445-3415

Middlesex County Chamber of Commerce
Small Business Development Center
393 Main St.
Middletown, CT 06457
860-344-2158
Fax: 860-346-1043

Greater New Haven Chamber of Commerce
Small Business Development Center
195 Church St.
New Haven, CT 06510-2009
203-782-4390 ext. 190
Fax: 203-787-6730

Southwestern Area Commerce and Industry
Association (SACIA)
Small Business Development Center
One Landmark Square
Stamford, CT 06901
203-359-3220 ext. 302
Fax: 203-967-8294

Greater Waterbury Chamber of Commerce
Small Business Development Center
101 Main St.
Waterbury, CT 06706-1042
203-757-8937
Fax: 203-756-9077

Eastern Connecticut State University
Small Business Development Center
83 Windham St.
Willmantic, CT 06226-2295
960-456-5349
Fax: 960-456-5670

Delaware

Lead Center:
Delaware Small Business Development
Center
University of Delaware
Purnell Hall, Suite 005
Newark, DE 19716
302-831-1555
Fax: 302-831-1423

Sussex County Department of Economic
Development
PO Box 610
Georgetown, DE 19947
302-856-1555
Fax: 302-856-5779

Delaware State University
1200 N. Dupont Highway
Dover, DE 19801
302-678-1555
Fax: 302-739-2333

Small Business Resource & Information
Center
1318 N. Market St.
Wilmington, DE 19801
302-571-1555

District of Columbia

Lead Center:
District of Columbia Small Business
Development Center
Howard University
6th and Fairmont St., NW
Room 128
Washington, DC 20059
202-806-1550
Fax: 202-806-1777

Small Business Clinic
720 20th St., NW
Washington, DC 20052
202-994-7463
Fax: 202-994-4946

Office of Latino Affairs
2000 14th St. NW, 2nd Floor
Washington, DC 20009
202-396-1200

Money For A Big Or Small Business

George Washington University
3101 MLK Jr. Ave. SE, 3rd Floor
Washington, DC 20010
202-561-4975 ext. 3006

Marshall Heights Community Development
Organization
3917 Minnesota Ave. NE
Washington, DC 20019
202-396-1200

Ward Five Community Development Corp.
Small Business Development Center
901 Newton St. NE, Suite 103
Washington, DC 20017
202-396-4106
Fax: 202-396-4106

Florida

Lead Center:
Florida Small Business Development Center
Network
University of West Florida
Downtown Center
19 W. Garden St., Suite 300
Pensacola, FL 32501
904-444-2060
Fax: 904-444-2070

Seminole Community College
Small Business Development Center
Seminole Chamber of Commerce
P.O. Box 150784
AltaMonte Springs FL 32715-0784
407-834-4404

Florida Atlantic University
Small Business Development Center
Building T-9
P.O. Box 3091
Boca Raton, FL 33431
407-362-5620
Fax: 407-362-5623

Brevard Community College
Small Business Development Center
1519 Clearlake Rd.
Cocoa, FL 32922
407-951-1060, ext. 2045

Small Business Development Center
46 SW 1st Ave.
Dania, FL 33304
305-987-0100

Small Business Development Center
Florida Atlantic University
Commercial Campus
1515 West Commercial Blvd., Room 11
Fort Lauderdale, FL 33309
954-771-6520
Fax: 954-776-6645

Indian River Community College
Small Business Development Center
3209 Virginia Ave., Room 114
Fort Pierce, FL 34981-5599
407-462-4796
Fax: 407-462-4796

University of South Florida
Small Business Development Center
Sabal Hall, Rooms 219 and 220
8099 College Parkway SW
Fort Myers, FL 33919
941-489-9200
Fax: 941-489-9051

University of West Florida
Fort Walton Beach Center
Small Business Development Center
1170 Martin Luther King, Jr. Blvd.
Fort Walton Beach, FL 32547
904-863-6543
Fax: 904-863-6564

Small Business Development Center
505 NW 2nd Ave., Suite D
P.O. Box 2518
Gainesville, FL 32601
352-377-5621
Fax: 352-372-4132

University of North Florida
Small Business Development Center
College of Business
4567 St. John's Bluff Rd., S.
Jacksonville, FL 32216
904-646-2476
Fax: 904-646-2594

Information USA, Inc.

Gulf Coast Community College
Small Business Development Center
2500 Minnesota Ave.
Lynn Haven, FL 32444
904-271-1108
Fax: 904-271-1109

Florida International University
Small Business Development Center
Trailer MO1, Tamiami Campus
Miami, FL 33199
305-348-2272

Small Business Development Center
600 N. Broadway, Suite 300
Bartow, FL 33830
941-534-4370
Fax: 941-533-1247

Daytona Beach Community College
Small Business Development Center
1200 W. International Speedway Blvd.
Daytona Beach, FL 32114
904-947-3141
Fax: 904-254-4465

Minority Business Development Center
5950 W. Oakland Park Blvd., Suite 307
Fort Lauderdale, FL 33313
954-485-5333
Fax: 954-485-2514

Florida Gulf Coast University
The Midway Ctr.
17595 Tamiami Tr., Suite 200
Fort Myers, FL 33908
941-590-1053

Miami Dade Community College--SBDC
6300 NW 7th Ave.
Miami, FL 33150
305-237-1906
Fax: 305-237-1908

Seminole Community College--SBDC
100 Weldon Blvd., Bldg. R
Sanford, FL 32707
407-328-4755 ext. 3341
Fax: 407-330-4489

Small Business Development Center
110 East Silver Springs Blvd.

P.O. Box 1210
Ocala, FL 32670
352-629-8051

University of Central Florida
Small Business Development Center
P.O. Box 161530
Orlando, FL 32816-1530
407-823-5554
Fax: 407-823-3073

University of West Florida
Small Business Development Center
Building 8, 11000 University Parkway
Pensacola, FL 32514
904-474-2908
Fax: 904-474-2126

Florida A & M University
Small Business Development Center
1157 Tennessee St.
Tallahassee, FL 32308
904-599-3407
Fax: 904-561-2395

University of South Florida
Small Business Development Center
College of Business Administration
4202 Minnesota Ave., BSN 3403
Tampa, FL 32444
813-974-4274

Small Business Development Center
Prospect Place, Suite 123
3111 S. Dixie Highway
West Palm Beach, FL 33405
407-837-5311

Georgia
Lead Center:
Georgia Small Business Development Center
University of Georgia
Chicopee Complex
1180 East Broad St.
Athens, GA 30602
706-542-6762
Fax: 706-542-6776

Small Business Development Center
Southwest Georgia District
Business and Technology Center

230 S. Jackson St., 3rd Floor, Suite 333
Albany, GA 31701-2885
912-430-4303
Fax: 912-430-3933

Small Business Development Center
University of Georgia
Chicopee Complex
1180 East Broad St.
Athens, GA 30602-5412
706-542-7436
Fax: 706-542-6823

Morris Brown College
Small Business Development Center
643 Martin Luther King Jr. Dr., NW
Atlanta, GA 30314
404-220-0205
Fax: 404-688-5985

Georgia State University
Small Business Development Center
Box 874, University Plaza
Atlanta, GA 30303-3083
706-651-3550
Fax: 706-651-1035

Small Business Development Center
1061 Katherine St.
Augusta, GA 30904-6105
706-737-1790
Fax: 706-731-7937

Small Business Development Center
1107 Fountain Lake Dr.
Brunswick, GA 31525-3039
912-264-7343
Fax: 912-262-3095

Small Business Development Center
928 45th St. North Bldg., Room 523
Columbus, GA 31904-6572
706-649-7433
Fax: 706-649-1928

DeKalb Chamber of Commerce
Small Business Development Center
750 Commerce Dr.
Decatur, GA 30030-2622
404-378-8000
Fax: 404-378-3397

Small Business Development Center
500 Jesse Jewel Parkway
Suite 304
Gainesville, GA 30501
706-531-5681
Fax: 706-531-5684

Small Business Development Center
P.O. Box 13212
401 Cherry St., Suite 701
Macon, GA 31208-3212
912-751-6592
Fax: 912-751-6607

Kennesaw State College
Small Business Development Center
1000 Chastian Rd.
Kennesaw, GA 30144-5591
770-423-6450
Fax: 770-423-6564

Clayton State College
Small Business Development Center
P.O. Box 285
Morrow, GA 30260
404-961-3440
Fax: 404-961-3428

Floyd College
Small Business Development Center
P.O. Box 1664
Rome, GA 30162-1864
404-295-6326
Fax: 404-295-6732

Small Business Development Center
450 Mall Blvd., Suite H
Savannah, GA 31406-4824
912-356-2755
Fax: 912-353-3033

Money For A Big Or Small Business

Small Business Development Center
3255 S. Main St.
Statesboro, GA 30460
912-681-5194
Fax: 912-681-0648

Small Business Development Center
Valdosta Area Office
Baytree West Professional Offices
Suite 9, Baytree Rd.
Valdosta, GA 31602-2782
912-245-3738
Fax: 912-245-3741

Middle Georgia Technical Institute
Small Business Development Center
151 Osigian Blvd.
Warner Robins, GA 31088
912-953-9356
Fax: 912-953-9376

Hawaii
Lead Center:
Hawaii Small Business Development Center
University of Hawaii at Hilo
200 W. Kawili St.
Hilo, HI 96720-4091
808-933-3515
Fax: 808-933-3683

Small Business Development Center - Kauai
Kauai Community College
3-1901 Kaumualii Highway
Lihue, HI 96766-9591
808-246-1748
Fax: 808-245-5102

Small Business Development Center - Maui
Maui Research and Technology Center
590 Lipoa Parkway
Kihei, HI 96753
808-875-2402

Small Business Development Center - Oahu
Business Action Center
130 N. Merchant St., Suite 1030
Honolulu, HI 96813
808-522-8131
Fax: 808-522-8135

Idaho
Lead Center:
Idaho Small Business Development Center
Boise State University
College of Business
1910 University Dr.
Boise, ID 83725
208-385-1640
Fax: 208-385-3877

Idaho State University
Small Business Development Center
2300 N. Yellowstone
Idaho Falls, ID 83401
208-523-1087
Fax: 208-523-1049

Lewis-Clark State College
Small Business Development Center
500 8th Ave.
Lewiston, ID 83501
208-799-2465
Fax: 208-799-2831

Boise Satellite Office
Small Business Development Center
Boise State University
305 E. Park St., Suite 405
McCall, ID 83638
208-634-2883

Idaho State University
Small Business Development Center
1651 Alvin Ricken Dr.
Pocatello, ID 83201
208-232-4921
Fax: 208-233-0268

North Idaho College
Small Business Development Center
525 W. Clearwater Loop
Post Falls, ID 83854
208-769-3296
Fax: 208-769-3223

College of Southern Idaho
Small Business Development Center
Region IV
315 Falls Ave.
Twin Falls, ID 83303

208-733-9554, ext. 2477
Fax: 208-733-9316

Illinois

Lead Center:
Illinois SBDC Network
Dept. of Commerce and Community Affairs
620 East Adams St., 3rd Floor
Springfield, IL 62701
217-524-5856
Fax: 217-785-6328

Waubonsee Community College/
Aurora Campus
Small Business Development Center
5 East Galena Blvd.
Aurora, IL 60506
708-892-3334, ext. 139
Fax: 708-892-3374

Southern Illinois University/Carbondale
Small Business Development Center
Carbondale, IL 62901-6702
618-536-2424
Fax: 618-453-5040

Kaskaskia College (Satellite)
Small Business Development Center
2710 College Rd.
Centralia, IL 62801
618-532-2049
Fax: 618-532-4983

Back of the Yards Neighborhood Council
(Sub-Center)
Small Business Development Center
1751 West 47th St.
Chicago, IL 60609
312-523-4419
Fax: 312-254-3525

Greater North Pulaski Economic
Development Corp.
Small Business Development Center
4054 West North Ave.
Chicago, IL 60639
312-384-2262
Fax: 312-384-3850

Women's Business Development Center
Small Business Development Center

8 S. Michigan, Suite 400
Chicago, IL 60603
312-853-3477
Fax: 312-853-0145

Olive-Harvey College
Small Business Development Center
10001 S. Woodlawn Dr.
Chicago, IL 60628
312-468-8700
Fax: 312-468-8086

Industrial Council of NW Chicago
Small Business Development Center
2023 West Carroll
Chicago, IL 60612
312-421-3941
Fax: 312-421-1871

Latin American Chamber of Commerce
Small Business Development Center
539 N. Kedzie, Suite 11
Chicago, IL 60647
312-252-5211
Fax: 312-252-7065

Eighteenth Street Development Corp.
Small Business Development Center
1839 S. Carpenter
Chicago, IL 60608
312-733-2287
Fax: 312-733-7315

Loop Small Business Development Center
DCCA, State of Illinois Center
100 West Randolph
Suite 3-400
Chicago, IL 60601
312-814-6111
Fax: 312-814-2807

McHenry County College
Small Business Development Center
8900 U.S. Highway 14
Crystal Lake, IL 60012-2761
815-455-6098
Fax: 815-455-9319

Danville Area Community College
Small Business Development Center
28 West North St.
Danville, IL 61832

Money For A Big Or Small Business

217-442-7232
Fax: 217-442-6228

Small Business Development Center
985 W. Pershing Rd., Suite F-4
305 East Locust
Decatur, IL 62526
217-875-8284
Fax: 217-875-8289

Sauk Valley College
Small Business Development Center
173 Illinois Route #2
Dixon, IL 61021-9110
815-288-5511
Fax: 815-288-5958

Southern Illinois University/Edwardsville
Small Business Development Center
Campus Box 1107
Edwardsville, IL 62026
618-692-2929
Fax: 618-692-2647

Elgin Community College
Small Business Development Center
1700 Spartan Dr.
Elgin, IL 60123
847-888-7675
Fax: 847-888-7995

Evanston Business and Technology Center
Small Business Development Center
1840 Oak Ave.
Evanston, IL 60201
847-866-1817
Fax: 847-866-1808

College of DuPage
Small Business Development Center
22nd and Lambert Rd.
Glen Ellyn, IL 60137
708-942-2600
Fax: 708-942-3789

College of Lake County
Small Business Development Center
19351 West Washington St.
Grayslake, IL 60030
708-223-3633
Fax: 708-223-9371

Southeastern Illinois College (Satellite)
303 S. Commercial
Harrisburg, IL 62946-2125
618-252-5001
Fax: 618-252-0210

Rend Lake College
Small Business Development Center
Route #1
Ina, IL 62846
618-437-5321, ext. 335
Fax: 618-437-5677

Joliet Junior College
Small Business Development Center
Renaissance Center
Room 319, 214 N. Ottawa St.
Joliet, IL 60431
815-727-6544, ext. 1313
Fax: 815-722-1895

Kankakee Community College
Small Business Development Center
101 S. Schuyler Ave.
Kankakee, IL 60901
815-933-0376
Fax: 815-933-0380

Western Illinois University
Small Business Development Center
114 Seal Hall
Macomb, IL 61455
309-298-2211
Fax: 309-298-2520

Black Hawk College
Small Business Development Center
301 42nd Ave
East Moline, IL 61244
309-755-2200 ext. 211
Fax: 309-755-9847

Maple City Business and Technology
(Satellite) SBDC
620 S. Main St.
Monmouth, IL 61462
309-734-4664
Fax: 309-734-8579

Illinois Valley Community College
Small Business Development Center
Building 11, Route 1

Oglesby, IL 61348
815-223-1740
Fax: 815-224-3033

Illinois Eastern Community College
Small Business Development Center
401 East Main St.
Olney, IL 62450
618-395-3011
Fax: 618-395-1922

Moraine Valley College
Small Business Development Center
10900 S. 88th Ave.
Palos Hills, IL 60465
708-974-5468
Fax: 708-974-0078

Bradley University
Small Business Development Center
141 N. Jobst Hall, 1st Floor
Peoria, IL 61625
309-677-2992
Fax: 309-677-3386

Rock Valley College
Small Business Development Center
1220 Rock St.
Rockford, IL 61102
815-968-4087
Fax: 815-968-4157

Lincoln Land Community College
Small Business Development Center
200 West Washington
Springfield, IL 62701
217-789-1017
Fax: 217-789-0958

East St. Louis
DCCA, State Office Building
10 Collinsville
East St. Louis, IL 62201
618-583-2272
Fax: 618-588-2274

Shawnee College (Satellite)
Small Business Development Center
Shawnee College Rd.
Ullin, IL 62992
618-634-9618
Fax: 618-634-9028

Governor's State University
Small Business Development Center
University Park, IL 60466
708-534-4929
Fax: 708-534-8457

Indiana
Lead Center:
Indiana Small Business Development Center
Economic Development Council
One N. Capitol, Suite 420
Indianapolis, IN 46204
317-264-6871
Fax: 317-264-3102

Greater Bloomington Chamber of Commerce
Small Business Development Center
116 W. 6th St.
Bloomington, IN 47404
812-339-8937
Fax: 812-336-0651

Columbus Enterprise Development Center,
Inc.
Small Business Development Center
4920 N. Warren Dr.
Columbus, IN 47203
812-372-6480
Fax: 812-372-0228

Evansville Chamber of Commerce
Small Business Development Center
100 NW Second St., Suite 200
Evansville, IN 47708
812-425-7232

Northeast Indiana Business Assistance
Corporation
Small Business Development Center
1830 Wayne Terrace
Fort Wayne, IN 46803
219-426-0040
Fax: 219-424-0024

Hoosier Valley Economic Opportunity
Corporation
Small Business Development Center
1613 E. 8th St.
Jeffersonville, IN 47130
812-288-6451
Fax: 812-284-8314

Indiana University
Small Business Development Center
342 Senate Ave.
Indianapolis, IN 46204
317-261-3030
Fax: 317-261-3053

Kokomo-Howard County Chamber of
Commerce
Small Business Development Center
106 N. Washington
Kokomo, IN 46901
317-457-5301
Fax: 317-452-4564

Greater Lafayette Progress, Inc.
Small Business Development Center
122 N. Third
Lafayette, IN 47901
317-742-2394
Fax: 317-742-6276

Madison Area Chamber of Commerce
Small Business Development Center
301 East Main St.
Madison, IN 47250
812-265-3127
Fax: 812-265-2923

Muncie-Delaware County Chamber
Small Business Development Center
401 S. High St.
Muncie, IN 47308
317-284-8144
Fax: 317-741-5489

Northwest
Indiana Forum

Northwest Indiana Forum, Inc.
Small Business Development Center
6100 Southport Rd.
Portage, IN 46368
219-762-1696
Fax: 219-942-5806

Richmond Area Chamber of Commerce
Small Business Development Center
33 S. 7th St.

Richmond, IN 47374
317-962-2887
Fax: 317-966-0882

South Bend Chamber of Commerce
Small Business Development Center
300 N. Michigan St.
South Bend, IN 46601
219-282-4350
Fax: 219-282-4344

Indiana State University
Small Business Development Center
School of Business
Terre Haute, IN 47809
812-237-7676
Fax: 812-237-7675

Bates Office of Economic Development
132 S. Main
Batesville, IN 47006
812-933-6110

Bedford Chamber of Commerce
Small Business Development Center
1116 W. 16th St.
Bedford, IN 47421
812-275-4493

Clay County Chamber of Commerce
Small Business Development Center
Twelve N. Walnut St.
Braxil, IN 47834
812-448-8457

Clinton Chamber of Commerce
Small Business Development Center
292 N. Ninth St.
Clinton, IN 47842
812-832-3844

Chamber of Commerce
Small Business Development Center
112 N. Main St.
Columbia City, IN 46725
219-248-8131

Connersville Small Business Development
Center
504 Central
Connersville, IN 47331
317-825-8328

Harrison County Development Center
The Harrison Center
405 N. Capitol, Suite 308
Corydon, IN 47112
812-738-8811

Montgomery County Chamber of
Commerce--SBDC
211 S. Washington St.
Crawfordsville, IN 47933
317-654-5507

Chamber of Commerce
Small Business Development Center
125 E. Monroe St.
Decatur, IN 46733
319-724-2604

City of Delphi Community Development
Small Business Development Center
20 S. Union
Delphi, IN 46923
317-564-6692

Elkhart Chamber of Commerce
Small Business Development Center
421 S. Second St.
Elkhart, IN 46515
219-522-5453

Elwood Chamber of Commerce
Small Business Development Center
108 S. Anderson St.
Elwood, IN 46063
317-552-0180

Clinton County Chamber of Commerce
Small Business Development Center
207 S. Main St.
Frankfort, IN 46041
317-654-5507

Northlake SBDC
Firth Avenue Mall
487 Broadway, Suite 201
Gary, IN 46402
219-882-2000

Greencastle Partnership Center
Small Business Development Center
Two S. Jackson St.

Greencastle, IN 46135
317-653-4517

Greensburg Area Chamber of Commerce
Small Business Development Center
125 W. Main St.
Greensburg, IN 47240
812-663-2832

Hammond Development Corp.
Small Business Development Center
649 Conkey St.
Hammond, IN 46324
219-853-6399

Blackford County Economic Development
Small Business Development Center
P.O. Box 43
Hartford, IN 47348
317-348-4944

Indiana Region 15 Planning Commission
Small Business Development Center
511 Fourth St.
Huntingburg, IN 47542
812-683-5699
812-683-4647

Kendallville Chamber of Commerce
Small Business Development Center
228 S. Main St.
Kendallville, IN 46755
219-347-1554

LaPorte Small Business Development Center
414 Lincolnway
LaPorte, IN 46350
219-326-7232

Dearborn County Chamber of Commerce
Small Business Development Center
213 Eads Parkway
Lawrenceburg, IN 47025
812-537-0814
Fax: 812-537-0845

Union County Chamber of Commerce
Small Business Development Center
102 N. Main St., #6
Liberty, IN 47353-1039
317-458-5976

Money For A Big Or Small Business

First Citizens Band
Small Business Development Center
515 N. Franklin Square
Michigan City, IN 46360
319-874-9245

Mitchell Chamber of Commerce
Small Business Development Center
First National Bank
Main Street
Mitchell, IN 47446
812-849-4441

White County Chamber of Commerce
Small Business Development Center
P.O. Box 1031
Monticello, IN 47960
219-583-6557

Mt. Vernon Chamber of Commerce
Small Business Development Center
405 E. Fourth St.
Mt. Vernon, IN 47602
812-838-3639

East Central Indiana Regional Small
Business Development Center
401 S. High St.
Muncie, IN 47308
317-284-8144
Fax: 317-741-5489

Brown County Chamber of Commerce
Small Business Development Center
P.O. Box 164
Nashville, IN 47448
812-988-6647

Floyd County Private Industry Council
Workforce Development Center
Small Business Development Center
3303 Plaza Dr., Suite 2
New Albany, IN 47150
812-945-2643

Jennings County Chamber of Commerce
Small Business Development Center
P.O. Box 340
North Vernon, IN 47265
812-346-2339

Private Industry Council Workforce, Orange
County

326 B. N. Gospel
Paoli, IN 47464
812-723-4206

Peru Area Chamber of Commerce
Small Business Development Center
Two N. Broadway, Suite 202
Peru, IN 46970
317-472-1923

Jay County Development Corp.
Small Business Development Center
121 W. Main St., Suite A
Portland, IN 47371
219-726-9311

Park County Economic Development
Small Business Development Center
P.O. Box 296
Rockville, IN 47872
317-569-0226

Rushville Chamber of Commerce
Small Business Development Center
P.O. Box 156
Rushville, IN 47173
317-932-2222

Seymour Chamber of Commerce
Small Business Development Center
P.O. Box 43
Seymour, IN 47274
812-522-3681

Sullivan Chamber of Commerce
Small Business Development Center
Ten S. Court St.
Sullivan, IN 47882
812-268-4836

Tell City Chamber of Commerce
Small Business Development Center
Regional Federal Bldg.
645 Main St.
Tell City, IN 47586
812-547-2385
Fax: 812-547-8378

Tipton County Economic Development
Corporation
Small Business Development Center
136 East Jefferson

Money For A Big Or Small Business

Tipton, IN 46072
317-675-7300

Porter County Small Business Development
Center
911 Wall St.
Valparaiso, IN 46383
219-477-5256

Vevay/Switzerland County Foundation
Small Business Development Center
P.O. Box 193
Vevay, IN 47043
812-427-2533

Vincennes University--SBDC
P.O. Box 887
Vincennes, IN 47591
812-885-5749

Wabash Area Chamber of Commerce
Small Business Development Center
67 S. Wabash
Wabash, IN 46922
219-563-1168

Washington, Davies County SBDC
One Train Depot St.
Washington, IN 47501
812-254-5262
Fax: 812-254-2550

Purdue University Small Business
Development Center
Business & Industrial Development Center
1220 Potter Dr.
West Layfayette, IN 47906
317-494-5858

Randolph County Economic Dev.
Foundation SBDC
111 S. Main St.
Winchester, IN 47394
317-584-3266

Iowa
Lead Center:
Iowa Small Business Development Center
Iowa State University
College of Business Administration
Chamblynn Building

137 Lynn Ave.
Ames, IA 50010
515-292-6351
Fax: 515-292-0020

ISU Small Business Development Center
ISU Audubon Branch
Circle West Incubator
P.O. Box 204
Audubon, IA 50025
712-563-2623
Fax: 712-563-2301

University of Northern Iowa
Small Business Development Center
Suite 5, Business Building
Cedar Falls, IA 50614-0120
319-273-2696
Fax: 319-273-6830

Iowa Western Community College
Small Business Development Center
2700 College Rd., Box 4C
Council Bluffs, IA 51502
712-325-3260
Fax: 712-325-3408

Southwestern Community College
Small Business Development Center
1501 West Townline
Creston, IA 50801
515-782-4161
Fax: 515-782-4164

Eastern Iowa Community College District
Small Business Development Center
304 West Second St.
Davenport, IA 52801
319-322-4499
Fax: 319-322-8241

Drake University
Small Business Development Center
Drake Business Center
2401 University
Des Moines, IA 50311-4505
515-271-2655
Fax: 515-271-4540

Dubuque Area Chamber of Commerce
Northeast Iowa Small Business Development
Center

770 Town Clock Plaza
Dubuque, IA 52001
319-588-3350
Fax: 319-557-1591

University of Iowa
Oakdale Campus
Small Business Development Center
108 Pappajohn Business Adm. Bldg.
Suite S-160
Iowa City, IA 52242-1000
319-335-3742
Fax: 319-335-2445

Kirkwood Community College
Small Business Development Center
2901 Tenth Ave.
Marion, IA 52302
319-377-8256
Fax: 319-377-5667

North Iowa Area Community College
Small Business Development Center
500 College Dr.
Mason City, IA 50401
515-421-4342
Fax: 515-423-0931

Indian Hills Community College
Small Business Development Center
525 Grandview Ave.
Ottumwa, IA 52501
515-683-5127
Fax: 515-683-5263

Western Iowa Tech Community College
Small Business Development Center
4647 Stone Ave., Bldg. B, Box 265
Sioux City, IA 51102-0265
712-274-6418
Fax: 712-274-6429

Iowa Lakes Community College
Small Business Development Center
Gateway Center
Highway 71 N.
Spencer, IA 51301
712-262-4213
Fax: 712-262-4047

Southeastern Community College
Small Business Development Center

Drawer F
West Burlington, IA 52655
319-752-2731, ext. 103
Fax: 319-752-3407

Kansas

Lead Center:
Kansas Small Business Development Center
Wichita State University
1845 Fairmount
Wichita, KS 67260-0148
316-689-3193
Fax: 316-689-3647

Butler County Community College
Small Business Development Center
600 Walnut
Augusta, KS 67010
316-775-1124

Neosho County Community College
Small Business Development Center
1000 S Allen
Chanute, KS 66720
316-431-2820, ext 219
Fax: 316-431-0082

Coffeyville Community College
Small Business Development Center
11th and Willow Sts.
Coffeyville, KS 67337-5064
316-252-7007
Fax: 316-252-7098

Colby Community College
Small Business Development Center
1255 S. Range
Colby, KS 67701
913-462-3984, ext. 239
Fax: 913-462-8315

Cloud County Community College
Small Business Development Center
2221 Campus Dr.
P.O. Box 1002
Concordia, KS 66901
913-243-1435
Fax: 913-243-1459

Dodge City Community College
Small Business Development Center
2501 N. 14th Ave.
Dodge City, KS 67801

316-227-9247, ext. 247
Fax: 316-227-9200

Emporia State University
Small Business Development Center
207 Cremer Hall
Emporia, KS 66801
316-342-7162
Fax: 316-341-5418

Fort Scott Community College
Small Business Development Center
2108 S Horton
Fort Scott, KS 66701
316-223-2700
Fax: 316-223-6530

Garden City Community College
Small Business Development Center
801 Campus Dr.
Garden City, KS 67846
316-276-9632
Fax: 316-276-9630

Fort Hays State University
Small Business Development Center
1301 Pine St.
Hays, KS 67601
913-628-5340
Fax: 913-628-1471

Hutchinson Community College
Small Business Development Center
815 N. Walnut, #225
Hutchinson, KS 67501
316-665-4950
Fax: 316-665-8354

Independence Community College
Small Business Development Center
College Ave. and Brookside, Box 708
Independence, KS 67301
316-331-4100
Fax: 316-331-5344

Allen County Community College
T.B.D.
Small Business Development Center
1801 N. Cottonwood
Iola, KS 66749
316-365-5116
Fax: 316-365-3284

Community College

Seward County Community College
Small Business Development Center
1801 N. Kansas
Liberal, KS 67905
316-624-1951, ext. 150
Fax: 316-624-0637

Kansas State University
Small Business Development Center
2323 Anderson Ave., Suite 100
Manhattan, KS 66502-2947
913-532-5529
Fax: 913-532-5827

Ottawa University
Small Business Development Center
College Ave., Box 70
Ottawa, KS 66067
913-242-5200, ext. 5457
Fax: 913-242-7429

Johnson County Community College
Small Business Development Center
CEC Building, Room 223
Overland Park, KS 66210-1299
913-469-3878
Fax: 913-469-4415

Labette Community College
Small Business Development Center
200 S. 14th
Parsons, KS 67357
316-421-6700
Fax: 316-421-0921

Pittsburg State University
Small Business Development Center
Shirk Hall
Pittsburg, KS 66762
316-235-4920
Fax: 316-232-6440

Pratt Community College
Small Business Development Center
Highway 61
Pratt, KS 67124

Money For A Big Or Small Business

316-672-5641
Fax: 316-672-5288

KSU-Salina College of Technology
Small Business Development Center
2409 Scanlan Ave.
Salina, KS 67401
913-826-2622,
Fax: 913-826-2936

Washburn University
Small Business Development Center
101 Henderson Learning Center
Topeka, KS 66621
913-231-1010, ext. 1305
Fax: 913-231-1063

Kentucky
Lead Center:
Kentucky Small Business Development Ctr.
University of Kentucky
Center for Business Development
College of Business and Economics
225 Business and Economics Building
Lexington, KY 40506-0034
606-257-7668
Fax: 606-258-1907

Ashland Small Business Development Center
Boyd-Greenup County Chamber of
Commerce Building
P.O. Box 830
207 15th St.
Ashland, KY 41105-0830
606-329-8011
Fax: 606-325-4607

Western Kentucky University
Bowling Green Small Business Development
Center
245 Grise Hall
Bowling Green, KY 42101
502-745-2901
Fax: 502-745-2902

Southeast Community College
Small Business Development Center
Room 113, Chrisman Hall
Cumberland, KY 40823
606-589-4514
Fax: 606-589-4941

Elizabethtown Small Business Development
Center
238 West Dixie Ave.
Elizabethtown, KY 42701
502-765-6737
Fax: 502-769-5095

Northern Kentucky University
North Kentucky Small Business
Development Center
BEP Center, Room 468
Highland Heights, KY 41099-0506
606-572-6524
Fax: 606-572-5566

Hopkinsville SBDC
300 Hammond Dr.
Hopkinsville, KY 42240
502-886-8666
Fax: 502-886-3211

University of Kentucky
Small Business Development Center
College of Business and Economics
c/o Downtown Public Library
140 Main St.
Lexington, KY 40507
606-257-7666
Fax: 606-257-1751

Bellarmine College
Small Business Development Center
School of Business
2001 Newburg Rd.
Louisville, KY 40205-0671
502-452-8282
Fax: 502-452-8288

University of Louisville
Small Business Development Center
Center for Entrepreneurship and Technology
Room 122, Burhans Hall
Louisville, KY 40292
502-588-7854
Fax: 502-588-8573

Morehead State University
Small Business Development Center
207 Downing Hall
Morehead, KY 40351
606-783-2895
Fax: 606-783-5023

Murray State University
West Kentucky SBDC
College of Business and Public Affairs
Murray, KY 42071
502-762-2856
Fax: 502-762-3049

Owensboro SBDC
3860 U.S. Highway 60 West
Owensboro, KY 42301
502-926-8085
Fax: 502-684-0714

Pikeville Small Business Development
Center
222 Hatcher Court
Pikeville, KY 41501
606-432-5848
Fax: 606-432-8924

Eastern Kentucky University
Small Business Development Center
107 West Mt. Vernon St.
Somerset, KY 42501
606-678-5520
Fax: 606-678-8349

Louisiana
Lead Center:
Louisiana Small Business Development
Center
Northeast Louisiana University
Adm. 2-57
Monroe, LA 71209
318-342-5506
Fax: 318-342-5510

Small Business Development Center
934 3rd St., Suite 510
Alexandria,, LA 71301
318-484-2123
Fax: 318-484-2126

Capital Small Business Development Center
1933 Wooddale Blvd. Suite E
Baton Rouge, LA 70806
504-922-0998
Fax: 504-922-0999

Southeastern Louisiana University
Small Business Development Center

Box 522, SLU Station
Hammond, LA 70402
504-549-3831
Fax: 504-549-2127

University of Southwestern Louisiana
Arcadiana Small Business Development
Center
Box 43732
Lafayette, LA 70504
318-262-5344
Fax: 318-262-5296

McNeese State University
Small Business Development Center
College of Business Administration
Lake Charles, LA 70609
318-475-5529
Fax: 318-475-5012

Northeast Louisiana University
College of Business Administration
Monroe, LA 71209
318-342-1215
Fax: 318-342-1209

Northwestern State University
Small Business Development Center
College of Business Administration
Natchitoches, LA 71497
318-357-5611
Fax: 318-357-6810

University of New Orleans
Small Business Development Center
LA International Trade
2 Canal St., Suite 2926
New Orleans, LA 70130
504-568-8222
Fax: 504-568-8228

Loyola University
Small Business Development Center
Box 134
New Orleans, LA 70118
504-865-3496
Fax: 504-865-3347

Southern University
Small Business Development Center
College of Business Administration
New Orleans, LA 70126

504-286-5308
Fax: 504-286-5131

University of New Orleans
Small Business Development Center
Lakefront Campus
College of Business Administration
New Orleans, LA 70148
504-539-9292
Fax: 504-539-9205

Louisiana Tech University
Small Business Development Center
Box 10318, Tech Station
Ruston, LA 71271-0046
318-257-3537
Fax: 318-257-4253

Louisiana State University at Shreveport
Small Business Development Center
College of Business Administration
1 University Place
Shreveport, LA 71115
318-797-5144
Fax: 318-797-5208

Nicholls State University
Small Business Development Center
P.O. Box 2015
Thibodaux, LA 70310
504-448-4242
Fax: 504-448-4922

Maine
Lead Center:
Maine Small Business Development Center
University of Southern Maine
96 Falmouth St.
P.O. Box 9300
Portland, ME 04101
207-780-4420
Fax: 207-780-4810

Androscoggin Valley Council of
Governments (AVCOG)
Small Business Development Center
125 Manley Rd.
Auburn, ME 04210
207-783-9186
Fax: 207-780-4810

Eastern Maine Development Corporation
Small Business Development Center
P.O. Box 2579
Bangor, ME 04402-2579
207-942-6389
Fax: 207-942-3548

Northern Maine Regional Planning
Commission
Small Business Development Center
P.O. Box 779
2 Main St.
Caribou, ME 04736
207-498-8736
Fax: 207-493-3108

Southern Maine Regional Planning
Commission
Small Business Development Center
Box Q
255 Main St.
Sanford, ME 04073
207-324-0316
Fax: 207-324-2958

Coastal Enterprises, Inc.
Small Business Development Center
Water St., Box 268
Wiscasset, ME 04578
207-882-4340
Fax: 207-882-4456

Maryland
Lead Center:
Small Business Development Center
1420 N. Charles St., Room 142
Baltimore, MD 21202
410-837-4141
Fax: 410-837-4151

Anne Arundel Office of Economic
Development
Small Business Development Center
2660 Riva Rd., Suite 200
Annapolis, MD 21401
410-224-4205
Fax: 410-222-7415

Business Resource Center
Small Business Development Center

217 E. Redwood St., 10th Floor
Baltimore, MD 21202
410-333-6552
Fax: 410-333-4460

Harford County Economic Development
Office
Small Business Development Center
220 S. Main St.
Bel Air, MD 21014
410-893-3837
Fax: 410-879-8043

Manufacturing and Technology
Small Business Development Center
Dingman Center for Entrepreneurship
College of Business and Management
University of Maryland
College Park, MD 20742-1815
301-405-2144
Fax: 301-314-9152

Howard County Economic Development
Office
Small Business Development Center
6751 Gateway Dr., Suite 500
Columbia, MD 21043
410-313-6552
Fax: 410-313-6556

Western Region Small Business
Development Center
3 Commerce Dr.
Cumberland, MD 21502
301-724-6716
Fax: 301-777-7504

Cecil Community College
Eastern Region Small Business
Development Center
135 E. Main St.
Elkton, MD 21921
410-392-0597
Fax: 410-392-6225

Arundel Center N
Small Business Development Center
101 Crain Highway NW, Room 110B
Glen Burnie, MD 21601
410-766-1910
Fax: 410-766-1911

Suburban Washington Small Business
Development Center
1400 McCormick Dr., Suite 282
Landover, MD 20785
301-883-6491
Fax: 301-883-6479

Eastern Shore Small Business Development
Center SubCenter
Salisbury State University
Power Professional Bldg. Suite 400
Salisbury, MD 21801
410-546-4325
Fax: 410-548-5389

Baltimore County Chamber of Commerce
Small Business Development Center
102 W. Pennsylvania Ave., Suite 402
Towson, MD 21204
410-832-5866
Fax: 410-821-9901

Carroll County Economic Development
Small Business Development Center
125 N. Court St., Room 103
Westminster, MD 21157
410-857-8166
Fax: 410-848-0003

Massachusetts
Lead Center:
Massachusetts Small Business Development
Center
University of Massachusetts
205 School of Management
Amherst, MA 01003
413-545-6301
Fax: 413-545-1273

University of Massachusetts at Amherst
Minority Business Assistance Center
250 Stuart St., 5th Floor
Boston, MA 02125-3393
617-287-7725
Fax: 617-287-7725

Boston College
Metropolitan Regional Small Business
Development Center
96 College Rd. - Rahner House
Chestnut Hill, MA 02167

Money For A Big Or Small Business

617-552-4091
Fax: 617-552-2730

Boston College
Capital Formation Service/East
Small Business Development Center
96 College Rd. - Rahner House
Chestnut Hill, MA 02167
617-552-4091
Fax: 617-552-2730

University of Massachusetts at Dartmouth
Southeastern Massachusetts Regional Small
Business Development Center
200 Pocasset St.
P.O. Box 2785
Fall River, MA 02722
508-673-9783
Fax: 508-674-1929

Salem State College
North Shore Regional Small Business
Development Center
197 Essex St.
Salem, MA 01970
508-741-6343
Fax: 508-741-6345

University of Massachusetts
Western Massachusetts Regional Small
Business Development Center
101 State St., Suite #424
Springfield, MA 01103
413-737-6712
Fax: 413-737-2312

Clark University
Central Massachusetts Regional Small
Business Development Center
950 Main St., Dana Commons
Worcester, MA 01610

508-793-7615
Fax: 508-793-8890

Michigan
Lead Center:
Michigan Small Business Development
Center
2727 Second Ave.
Detroit, MI 48201
313-964-1798
Fax: 313-964-3648

Ottawa County Economic Development
Office, Inc.
Small Business Development Center
6676 Lake Michigan Dr.
P.O. Box 539
Allendale, MI 49401-0539
616-892-4120
Fax: 616-895-6670

Merra Specialty Business Development
Center
Small Business Development Center
2200 Commonwealth, Suite 230
Ann Arbor, MI 48106-1485
313-769-4110
Fax: 313-769-4064

Huron County Economic Development
Corporation (Satellite)
Small Business Development Center
Huron County Building, Room 303
Bad Axe, MI 48413
517-269-6431
Fax: 517-269-7221

Kellogg Community College
Small Business Development Center
34 W. Jackson, Suite A
Battle Creek, MI 49017
616-962-4076

Lake Michigan College
Small Business Development Center
Corporate and Community Services
2755 E. Napier
Benton Harbor, MI 49022
616-927-8179
Fax: 616-927-8103

Information USA, Inc.   317

Ferris State University
Small Business Development Center
330 Oak St., W115
Big Rapids, MI 49307
616-592-3553
Fax: 616-592-3539

Tuscola County Economic Development
Corporation
Small Business Development Center
194 N. State, Suite 200
Caro, MI 48723
517-673-2849
Fax: 517-673-2517

NILAC-Marygrove College
Small Business Development Center
8425 West McNichols
Detroit, MI 48221
313-945-2159
Fax: 313-864-6670

Wayne State University
Small Business Development Center
School of Business Administration
2727 Second Ave.
Detroit, MI 48201
313-577-4850
Fax: 313-577-8933

1st Step, Inc.
Small Business Development Center
2415 14th Ave., S.
Escanaba, MI 49829
906-786-9234
Fax: 906-786-4442

Genesee Economic Area Revitalization, Inc.
(Satellite)
Small Business Development Center
711 N. Saginaw St., Suite 123
Flint, MI 48503
810-239-5847
Fax: 810-239-5575

Grand Rapids Community College
Small Business Development Center
Applied Technology Center
151 Fountain NE
Grand Rapids, MI 49503
616-771-0571
Fax: 616-458-3768

Oceana Economic Development Corporation
(Satellite)
Small Business Development Center
P.O. Box 168
100 State St.
Hart, MI 49420-0168
616-873-7141
Fax: 616-873-5914

Michigan Technological University
Small Business Development Center
Bureau of Industrial Development
1400 Townsend Dr.
Houghton, MI 49931
906-487-2470
Fax: 906-487-2858

Kalamazoo College
Small Business Development Center
Stryker Center for Management Studies
1327 Academy St.
Kalamazoo, MI 49006-3200
616-337-7350
Fax: 616-337-7415

Lansing Community College
Small Business Development Center
P.O. Box 40010, 333 N. Washington Sq.
Lansing, MI 48901-7210
517-483-1921
Fax: 517-483-1675

Lapeer Development Corporation (Satellite)
449 McCormick Dr.
Lapeer, MI 48446
313-667-0080
Fax: 313-667-3541

Macomb County Business Assistance
Network
115 S. Groesbeck Hwy.
Mt. Clemens, MI 48043
810-469-5118
Fax: 810-469-6787

Central Michigan University
Small Business Development Center
256 Applied Business Studies Complex
Mt. Pleasant, MI 48859
517-774-3270
Fax: 517-774-7992

Money For A Big Or Small Business

Muskegon Economic Growth Alliance
Small Business Development Center
230 Terrace Plaza
P.O. Box 1087
Muskegon, MI 49443-1087
616-722-3751
Fax: 616-728-7251

Sanilac County Economic Growth (Satellite)
175 East Aitken Rd.
Peck, MI 48466
313-648-4311
Fax: 313-648-4617

St. Claire County Community College
Small Business Development Center
800 Military St., Suite 320
Port Huron, MI 48060
810-982-9511
Fax: 810-982-9531

Saginaw Future, Inc.
Small Business Development Center
301 East Genesee, Third Floor
Saginaw, MI 48607
517-754-8222
Fax: 517-754-1715

West Shore Community College (Satellite)
Business and Industrial Development
3000 N. Stiles Rd., P.O. Box 277
Scottville, MI 49454-0277
616-845-6211
Fax: 616-845-0207

Montcalm Community College (Satellite)
2800 College Dr. SW
Sidney, MI 48885
517-328-2111
Fax: 517-328-2950

Sterling Heights Area Chamber of
Commerce (Satellite)
12900 Hall Rd., Suite 110
Sterling Heights, MI 48313
810-731-5400
Fax: 810-731-3521

Northwestern Michigan College
Center for Business and Industry
1701 East Front St.
Traverse City, MI 49686

616-922-1720
Fax: 616-922-1722

Travers Bay Economic Development
Corporation
Traverse City SBDC
202 E. Grandview Parkway
Traverse City, MI 49684
616-947-5075
Fax: 616-946-2565

Greater Northwest Regional CDC
2200 Dendrinos Dr., P.O. Box 506
Traverse City, MI 49685-0506
616-929-5000
Fax: 616-929-5012

Walsh/O.C.C. Business Enterprise
Development Center
1301 W. Long Lanke, Suite 150
Troy, MI 48098
810-952-5800
Fax: 810-952-1875

Saginaw Valley State University (Satellite)
Business and Industrial Development
Institute
7400 Bay Rd.
University Center, MI 48710
517-790-4388
Fax: 517-790-4983

Minnesota
Lead Center:
Minnesota Small Business Development
Center
Department of Trade and Economic
Development
500 Metro Square
121 7th Place E.
St. Paul, MN 55101-2146
612-297-5770
Fax: 612-296-1290

Customized Training Center
Small Business Development Center
Bemidji Technical College
905 Grant Ave., SE
Bemidji, MN 56601
218-755-4286
Fax: 218-755-4289

Money For A Big Or Small Business

Normandale Community College
Small Business Development Center
9700 France Ave. S.
Bloomington, MN 55431
612-832-6560
Fax: 612-832-6352

Brainerd Technical College
Small Business Development Center
300 Quince St.
Brainerd, MN 56401
218-828-5302
Fax: 218-828-5321

University of Minnesota at Duluth
Small Business Development Center
10 University Dr., 150 SBE
Duluth, MN 55812
218-726-8758
Fax: 218-726-6338

Itasca Development Corporation
Grand Rapids SBDC
19 NE Third St.
Grand Rapids, MN 55744
218-327-2241
Fax: 218-327-2242

Hibbing Community College
Small Business Development Center
1515 East 25th St.
Hibbing, MN 55746
218-262-6703
Fax: 218-262-6717

Small Business Development Center
Rainy River Community College
1501 Hwy 71
International Falls, MN 56649
218-285-2255
Fax: 218-285-2239

Mankato State University
Small Business Development Center
P.O. Box 3367
410 Jackson St.
Mankato, MN 56001
507-387-5643
Fax: 507-387-7105

Southwest State University
Small Business Development Center

ST #105
Marshall, MN 56258
507-537-7386
Fax: 507-537-6094

Minnesota Project Innovation
Small Business Development Center
Suite 100, 111 Third Ave. S.
Minneapolis, MN 55401
612-338-3280
Fax: 612-338-3483

Small Business Development Center
University of St. Thomas
1000 LaSalle Ave., Suite MPL100
Minneapolis, MN 55403
612-962-4500
Fax: 612-962-4410

Moorhead State University
Small Business Development Center
1104 7th Ave.S
MSU Box 303
Moorhead, MN 56563
218-226-2289
Fax: 218-236-2280

Small Business Development Center
Owatonna Incubator, Inc.
P.O. Box 505
560 Dunnell Dr., Suite #203
Owatonna, MN 55060
507-451-0517
Fax: 507-455-2788

Pine Technical College
Small Business Development Center
1100 4th St.
Pine City, MN 55063
612-629-7340
Fax: 612-629-7603

Small Business Development Center
Hennepin Technical College
1820 N. Xenium Lane
Plymouth, MN 55441
612-550-7218
Fax: 612-550-7272

Pottery Bus. & Tech. Ctr.
Small Business Development Center
2000 Pottery Place Dr., Suite 339

320   *Information USA, Inc.*

Money For A Big Or Small Business

Red Wing, MN 55066
612-388-4079
Fax: 612-385-2251

Rochester Community College
Small Business Development Center
851 30th Ave., SE
Rochester, MN 55904
507-285-7536
Fax: 507-280-5502

Dakota County Technical Institute
Small Business Development Center
1300 145th St. East
Rosemount, MN 55068
612-423-8262
Fax: 612-322-5156

Small Business Development Center
SE Minnesota Development Corp.
111 W. Jessie St.
Rushford, MN 55971
507-864-7557
Fax: 507-864-2091

St. Cloud State University
Small Business Development Center
Business Resource Center
4191 2nd St. S
St. Cloud, MN 56301-3761
612-255-4842
Fax: 612-255-4957

Minnesota Technology Inc.
Small Business Development Center
Olcott Plaza
820 N. 9th St.
Virginia, MN 55792
218-741-4251
Fax: 218-741-4249

Wadena Technical College
Small Business Development Center
222 Second St., SE
Wadena, MN 56482
218-631-1502
Fax: 218-631-2396

North/East Metro Technical College
Small Business Development Center
3300 Century Ave. N, Suite 200D
White Bear Lake, MN 55110-1894

612-779-5764
Fax: 612-779-5802

Mississippi
Lead Center:
Mississippi Small Business Development
Center
University of Mississippi
Old Chemistry Building, Suite 216
University, MS 38677
601-232-5001
Fax: 601-232-5650

Northeast Mississippi Community College
Small Business Development Center
Cunningham Blvd.
Holliday Hall, 2nd Floor
Booneville, MS 38829
601-728-7751
Fax: 601-728-1165

Delta State University
Small Business Development Center
P.O. Box 3235 DSU
Cleveland, MS 38733
601-846-4236
Fax: 601-846-4235

East Central Community College Small
Business Development Center
P.O. Box 129
Decatur, MS 39327
601-635-2111
Fax: 601-635-2150

Jones Jr College Small Business
Development Center
900 Court St.
Ellisville, MS 39437
601-477-4165
Fax: 601-477-4152

Mississippi Gulf Coast Community College
Small Business Development Center
Jackson County Campus
P.O. Box 100
Gautier, MS 39553
601-497-9595
Fax: 601-497-9604

Delta Community College
Small Business Development Center
P.O. Box 5607

Greenville, MS 38704-5607
601-378-8183
Fax: 601-378-5349

MS Contract Procurement Center
Small Business Development Center
3015 12th St.
P.O. Box 610
Gulfport, MS 39502-0610
601-864-2961
Fax: 601-864-2969

Pearl River Community College
Small Business Development Center
5448 U.S. Highway 49 S.
Hattiesburg, MS 39401
601-544-0030
Fax: 601-544-0032

Mississippi Valley State University Small
Business Development Center
MS Valley State University
Itta Bena, MS 38941
601-254-3601
Fax: 601-254-6704

Jackson State University
Small Business Development Center
Suite A1, Jackson Enterprise Center
931 Highway 80 West
Jackson, MS 39204
601-968-2795
Fax: 601-968-2796

University of Southern Mississippi
Small Business Development Center
136 Beach Park Place
Long Beach, MS 39560
601-865-4578
Fax: 601-865-4581

Alcorn State University
Small Business Development Center
P.O. Box 90
Lorman, MS 39095-9402
601-877-6684
Fax: 601-877-6266

Meridian Community College
Small Business Development Center
910 Highway 19 N.
Meridian, MS 39307

601-482-7445
Fax: 601-482-5803

Mississippi State University
Small Business Development Center
P.O. Drawer 5288
Mississippi State, MS 39762
601-325-8684
Fax: 601-325-4016

Copiah-Lincoln Community College
Small Business Development Center
823 Hwy. 61 N.
Natchez, MS 39120
601-445-5254
Fax: 601-445-5254

Hinds Community College
Small Business Development Center
International Trade Center
P.O. Box 1170
Raymond, MS 39154
601-857-3537
Fax: 601-857-3535

Holmes Community College Small Business
Development Center
412 West Ridgeland Ave.
Ridgeland, MS 39159
601-853-0827
Fax: 601-853-0844

Northwest MS Comm. College Small
Business Development Center
Desoto Center
8700 Northwest Dr.
Southaven, MS 38671
601-342-7648
Fax: 601-342-7648

Southwest MS Comm. College Small
Business Development Center
College Dr.
Summit, MS 39666
601-276-3890
Fax: 601-276-3867

Itawamba Community College
Small Business Development Center
653 Eason Blvd.
Tupelo, MS 38801
601-680-8515
Fax: 601-842-6885

University of Mississippi
Small Business Development Center
Old Chemistry Building, Suite 216
University, MS 38677
601-234-2120
Fax: 601-232-5650

Missouri
Lead Center:
Missouri Small Business Development
Center
University of Missouri
Suite 300, University Place
Columbia, MO 65211
573-882-0344
Fax: 573-884-4297

Camden County Extension Center
Small Business Development Center
113 Kansas
P.O. Box 1405
Camdenton, MO 65020
573-346-2644
Fax: 573-346-2694

Southwest Missouri State University
Small Business Development Center
222 N. Pacific
Cape Girardeau, MO 63701
573-290-5965
Fax: 573-290-5005

Small Business Development Center
Chillicothe City Hall
715 Washington St.
Chillicothe, MO 64601
816-646-6920
Fax: 816-646-6811

St. Louis County Extension Center
Small Business Development Center
121 S Meramac, Suite 501
Clayton, MO 63105
314-889-2911
Fax: 314-854-6147

Boone County Extension Center
Small Business Development Center
1012 N. Hwy UU
Columbia, MO 65203
573-445-9792
Fax: 573-445-9807

University of Missouri at Columbia
Small Business Development Center
1800 University Place
Columbia, MO 65211
573-882-3597
Fax: 573-884-4297

Hannibal Satellite Center
Small Business Development Center
Hannibal, MO 63401
816-385-6550
Fax: 816-385-6568

Jefferson County Extension Center
Small Business Development Center
Courthouse, #203
725 Maple St.
P.O. Box 497
Hillsboro, MO 63050
573-789-5391
Fax: 573-789-5059

Jackson County Extension Center
Small Business Development Center
1507 S. Noland Rd.
Independence, MO 64055-1307
816-252-5051
Fax: 816-252-5575

Cape Girardeau County Extension Center
Small Business Development Center
P.O. Box 408
815 Highway 25S
Jackson, MO 63755
573-243-3581 ext. 283
Fax: 573-243-1606

Cole County Extension Center
Small Business Development Center
2436 Tanner Bridge Rd.
Jefferson City, MO 65101
573-634-2824
Fax: 573-634-5463

Money For A Big Or Small Business

Missouri Southern State College
Small Business Development Center
107 Mathews Hall, 3950 Newman Rd.
Joplin, MO 64801-1595
417-625-9313
Fax: 417-926-4588

Rockhurst College
Small Business Development Center
1100 Rockhurst Rd.
Kansas City, MO 64110-2599
816-926-4572
Fax: 816-926-4646

Three Rivers Community College
Small Business Development Center
Business Incubator Bldg.
3019 Fair St.
Poplar Bluff, MO 63901
314-686-3499
Fax: 314-686-5467

Washington County
102 N. Missouri
Potosi, MO 63664
573-438-2671

MO Enterprise Bus. Assistance Center
800 W 14th St., Suite 111
Rolla, MO 65401
573-364-8570
Fax: 573-341-6495

St. Louis County Extension Center
207 Marillac, UMSL
8001 Natural Bridge Rd.
St. Louis, MO 63121
314-553-5944

MO PAC--Eastern Region
975 Hornet Dr., Bldg
279 Wing B
St. Louis, MO 63042
314-731-3533

Northeast Missouri State University
Small Business Development Center
207 East Patterson
Kirksville, MO 63501-4419
816-785-4307
Fax: 816-785-4181

Thomas Hill Enterprise Center
Small Business Development Center
P.O. Box 246
Macon, MO 63552
816-385-6550
Fax: 816-385-6568

Northwest Missouri State University
Small Business Development Center
127 S. Buchanan
Maryville, MO 64468
816-562-1701
Fax: 816-562-1900

Audrain County Extension Center
Small Business Development Center
101 N. Jefferson
4th Floor Courthouse
Mexico, MO 65265
573-581-3231
Fax: 573-581-3232

Randolph County Extension Center
Small Business Development Center
417 E. Urbandale
Moberly, MO 65270
816-263-3534
Fax: 816-263-1874

Small Business Development Center
Mineral Area College
P.O. Box 1000
Park Hills, MO 63601-1000
314-431-4593
Fax: 314-431-2144

Three Rivers Community College
Small Business Development Center
Business Incubator Building
3019 Fair St.
Poplar Bluff, MO 63901
314-686-3499
Fax: 314-686-5467

Washington County Extension Center
Small Business Development Center
102 N. Missouri
Potosi, MO 63664
314-438-2671
Fax: 314-438-2079

MO Enterprise Business Assistance Center
Small Business Development Center
800 W. 14th St., Suite 111
Rolla, MO 65401
314-364-8570
Fax: 314-364-6323

Phelps County Extension Center
Small Business Development Center
Courthouse
200 N. Main
P.O. Box 725
Rolla, MO 65401
314-364-3147
Fax: 314-364-0436

Center for Technology Transfer and
Economic Development
University of Missouri at Rolla
Room 104, Nagogami Terrace
Rolla, MO 65401-0249
314-341-4559
Fax: 314-341-6495

Pettis County Extension Center
Small Business Development Center
1012 A Thompson Blvd.
Sedalia, MO 65301
816-827-0591
Fax: 816-826-8599

Southwest Missouri State University
Small Business Development Center
Center for Business Research
901 S. National
Springfield, MO 65804-5685
417-836-5685
Fax: 417-836-6337

St. Louis County Extension Center
207 Marillac, UMSI
8001 Nttl. Bridge Rd
St. Louis, MO 63121
314-533-5944
Fax: 314-977-7241

St. Louis University
Small Business Development Center
3750 Lindell Blvd.
St. Louis, MO 63108
314-534-7232
Fax: 314-534-7023

St. Charles County Extension Center
Small Business Development Center
260 Brown Rd.
St. Peters, MO 63376
314-970-3000
Fax: 314-970-3000

Franklin County Extension Center
Small Business Development Center
414 E. Main
P.O. Box 71
Union, MO 63084
573-583-5141
Fax: 573-583-5145

Central Missouri State
Center for Technology
Grinstead #75
Warrensburg, MO 64093-5037
816-543-4402
Fax: 816-747-1653

Howell County Extension Center
Small Business Development Center
217 S. Aid Ave.
West Plains, MO 65775
417-256-2391
Fax: 417-256-8569

Montana
Lead Center:
Montana Small Business Development
Center
Department of Commerce
1424 Ninth Ave.
Helena, MT 59620
406-444-4780
Fax: 406-444-1872

Billings Area Business Incubator
Small Business Development Center
115 N. Broadway, 2nd Floor
Billings, MT 59101
406-256-6875
Fax: 406-256-6877

Bozeman Human Resources Development
Council
Small Business Development Center
321 E. Main, Suite 413
Bozeman, MT 59715

406-587-3113
Fax: 406-587-9565

Butte REDI
Small Business Development Center
305 W. Mercury St., Suite 211
Butte, MT 59701
406-782-7333
Fax: 406-782-9675

Haver Small Business Development Center
Bear Paw Development Corporation
P.O. Box 1549
Haver, MT 59501
406-265-9226
Fax: 406-265-3777

Flathead Valley Community College
Small Business Development Center
777 Grandview Dr.
Kalispell, MT 59901
406-756-8333
Fax: 406-786-3815

Missoula Incubator
Small Business Development Center
127 N. Higgins, 3rd Floor
Missoula, MT 59802
406-278-9234
Fax: 406-721-4584

Sidney Small Business Development Center
123 W. Main
Sidney, MT 59270
406-482-5024
Fax: 406-482-5306

Great Falls Small Business Development
Center
High Plains Dev. Authority
710 First Ave. N
Great Falls, MT 59403
406-454-1934
Fax: 406-454-2995

Nebraska
Lead Center:
Nebraska Small Business Development
Center
Omaha Business and Tech. Center
2505 N. 24th St., Suite 101

Omaha, NE 68110
402-595-3511

Chadron State College
Small Business Development Center
Administration Building
Chadron, NE 69337
308-432-6282
Fax: 308-432-6430

University of Nebraska at Kearney
Small Business Development Center
Welch Hall
19th and College Dr.
Kearney, NE 68849-3035
308-865-8344
Fax: 308-865-8153

University of Nebraska at Lincoln
Small Business Development Center
Cornhusker Bank Bldg.
11th and Cornhusker Hwy., Suite 302
Lincoln, NE 68521
402-472-3358
Fax: 402-482-0328

Mid-Plains Community College
Small Business Development Center
416 N. Jeffers, Room 26
North Platte, NE 69101
308-534-5115
Fax: 308-534-5117

University of Nebraska at Omaha
Small Business Development Center
Peter Keiwit Conference Center
1313 Farnam, Suite 132
Omaha, NE 68182-0248
402-595-2381
Fax: 402-595-2385

Peru State College
Small Business Development Center
T.J. Majors Building, Room 248
Peru, NE 68421
402-872-2274
Fax: 402-872-2422

Small Business Development Center
Nebraska Public Power Building
1721 Broadway, Room 408
Scottsbluff, NE 69361

308-635-7513
Fax: 308-635-6596

Wayne State College
Small Business Development Center
Garner Hall, 111 Main St.
Wayne, NE 68787
402-375-7575
Fax: 402-375-7574

Nevada
Lead Center:
Nevada Small Business Development Center
University of Nevada at Reno
College of Business Administration
Room 411, Business Bldg.
Reno, NV 89577-0100
702-784-1717
Fax: 702-784-4337

FOREIGN TRADE
ZONE OFFICE

Great Basin College SBDC
1500 College Pkwy.
Elko, NV 89801
702-753-2245
Fax: 702-753-2242

University of Nevada at Las Vegas
Small Business Development Center
College of Business and Economics
Box 456011
Las Vegas, NV 89154-0611
702-895-0852
Fax: 702-895-4095

Carson City Chamber of Commerce
Small Business Development Center
1900 S. Carson St., #100
Carson City, NV 89701
702-882-1565
Fax: 702-882-4179

Incline Village Crystal Bay
Chamber of Commerce SBDC
969 Tahoe Blvd.

Incline Village, NV 89451
702-831-4440
Fax: 702-832-1605

X Foreign Trade Zone Office SBDC
111 Grier Dr.
Las Vegas, NV 89119
702-896-4496
Fax: 702-896-8351

Small Business Development Center
19 W. Fourth St.
North Las Vegas, NV 89030
702-399-6300
Fax: 702-399-6301

Tri-County Development Authority
Small Business Development Center
P.O. Box 820
50 W. Fourth St.
Winnemucca, NV 89446
702-623-5777
Fax: 702-623-5999

New Hampshire
Lead Center:
New Hampshire Small Business
Development Center
University of New Hampshire
108 McConnell Hall
Durham, NH 03824 3593
603-862-2200
Fax: 603-862-4876

Keene State College
Small Business Development Center
Blake House
Keene, NH 03431
603-358-2602
Fax: 603-358-2612

Small Business Development Center
120 Main St.
Littleton, NH 03561
603-444-1053
Fax: 603-444-5463

Small Business Development Center
1000 Elm St., 14th Floor
Manchester, NH 03101

603-634-2796
Fax: 603-634-2449

Plymouth State College
Small Business Development Center
Hyde Hall
Plymouth, NH 03264
603-535-2523
Fax: 603-535-2611

Center for Economic Development
Small Business Development Center
1 Indian Head Plaza
Nashua, NH 03060
603-886-1233
Fax: 603-598-1164

First National Bank of Portsmouth
Small Business Development Center
One 3rd St., Suite 2
Dover, NH 03820
603-749-4264

Micro Enterprise Assistance Program
Small Business Development Center
Portsmouth City Hall, Room 325
P.O. Box 628
Portsmouth, NH 03802-0628
603-431-2006
Fax: 603-427-1526

New Jersey
Lead Center:
New Jersey Small Business Development
Center
Rutgers Graduate School of Management
University Heights
180 University Ave.
Newark, NJ 07102
201-648-5950
Fax: 201-648-1110

Small Business Development Center
Greater Atlantic City Chamber of Commerce
1301 Atlantic Ave.
Atlantic City, NJ 08401
609-345-5600
Fax: 609-345-4524

Rutgers - The State University Of New
Jersey at Camden

Small Business Development Center
Business and Science Building
Second Floor
Camden, NJ 08102
609-756-6221
Fax: 609-225-6231

Brookdale Community College
Small Business Development Center
Newman Springs Rd.
Lincroft, NJ 07738
908-842-1900
Fax: 908-842-0203

Rutgers - The State University of New Jersey
at Camden
Small Business Development Center
University Heights
180 University Ave.
3rd Floor, Ackerson Hall
Newark, NJ 07102
201-648-5950
Fax: 201-648-1110

Bergen Community College
Small Business Development Center
400 Paramus Rd
Paramus, NJ 07552
201-447-7841
Fax: 201-447-7495

Mercer County Community College
Small Business Development Center
P.O. Box B
Trenton, NJ 08690
609-586-4800, ext. 469
Fax: 609-890-6338

Kean College of New Jersey
Small Business Development Center
East Campus, Room 242
Union, NJ 07083
908-527-2946
Fax: 908-527-2960

Warren County Community College
Small Business Development Center
Route 57 West, Box 55A
Washington, NJ 07882-9605
908-689-9620
Fax: 908-689-7488

Money For A Big Or Small Business

New Mexico

Lead Center:
New Mexico Small Business Development
Center
Santa Fe Community College
P.O. Box 4187
Santa Fe, NM 87502-4187
505-438-1362
Fax: 505-438-1237

New Mexico State University at Alamogordo
Small Business Development Center
1000 Madison
Alamogordo, NM 87310
505-434-5272

Albuquerque Technical Vocational Institute
Small Business Development Center
525 Buena Vista SE
Albuquerque, NM 87106
505-224-4246
Fax: 505-224-4251

New Mexico State University at Carlsbad
Small Business Development Center
P.O. Box 1090
Carlsbad, NM 88220
505-887-6562
Fax: 505-885-0818

Clovis Community College
Small Business Development Center
417 Schepps Blvd
Clovis, NM 88101
505-769-4136
Fax: 505-769-4190

Northern New Mexico Community College
Small Business Development Center
1002 N. Onate St
Espanola, NM 87532
505-747-2236
Fax: 505-747-2180

San Juan College
Small Business Development Center
4601 College Blvd.
Farmington, NM 87402
505-599-0528

University of New Mexico at Gallup
Small Business Development Center
P.O. Box 1395
Gallup, NM 87305
505-722-2220
Fax: 505-863-6006

New Mexico State University at Grants
Small Business Development Center
709 E. Roosevelt Ave
Grants, NM 87020
505-287-8221
Fax: 505-287-2125

New Mexico Junior College
Small Business Development Center
5317 Lovington Highway
Hobbs, NM 88240
505-392-4510
Fax: 505-392-2526

Dona Ana Branch Community College
Small Business Development Center
Box 30001, Department 3DA
Las Cruces, NM 88003-0001
505-527-7601
Fax: 505-527-7515

Luna Vocational Technical Institute
Small Business Development Center
Luna Camp
P.O. Drawer K
Las Vegas, NM 88701
505-454-2595
Fax: 505-454-2518

University of New Mexico at Los Alamos
Small Business Development Center
P.O. Box 715
901 8th St., #18
Los Alamos, NM 87544
505-662-0001
Fax: 505-662-0099

University of New Mexico at Valencia
Small Business Development Center
280 La Entrada
Los Lunas, NM 87031
505-866-5348
Fax: 505-865-3095

Eastern New Mexico University at Roswell
Small Business Development Center
P.O. Box 6000
57 University Ave.
Roswell, NM 88201-6000
505-624-7133
Fax: 505-624-7132

Santa Fe Community College
Small Business Development Center
S. Richards Ave.
P.O. Box 4187
Santa Fe, NM 87502-4187
505-438-1343
Fax: 505-438-1237

Western New Mexico University
Southwest Small Business Development
Center
P.O. Box 2672
Silver City, NM 88062
505-538-6320
Fax: 505-538-6341

Tucumcari Area Vocational School
Small Business Development Center
P.O. Box 1143
Tucumcari, NM 88401
505-461-4413
Fax: 505-461-1901

New York
Lead Center:
New York Small Business Development
Center
State University of New York
State University Plaza, S-523
Albany, NY 12246
518-443-5398
Fax: 518-465-4992
1-800-732-7232

State University of New York at Albany
(SUNY)
Small Business Development Center
Draper Hall, Room 107
135 Western Ave.
Albany, NY 12222
518-442-5577
Fax: 518-442-5582

SUNY at Binghamton
Small Business Development Center
P.O. Box 6000
Binghamton, NY 13902-6000
607-777-4024
Fax: 607-777-4029

Small Business Development Center
74 N. Main St.
Brockport, NY 14420
716-637-6660
Fax: 716-637-2102

Bronx Community College
Small Business Development Center
McCracken Hall, Room 14
West 181st St. and University Ave.
Bronx, NY 10453
718-563-3570
Fax: 718-563-3572

Kingsborough Community College
2001 Oriental Blvd
Bldg. Tr Room 4204
Brooklyn, NY 11235
718-368-4619
Fax: 718-368-4629

Downtown Outreach Center
Small Business Development Center
395 Flatbush Ave.
Brooklyn, NY 11201
718-260-9783
Fax: 718-260-9797

State University College at Buffalo
Small Business Development Center
1300 Elmwood Ave., BA 117
Buffalo, NY 14222
716-878-4030
Fax: 716-878-4067

Cobleskill Outreach Center
Small Business Development Center
SUNY Cobleskill
Warner Hall, Room 218
Cobleskill, NY 12043
518-234-5528
Fax: 518-234-5272

Money For A Big Or Small Business

Corning Community College
Small Business Development Center
24 Denison Parkway West
Corning, NY 14830
607-962-9461
Fax: 607-936-6642

Mercy College Outreach Ctr.
Small Business Development Center
555 Broadway
Dobbs Ferry, NY 10522-1189
914-674-7845
Fax: 914-693-4996

State Univ. College of Technology at
Farmingdale
Small Business Development Center
Campus Commons
Farmingdale, NY 11735
516-420-2765
Fax: 516-293-5343

Marist College
Small Business Development Center
Fishkill Extension Center
2600 Route 9, Unit 90
Fishkill, NY 12524-2001
914-897-2607
Fax: 914-897-4653

SUNY Geneseo
Small Business Development Center
1 College Circle
Geneseo, NY 14454-1485
716-245-5429
Fax: 716-245-5430

Geneva Outreach Center
Small Business Development Center at
Geneva
122 N. Genesee St
Geneva, NY 14456
315-781-1253

EOC Hempstead Outreach Center
Small Business Development Center
269 Fulton Ave
Hempstead, NY 11550
516-564-8672/1895
Fax: 516-481-4938

York College
Small Business Development Center
Science Building, Room 107
The City University of New York
Jamaica, NY 11451
718-262-2880
Fax: 718-262-2881

Jamestown Community College
Small Business Development Center
P.O. Box 20
Jamestown, NY 14702-0020
716-665-5754
1-800-522-7232
Fax: 716-665-6733

Kingston Small Business Development
Center
1 Development Court
Kingston, NY 12401
914-339-0025
Fax: 914-339-1631

Harlem Outreach Center
Small Business Development Center
163 W. 125th St, Room 1307
New York, NY 10027
212-346-1900
Fax: 212-534-4576

East Harlem Outreach Center
Small Business Development Center
145 E 116th St, 3rd Floor
New York, NY 10029
212-534-2729/4526
Fax: 212-410-1359

Midtown Outreach Center
Small Business Development Center
Baruch College
360 Park Ave. S., Room 1101
New York, NY 10010
212-802-6620
Fax: 212-802-6613

Pace University
Small Business Development Center
1 Pace Plaza, Room W483
New York, NY 10038
212-346-1900
Fax: 212-346-1613

Money For A Big Or Small Business

SUNY at Oswego
Small Business Development Center
Operation Oswego County
44 W. Bridge St.
Oswego, NY 13126
315-343-1545
Fax: 315-343-1546

Clinton Community College
Small Business Development Center
Lake Shore Rd, Suite 9 S.
136 Clinton Point Dr.
Plattsburgh, NY 12901
518-562-4260
Fax: 518-563-9759

Riverhead Outreach Center
Small Business Development Center
Suffolk County Community College
Riverhead, NY 11901
516-369-1409/1507
Fax: 516-369-3255

Small Business Development Center-SUNY
Brockport
Temple Bldg
14 Franklin St, Suite 200
Rochester, NY 14604
716-232-7310
Fax: 716-637-2182

Niagara County Community College at
Sanborn
Small Business Development Center
3111 Saunders Settlement Rd.
Sanborn, NY 14132
716-693-1910
Fax: 716-731-3595

Southampton Outreach Center
Small Business Development Center
Long Island University at Southampton
Abney Peak, Montauk Highway
Southampton, NY 11968
516-287-0059/0071
Fax: 516-287-8287

The College of Staten Island
Small Business Development Center
2800 Victory Blvd.
Staten Island, NY 10314-9806

718-982-2560
Fax: 718-982-2323

SUNY at Stony Brook
Small Business Development Center
Harriman Hall, Room 109
Stony Brook, NY 11794-3775
516-632-9070
Fax: 516-632-7176

Rockland Community College at Suffern
Small Business Development Center
145 College Rd.
Suffern, NY 10901-3620
914-356-0370
Fax: 914-356-0381

Onondaga Community College at Syracuse
Small Business Development Center
Excell Bldg, Room 108
4969 Onondaga Rd.
Syracuse, NY 13215
315-492-3029
Fax: 315-492-3704

Manufacturing Technology Center
Small Business Development Center
New York Manufacturing Partnership
385 Jordan Rd
Troy, NY 12180-7602
518-286-1014
Fax: 518-286-1006

SUNY College of Technology at Utica/Rome
Small Business Development Center
P.O. Box 3050
Utica, NY 13504-3050
315-792-7546
Fax: 315-792-7554

Information USA, Inc.

Jefferson Community College
Small Business Development Center
Watertown, NY 13601
315-782-9262
Fax: 315-782-0901

The Small Business Resource Center
Small Business Development Center
222 Bloomingdale Rd, 3rd Floor
White Plains, NY 10605-1500
914-644-4116
Fax: 914-644-2184

North Carolina

Lead Center:
North Carolina Small Business Development
Center
University of North Carolina
333 Fayette St. Mall, Suite 1150
Raleigh, NC 27601
919-715-7272
Fax: 919-715-7777

Asheville Office
Small Business Development Center
34 Wall St, Suite 707
Public Services Bldg
Asheville, NC 28805
704-251-6025

Appalachian State University
Small Business Development Center
Northwestern Region
Walker College of Business
Boone, NC 28608
704-262-2492
Fax: 704-262-2027

Small Business Development Center
Central Carolina Region
608 Airport Rd., Suite B
Chapel Hill, NC 27514
919-962-0389
Fax: 919-962-3291

Small Business Development Center
Southern Piedmont Region
The Ben Craig Center
8701 Mallard Creek Rd.
Charlotte, NC 28262
704-548-1090
Fax: 704-548-9050

Small Business Development Center
Center for Improving Mountain Living
Western Carolina University
Bird Building
Cullowhee, NC 28723
704-227-7494
Fax: 704-227-7422

Elizabeth City State University
Small Business Development Center
Northeastern Region
P.O. Box 874
Elizabeth City, NC 27909
919-335-3247
Fax: 919-335-3648

Fayetteville State University
Small Business Development Center
Cape Fear Region
Continuing Education Center
P.O. Box 1334
Fayetteville, NC 28302
910-486-1727
Fax: 910-486-1949

NC A&T University/CH Moore Agricultural
Research Center
Small Business Development Center
Box D-22, 1602 E. Market St.
Greensboro, NC 27411
910-334-7005
Fax: 910-334-7073

East Carolina University
Small Business Development Center
Eastern Region
300 E. 1st St., Willis Bldg.
Greenville, NC 27858-4353
919-328-6157
Fax: 919-328-6992

Catawba Valley Region
Small Business Development Center
514 Hwy 321, Suite A
Hickory, NC 28601
704-345-1110
Fax: 704-326-9117

Pembroke State University
Office of Economic Development and
SBTDC
Pembroke, NC 28372

910-521-6603
Fax: 910-521-6550

MCI Small Business Resource Center
800 1/2 S. Salisbury St
Raleigh, NC 27601
919-715-0520
Fax: 919-715-0518

NC Wesleyan College
Small Business Development Center
3400 N. Wesleyan Blvd
Rocky Mount, NC 27804
919-985-5130
Fax: 919-977-3701

University of North Carolina at Wilmington
Small Business Development Center
Southeastern Region
601 S. College Rd.
Wilmington, NC 28403
919-395-3744
Fax: 910-350-3990

Winston-Salem University
Small Business Development Center
Northern Piedmont Region
P.O. Box 13025
Winston-Salem, NC 27110
910-750-2030
Fax: 910-750-2031

North Dakota
Lead Center:
North Dakota Small Business Development
Center
University of North Dakota
118 Gamble Hall, Box 7308
Grand Forks, ND 58202-7308
701-777-3700
Fax: 701-777-3225

Small Business Development Center
Bismarck Regional Center
400 East Broadway, Suite 416
Bismarck, ND 58501
701-223-8583
Fax: 701-252-3843

Devils Lake Outreach Center
Small Business Development Center

417 5th St
Devils Lake, ND 58301
800-445-7232

Small Business Development Center
Dickinson Regional Center
314 3rd Ave. West, Drawer L
Dickinson, ND 58602
701-227-2096
Fax: 701-225-5116

Small Business Development Center
Fargo Regional Center
417 Main Ave.
Fargo, ND 58103
701-237-0986
Fax: 701-237-9734

Grafton Outreach Center
Red River Regional Planning Council
Small Business Development Center
P.O. Box 633
Grafton, ND 58237
800-445-7232

Small Business Development Center
Grand Forks Regional Center
The Hemp Center
1407 24th Ave. S, Suite 201
Grand Forks, ND 58201
701-772-8502
Fax: 701-775-2772

Jamestown Outreach Center
Small Business Development Center
210 10th St. SE
Box 1530
Jamestown, ND 58402
701-252-9243
Fax: 701-251-2488

Small Business Development Center
Minot Regional Center
1020 20th Ave. SW
P.O. Box 940
Minot, ND 58702
701-852-8861
Fax: 701-838-2488

Williston Outreach Center
Tri-County Economic Development Assn.
Small Business Development Center

Box 2047
Williston, ND 58801
800-445-7232

Ohio
Lead Center:
Ohio Small Business Development Center
Department of Development
77 S. High St., 28th Floor
Columbus, OH 43226-0101
614-466-2480
Fax: 614-466-0829

Small Business Development Center
Akron Regional Development Board
One Cascade Plaza, 8th Floor
Akron, OH 44308
216-379-3170
Fax: 216-379-3164

Ohio University
Small Business Development Center
Innovation Center
20 E. Circle Dr
Athens, OH 45701
614-593-1797
Fax: 614-593-1795

Athens Small Business Center, Inc
900 East State St.
Athens OH 45701
614-592-1188
Fax: 614-593-8283

Wood County Small Business Development
Center
WSOS Community Action Commission, Inc.
P.O. Box 539
121 E. Wooster St
Bowling Green, OH 43402
419-352-7469
Fax: 419-353-3291

Wright State University
Lake Campus
Small Business Development Center
7600 State Route 703
Celina, OH 45882
419-586-0355
Fax: 419-586-0358

Cincinnati Small Business Development
Center
IAMS Research Park, MC189
1111 Edison Ave.
Cincinnati, OH 45216-2265
513-948-2082
Fax: 513-948-2007

Clemont County Chamber of Commerce
Small Business Development Center
4440 Glen Este-Withamsville Rd.
Cincinnati, OH 45245
513-753-7141
Fax: 513-753-7146

Northern Ohio Mfg. Small Business
Development Center
Prospect Pk. Bldg.
4600 Prospect Ave.
Cleveland, OH 44103-4314
216-432-5364
Fax: 216-361-2900

Greater Cleveland Growth Association
Small Business Development Center
200 Tower City Center
50 Public Square
Cleveland, OH 44113-2291
216-621-3300
Fax: 216-621-4617

Columbus Small Business Development
Center
Columbus Area Chamber of Commerce
37 N. High St.
Columbus, OH 43215
614-225-6082
Fax: 614-469-8250

Dayton Satellite
Center for Small Business Assistance
College of Business, 310 Rike Hall
Dayton, OH 45433
513-873-3503
Fax: 523-873-3545

Northwest SBDC
1935 E. Second St, Suite D
Defiance, OH 43512
419-784-3777
Fax: 419-782-4649

North Central Small Business Development
Center
Fremond Office
Terra Technical College
1220 Cedar St.
Freemont, OH 43420
419-332-1002
Fax: 419-334-2300

Enterprise Center Small Business
Development Center
129 E. Main St
Hillsboro, OH 45132
513-393-9599
Fax: 513-393-8159

Ashtabula County Economic Development
Council, Inc.
Small Business Development Center
36 West Walnut St.
Jefferson, OH 44047
216-576-9134
Fax: 216-576-5003

Kent Regional Business Alliance Small
Business Development Center
Kent State Univ. Partnership
College of Business Admin., Room 302
Kent, OH 44242
216-672-2772 ext. 254
Fax: 216-672-2448

EMTEC/Small Business Development
Center
Southern Area Mfg. Small Business
Development Center
3171 Research Park
Kettering, OH 45420
513-259-1361
Fax: 513-259-1303

Lima Technical College
Small Business Development Center
545 West Market St., Suite 305
Lima, OH 45801-4717
419-229-5320
Fax: 419-229-5424

Lorain County Chamber of Commerce
Small Business Development Center
6100 S. Broadway
Lorain, OH 44053

216-233-6500
Fax: 216-246-4050

Mid-Ohio SBDC
246 E. 4th St
P.O. Box 44901
Mansfield, OH 44901
800-366-7232
Fax: 419-522-6811

Marietta College
Small Business Development Center
213 4th St
Marietta, OH 45750
614-376-4901
Fax: 614-376-4832

Marion SBDC
Marion Area Chamber of Commerce
206 S. Prospect St.
Marion, OH 43302
614-387-0188
Fax: 614-387-7722

Lakeland Community College
Lake County Economic Development Center
Small Business Development Center
750 Clocktower Dr.
Mentor, OH 44080
216-951-1290
Fax: 216-951-7336

Women's Network
1540 W. Market St., Suite 100
Akron, OH 44313
330-864-5636
Fax: 330-884-6526

Women's Entrepreneurial Growth
Organization
Small Business Development Center
The University of Akron
Buckingham Bldg., Room 55
Akron, OH 44309
330-972-5179
330-972-5513

Women's Business Development Center
2400 Cleveland Ave. NW
Canton, OH 44709
216-453-3867
Fax: 216-773-2992

Kent State Univ./Salem Campus
Small Business Development Center
2491 State Route 45 S.
Salem, OH 44460
330-332-0361
Fax: 330-332-9256

Youngstown/Warren SBDC
Region Chamber of Commerce
180 E. Market St.
Warren, OH 44482
330-393-2565
Fax: 330-392-6040

VOCATIONAL SCHOOL

Tuscarawas Chamber of Commerce
Small Business Development Center
330 University Dr, NE
New Philadelphia, OH 44663-9447
216-339-3391 ext. 279
Fax: 216-339-2637

Miami University Small Business
Development Center
Dept. of Decision Sciences
336 Upham Hall
Oxford, OH 44046
513-529-4841
Fax: 513-529-1469

Upper Valley Joint Vocational School
Small Business Development Center
8811 Career Dr.
North County Rd. 25A
Piqua, OH 45356
513-778-8419
Fax: 513-778-9237

Portsmouth Area Chamber of Commerce
Small Business Development Center
1208 Waller St.
P.O. Box 1757
Portsmouth, OH 45662
614-353-8395
Fax: 614-353-2695

Lawrence County Chamber of Commerce
Small Business Development Center
U.S. Route 52 and Solida Rd.
P.O. Box 488
Southpoint, OH 45680
614-894-3838
Fax: 614-894-3836

Springfield Small Business Development
Center, Inc.
300 E. Auburn Ave
Springfield, OH 45505
513-322-7821
Fax: 513-322-7824

Department of Development of the CIC of
Belmont County
Small Business Development Center
St. Clairsville Office
100 East Main St.
St. Clairsville, OH 43950
614-695-9678
Fax: 614-695-1536

Greater Steubenville Chamber of Commerce
Small Business Development Center
630 Market St.
P.O. Box 278
Steubenville, OH 43952
614-282-6226
Fax: 614-282-6285

Northwest Ohio Women's Business
Entrepreneurial Network
Small Business Development Center
Toledo Regional Growth Partnership
300 Madison Ave
Toledo, OH 43604
419-252-2700
Fax: 419-252-2724

Youngstown State University
Cushwa Center for Industrial Development
Small Business Development Center
241 Federal Plaza W.
Youngstown, OH 44503
330-746-3350
Fax: 330-746-3324

Zanesville Area Chamber of Commerce
Small Business Development Center

217 N. Fifth St.
Zanesville, OH 43701
614-452-4868
Fax: 614-454-2963

Oklahoma

Lead Center:
Oklahoma Small Business Development
Center Network
Southeastern Oklahoma State University
517 University
Durant, OK 74701
405-924-0277
1-800-522-6154
Fax: 405-920-7471

East Central State University
Small Business Development Center
1036 East 10th
Ada, OK 74820
405-436-3190
Fax: 405-436-3190

Northwestern State University
Small Business Development Center
709 Oklahoma Blvd
Alva, OK 73717
405-327-8608
Fax: 405-327-0560

Southeastern State University
Small Business Development Center
517 University
Durant, OK 74701
405-924-0277
Fax: 405-920-7471

Phillips University
Enid Satellite Center
100 S. University Ave.
Enid, OK 73701
405-242-7989
Fax: 405-237-1607

Langston University
Minority Assistance Center
Hwy. 33 East
Langston, OK 73050
405-466-3256
Fax: 405-466-2909

Lawton Satellite Center
Small Business Development Center
American National Bank Building
601 SW "D", Suite 209
Lawton, OK 73501
405-248-4946
Fax: 405-355-3560

Miami Satellite
215 I St. NE
Miami, OK 74354
918-540-0575
Fax: 918-540-0575

Rose State College
Procurement Specialty Center
6420 SE 15th St.
Midwest City, OK 73110
405-733-7348
Fax: 405-733-7495

University of Central Oklahoma
Small Business Development Center
P.O. Box 1439, 115 Park Ave.
Oklahoma City, OK 73101-1439
405-232-1968
Fax: 405-232-1967

Carl Albert Junior College
Poteau Satellite Center
Small Business Development Center
1507 S. McKenna
Poteau, OK 74953
918-647-4019
Fax: 918-647-1218

Northeastern State University
Small Business Development Center
Tahlequah, OK 74464
918-458-0802
Fax: 918-458-2105

Tulsa Satellite Center
State Office Building
440 S. Houston, Suite 507
Tulsa, OK 74127
918-581-2502
Fax: 918-581-2745

Southwestern State University
Small Business Development Center

100 Campus Dr.
Weatherford, OK 73096
405-774-1040
Fax: 405-774-7091

Oregon
Lead Center:
Oregon Small Business Development Center
44 W. Broadway, Suite 501
Eugene, OR 97401-3021
503-726-2250
Fax: 503-345-6006

Linn-Benton Community College
Small Business Development Center
6500 SW Pacific Blvd.
Albany, OR 97321
541-917-4923
Fax: 541-917-4445

Southern Oregon State College
Small Business Development Center
Regional Service Institute
Ashland, OR 97520
541-482-5838
Fax: 541-482-5838

Central Oregon Community College
Small Business Development Center
2600 NW College Way
Bend, OR 97701
541-383-7290
Fax: 541-383-7503

Southwestern Oregon Community College
Small Business Development Center
340 Central
Coos Bay, OR 97420
541-269-0123
Fax: 541-269-0323

Lane Community College
Small Business Development Center
1059 Willamette St.
Eugene, OR 97401
503-726-2255
Fax: 503-686-0096

Rogue Community College
Small Business Development Center
214 SW 4th St

Grants Pass, OR 97526
541-471-3515
Fax: 541-471-3589

Mount Hood Community College
Small Business Development Center
323 NE Roberts St.
Gresham, OR 97030
503-667-7658
Fax: 503-666-1140

Oregon Institute of Technology
Small Business Development Center
3201 Campus Dr., South 314
Klamath Falls, OR 97601
541-885-1760
Fax: 541-885-1855

Small Business Development Center
229 N. Bartlett
Medford, OR 97501
503-772-3478
Fax: 503-776-2224

Clackamas Community College
Small Business Development Center
7616 SE Harmony Rd.
Milwaukie, OR 97222
503-656-4447
Fax: 503-652-0389

Treasure Valley Community College
Small Business Development Center
88 SW Third Ave.
Ontario, OR 97914
541-889-2617
Fax: 541-889-8331

Blue Mountain Community College
Small Business Development Center
37 SE Dorion
Pendleton, OR 97801
541-276-6233
Fax: 541-276-6819

Portland Community College
Small Business Development Center
123 NW 2nd Ave., Suite 321
Portland, OR 97209
503-414-2828
Fax: 503-294-0725

Money For A Big Or Small Business

Small Business International Trade Program
121 SW Salmon St., Suite 210
Portland, OR 97204
503-274-7482
Fax: 503-228-6350

Umpqua Community College
Small Business Development Center
744 SE Rose
Rosenburg, OR 97470
541-672-2535
Fax: 541-672-3679

Chemeketa Community College
Small Business Development Center
365 Ferry St. SE
Salem, OR 97301
503-399-5181
Fax: 503-581-6017

Clatsop Community College
Small Business Development Center
1240 S. Holladay
Seaside, OR 97138
503-738-3347
Fax: 503-738-7843

Columbia Gorge Community College
Small Business Development Center
212 Washington
The Dalles, OR 97058
541-298-3118
Fax: 541-298-3119

Tillamook Bay Community College Service
District SBDC
401 B Main St.
Tillamook, OR 97141
503-842-2551
Fax: 503-842-2555

Pennsylvania
Lead Center:
Pennsylvania Small Business Development
Center
University of Pennsylvania
The Wharton School
409 Vance Hall
Philadelphia, PA 19104-6374
215-898-4861
Fax: 215-898-1063

Lehigh University
Small Business Development Center
Rauch Business Center #37
Bethlehem, PA 18015
610-758-3980
Fax: 610-758-5205

Clarion University of Pennsylvania
Small Business Development Center
Dana Still Building, Room 102
Clarion, PA 16214
814-226-2060
Fax: 814-226-2636

Gannon University
Small Business Development Center
Carlisle Building, 3rd Floor
Erie, PA 16541
814-871-7714
Fax: 814-871-7383

Kutztown University
Small Business Development Center
University Center
2986 N. 2nd St.
Harrisburg, PA 17110
717-720-4230
Fax: 717-233-3181

Indiana University of PA
Small Business Development Center
Robt. Shaw Bldg.
Indiana, PA 15705
412-357-7915
Fax: 412-357-4514

St. Vincent College
Small Business Development Center
Alfred Hall, 4th Floor
Latrobe, PA 15650
412-537-4572
Fax: 412-537-0919

Bucknell University
Small Business Development Center
126 Dana Engineering Building
Lewisburg, PA 17837
717-524-1249
Fax: 717-524-1768

St. Francis College
Small Business Development Center

340 *Information USA, Inc.*

Business Resource Center
Loretto, PA 15940
814-472-3200
Fax: 814-472-3202

Temple University
Small Business Development Center
Room 6, Speakman Hall 006-00
Philadelphia, PA 19122
215-204-7282

LaSalle University
Small Business Development Center
1900 W. and Olney Ave
Philadelphia, PA 19141
215-951-1416
Fax: 215-951-1597

University of Pennsylvania
Small Business Development Center
The Wharton School
423 Vance Hall
Philadelphia, PA 19104-6374
215-898-1219
Fax: 215-898-2135

Duquesne University
Small Business Development Center
Rockwell Hall-Room 10 Concourse
600 Forbes Ave.
Pittsburgh, PA 15282
412-396-6233
Fax: 412-396-5884

University Small Business Development
Center
208 Bellefield Hall
315 S. Bellefield Ave.
Pittsburgh, PA 15260
412-648-1544
Fax: 412-648-1636

University of Scranton
Small Business Development Center
St. Thomas Hall, Room 588
Scranton, PA 18510
717-941-7588
Fax: 717-941-4053

Wilkes College
Small Business Development Center
Hollenback Hall

192 S. Franklin St.
Wilkes-Barre, PA 18766-0001
717-831-4340
Fax: 717-824-2245

Rhode Island
Lead Center:
Rhode Island Small Business Development
Center
Bryant College
1150 Douglas Pike
Smithfield, RI 02917
401-232-6416
Fax: 401-232-6111

Salve Regina University
Small Business Development Center
Miley Hall, Room 006
Newport, RI 02840
401-849-6900
Fax: 401-847-0372

Rhode Island Small Business Development
Center
Quonset P/D Industrial Park
35 Belver Ave., Room 2127
North Kingstown, RI 02852-7556
401-294-1227
Fax: 401-294-6897

Rhode Island Small Business Development
Center
CCRI-Providence Campus
One Hilton St
Providence, RI 02905
401-455-6088
Fax: 401-455-6047

Bryant College
Small Business Development Center
30 Exchange Terrace, 4th Floor
Providence, RI 02903
401-831-1330
Fax: 401-454-2819

South Carolina
Lead Center:
South Carolina Small Business Development
Center
University of South Carolina
College of Business Administration

Columbia, SC 29208
803-777-4907
Fax: 803-777-4403

University of South Carolina
Alkan Office
Small Business Development Center
171 University Pkwy., Suite 100
School of Business
Alkan, SC 29801
803-641-3646
Fax: 803-641-3647

University of South Carolina at Beaufort
Small Business Development Center
800 Carterat St.
Beaufort, SC 29902
803-521-4143
Fax: 803-521-4198

Clemson University
Small Business Development Center
425 Sirrine Hall
College of Commerce
Clemson, SC 29634-1392
803-656-3227
Fax: 803-656-4869

University of South Carolina
USC Regional Small Business Development
Center
College of Business Administration
Columbia, SC 29208
803-777-5118
Fax: 803-777-4403

Coastal Carolina
Small Business Development Center
School of Business Administration
P.O. Box 1954
Conway, SC 29526
803-349-2170
Fax: 803-349-2445

Florence Darlington Technical College
Small Business Development Center
P.O. Box 100548
Florence, SC 29501-0548
803-661-8256
Fax: 803-661-8041

Greenville Chamber of Commerce
Small Business Development Center

24 Cleveland St
Greenville, SC 29601
803-271-4259
Fax: 803-282-8549

Upper Savannah Council of Governments
Small Business Development Center
Exchange Building
222 Phoenix St., Suite 200
P.O. Box 1366
Greenwood, SC 29648
803-941-8071
Fax: 803-941-8090

University of South Carolina at Hilton Head
Small Business Development Center
Suite 300, Kiawah Bldg.
10 Office Park Rd.
Hilton Head, SC 29928
803-785-3995
Fax: 803-777-0333

South Carolina State College
Small Business Development Center
School of Business
300 College Ave
Orangeburg, SC 29117
803-536-8445
Fax: 803-536-8066

Winthrop University
Small Business Development Center
119 Thurmond Building
Rock Hill, SC 29733
803-323-2283
Fax: 803-323-4281

Spartanburg Chamber of Commerce
Small Business Development Center
P.O. Box 1636
105 N. Pine St

Spartanburg, SC 29304
803-594-5080
Fax: 803-594-5055

South Dakota
Lead Center:
South Dakota Small Business Development
Center
University of South Dakota
414 East Clark
Vermillion, SD 57069
605-677-5498
Fax: 605-677-5272

Small Business Development Center
226 Citizens Building
Aberdeen, SD 57401
605-626-2252
Fax: 605-626-2667

Small Business Development Center
105 S. Euclid, Suite C
Pierre, SD 57501
605-773-5941
Fax: 605-773-5942

Small Business Development Center
444 Mount Rushmore Rd., Room 208
Rapid City, SD 57701
605-394-5311
Fax: 605-394-6140

Small Business Development Center
200 N. Phillips, Suite 302
Sioux Falls, SD 57102
605-367-5757
Fax: 605-367-5755

Tennessee
Lead Center:
Tennessee Small Business Development
Center
Memphis State University
South Campus (Getwell Rd.), Building #1
Memphis, TN 38152
901-678-2500
Fax: 901-678-4072

Chattanooga State Technical Community
College
Small Business Development Center

4501 Amnicola Highway
Chattanooga, TN 37406-1097
615-697-4410, ext. 505
Fax: 615-698-5653

Southeast Tennessee Development District
Small Business Development Center
P.O. Box 4757
Chattanooga, TN 37405
423-266-5781
Fax: 423-267-7705

Austin Peay State University
Small Business Development Center
College of Business
Clarksville, TN 37044-0001
615-648-7764
Fax: 615-648-5985

Cleveland State Community College
Small Business Development Center
Business and Technology
P.O. Box 3570
Cleveland, TN 37320
423-478-6247
Fax: 423-478-6251

Small Business Development Center
Memorial Building
Room 205, 308 West 7th St.
Columbia, TN 38401
615-388-5674
Fax: 615-388-5474

Tennessee Technological University
Small Business Development Center
College of Business Administration
P.O. Box 5023
Cookeville, TN 38505
615-372-6634
Fax: 615-372-6249

Dyersburg Community College
Small Business Development Center
1510 Lake Rd.
Dyersburg, TN 38024
901-286-3201
Fax: 901-286-3271

Four Lakes Regional Industrial Development
Authority
Small Business Development Center

P.O. Box 63
Hartsville, TN 37074-0063
615-374-9521
Fax: 615-374-4608

Jackson State Community College
Small Business Development Center
2046 N. Parkway St.
Jackson, TN 38305
901-424-5389
Fax: 901-425-2647

East Tennessee State University
Small Business Development Center
College of Business
P.O. Box 70, 698A
Johnson City, TN 37614-0698
423-929-5630
Fax: 423-461-7080

International Trade Center
301 E. Church Ave.
Knoxville, TN 37915
423-637-4283
Fax: 423-523-2071

Memphis State University
Small Business Development Center
320 S. Dudley St.
Memphis, TN 38104
901-527-1041
Fax: 901-527-1047

Memphis State University
Small Business Development Center
International Trade Center
Memphis, TN 38152
901-678-4174
Fax: 901-678-4072

Walters State Community College
Small Business Development Center
Business/Industrial Services
500 S. Davy Crockett Parkway
Morristown, TN 37813
423-585-2675
Fax: 423-585-2679

Middle Tennessee State University
Small Business Development Center
School of Business
1417 E. Main St.

P.O. Box 487
Murfreesboro, TN 37132
615-898-2745
Fax: 615-898-2861

Tennessee State University
Small Business Development Center
School of Business
330 10th Ave. N.
Nashville, TN 37203-3401
615-963-7179
Fax: 615-963-7160

Texas
Lead Centers:
North Texas Small Business Development
Center
Dallas County Community College
1402 Corinth St.
Dallas, TX 75215
214-860-5831
Fax: 214-860-5813

Houston Small Business Development
Center
University of Houston
1100 Louisiana, Suite 500
Houston, TX 77002
713-752-8444
Fax: 713-756-1500

Northwest Texas Small Business
Development Center
Center for Innovation
2579 S. Loop 289, Suite 114
Lubbock, TX 79423
806-745-3973
Fax: 806-745-6207

South Texas Border Small Business
Development Center
University of Texas at San Antonio
1222 N. Main, Suite 450
San Antonio, TX 78205
210-558-2450
Fax: 210-558-2464

Abilene Christian University
Caruth Small Business Development Center
College of Business Administration
648 E. Highway 80

Abilene, TX 79601
915-670-0300
Fax: 915-670-0311

Alvin Community College
Small Business Development Center
3110 Mustang Rd.
Alvin, TX 77511-4898
713-338-4686
Fax: 713-388-4903

West Texas State University
Panhandle SBDC
T. Boone Pickens School of Business
1800 S. Washington, Suite 209
Amarillo, TX 79102
806-372-5151
Fax: 806-372-5261

Trinity Valley Small Business Development
Center
500 S. Prairieville
Athens, TX 75751
903-675-7403
Fax: 903-675-6316

Austin Small Business Development Center
221 S. IH 35, Suite 103
Austin, TX 78767
512-473-3510
Fax: 512-443-4094

Lee College
Small Business Development Center
P.O. Box 818
Baytown, TX 77522-0818
713-425-6307
Fax: 713-425-6309

John Gray Institute/Lamar University
Small Business Development Center
855 Florida Ave.
Beaumont, TX 77705
409-880-2367
Fax: 409-880-2201

Bonham Small Business Development Center
(Satellite)
110 W. First
Bonham, TX 75418
903-583-4811
Fax: 903-583-6706

Blinn College
Small Business Development Center
902 College Ave.
Brenham, TX 77833
409-830-4137
Fax: 409-830-4135

Bryan/College Station Chamber of
Commerce
Small Business Development Center
4001 E. 29th St.
Bryan, TX 77805
409-260-5222
Fax: 409-260-5208

Corpus Christi Chamber of Commerce
Small Business Development Center
1201 N. Shoreline
Corpus Christi, TX 78539
512-881-1888
Fax: 512-882-4256

Navarro SBDC
120 N. 12th St.
Corsicana, TX 75110
903-874-0658
Fax: 903-874-4187

International Business Center
2050 Stemmons Freeway
World Trade Center, Suite #150
P.O. Box 58299
Dallas, TX 75258
214-747-1300
Fax: 214-748-5774

Grayson SBDC
6101 Grayson Dr.
Denison, TX 75020
903-786-3551
Fax: 903-786*6284

Denton Small Business Development Center
(Satellite)
P.O. Drawer P
Denton, TX 76202
817-380-1849
Fax: 817-382-0040

University of Texas/Pan American
Small Business Development Center
1201 West University Dr.

Edinburg, TX 78539-2999
210-381-3361
Fax: 210-381-2322

El Paso Community College
Small Business Development Center
103 Montana Ave., Room 202
El Paso, TX 79902-3929
915-534-3410
Fax: 915-534-4625

Tarrant Small Business Development Center
1500 Houston St., Room 163
7917 Highway 80 West
Fort Worth, TX 76102
817-794-5900
Fax: 817-794-5952

Cooke Small Business Development Center
1525 West California
Gainesville, TX 76240
817-668-4220
Fax: 817-668-6049

Galveston College
Small Business Development Center
4015 Avenue Q
Galveston, TX 77550
409-740-7380
Fax: 409-740-7381

North Harris Community College District
Small Business Development Center
250 N. Sam Houston Parkway
Houston, TX 77060
713-591-9320
Fax: 713-591-3513

Sam Houston State University
Small Business Development Center
College of Business Administration
P.O. Box 2058
Huntsville, TX 77341-2058
409-294-3737
Fax: 409-294-3738

Kingsville Chamber of Commerce
Small Business Development Center
635 E. King
Kingsville, TX 78363
512-595-5088
Fax: 512-592-0866

Brazosport College
Small Business Development Center
500 College Dr.
Lake Jackson, TX 77566
409-266-3380
Fax: 409-265-7208

Laredo Development Foundation
Small Business Development Center
616 Leal St.
Laredo, TX 78041
210-722-0563
Fax: 210-722-6247

Kilgore College
Small Business Development Center
100 Triple Creek Dr., Suite 70
Longview, TX 75601
903-757-5857
Fax: 903-753-7920

Texas Tech University
Small Business Development Center
Center for Innovation
2579 S. Loop 289, Suite 210
Lubbock, TX 79423
806-745-1637
Fax: 806-745-6217

Angelina Community College
Small Business Development Center
P.O. Box 1768
Lufkin, TX 75902
409-639-1887
Fax: 409-639-1887

Northeast Texarkana Small Business
Development Center
P.O. Box 1307
Mt. Pleasant, TX 75455
214-572-1911
Fax: 903-572-0598

University of Texas/Permian Basin
Small Business Development Center
4901 East University
Odessa, TX 79762
915-552-2455
Fax: 915-552-2433

Paris Small Business Development Center
2400 Clarksville St.

Paris, TX 75460
214-784-1802
Fax: 903-784-1801

STATE COLLEGE

Collin County Small Business Development
Center
4800 Preston Park Blvd.
Plano, TX 75093
214-985-3770
Fax: 214-985-3775

Angelo State University
Small Business Development Center
2610 West Ave. N
Campus Box 10910
San Angelo, TX 76909
915-942-2098
Fax: 915-942-2096

UTSA
International Small Business Development
Center
1222 N. Main
San Antonio, TX 78212
210-558-2470
Fax: 210-558-2464

Houston Community College System
Small Business Development Center
13600 Murphy Rd.
Stafford, TX 77477
713-499-4870
Fax: 713-499-8194

Tarleton State University
Small Business Development Center
Box T-0650
Stephenville, TX 76402
817-968-9330
Fax: 817-968-9329

College of the Mainland
Small Business Development Center
8419 Emmett F. Lowry Expressway

Texas City, TX 77591
409-938-7578
Fax: 409-935-5816

Tyler Small Business Development Center
1530 S. SW Loop 323, Suite 100
Tyler, TX 75701
903-510-2975
Fax: 903-510-2978

University of Houston-Victoria
Small Business Development Center
700 Main Center, Suite 102
Victoria, TX 77901
512-575-8944
Fax: 512-575-8852

McLennan Small Business Development
Center
4601 N. 19th St., Suite A-15
Waco, TX 76708
817-750-3600
Fax: 817-750-3620

Wharton County Junior College
Small Business Development Center
Administration Building, Room 102
911 Boling Highway
Wharton, TX 77488-0080
409-532-0604
Fax: 409-532-2410

Midwestern State University
Small Business Development Center
Division of Business
3400 Taft Blvd.
Wichita Falls, TX 76308
817-689-4373
Fax: 817-689-4374

Utah
Lead Center:
Utah Small Business Development Center
University of Utah
102 West 500 South, Suite 315
Salt Lake City, UT 84101
801-581-7905
Fax: 801-581-7814

Southern Utah University
Small Business Development Center

351 West Center
Cedar City, UT 84720
801-586-5400
Fax: 801-586-5493

Snow College SBDC
345 West First North
Ephraim, UT 84627
801-283-4021
801-283-6890
Fax: 801-283-6913

Utah State University
Small Business Development Center
East Campus Building
Logan, UT 84322-8330
801-797-2277
Fax: 801-797-3317

Weber State University
Small Business Development Center
College of Business and Economics
Ogden, UT 84408-3806
801-626-7232
Fax: 801-626-7423

College of Eastern Utah
Small Business Development Center
451 East 400 North
Price, UT 84501
801-637-1995
Fax: 801-637-4102

Utah State College
Small Business Development Center
School of Management
800 W. 1200 S
Orem, UT 84058
801-222-8230
Fax: 801-225-1229

Uintah Basin Applied Technology Center
Small Business Development Center
1100 East Lagoon
P.O. Box 124-5
Roosevelt, UT 84066
801-722-4523
Fax: 801-722-5804

Dixie College SBDC
225 South 700 East
St. George, UT 84770

801-673-4811, ext 353
Fax: 801-674-5839

Vermont
Lead Center:
Vermont Small Business Development
Center
Vermont Tech. College
P.O. Box 422
Randolph, VT 05060-0422
802-728-9101
Fax: 802-728-3026

Northwestern Vermont Small Business
Development Center
P.O. Box 786 NW VT SBDC
Burlington, VT 05402-0786
802-658-9228
Fax: 802-860-1899

Southwestern Vermont Small Business
Development Center
256 N. Main St.
Rutland, VT 05701
802-773-9147
Fax: 802-773-2772

Southeastern Vermont Small Business
Development Center
P.O. Box 58
Springfield, VT 05156-0058
802-885-2071
Fax: 802-885-3027

Central Vermont Small Business
Development Center
Green Mountain SBDC
P.O. Box 246
White River Jct., VT 05001-0246
802-295-3710
Fax: 802-295-3779

Brattleboro Dev. Credit Corp.
Small Business Development Center
P.O. Box 1177
Brattleboro, VT 05301-1177
802-257-7731
Fax: 802-258-3886

Addison County Economic Development
Corporation SBDC
2 Court St.
Middlebury, VT 05753

802-388-7953
Fax: 802-388-8066

Central VT Economic Development Center
Small Business Development Center
P.O. Box 1439
Montpelier, VT 05601-1439
802-223-4654
Fax: 802-223-4655

Lamoille Economic Development Center
Small Business Development Center
P.O. Box 455
Morrisville, VT 05661-0455
802-888-4923
Fax: 802-888-5640

Bennington Co. Industrial Corp.
Small Business Development Center
P.O. Box 357
No. Bennington, VT 05257
802-442-8975
Fax: 802-442-1101

Lake Champlain Islands
Chamber of Commerce Small Business
Development Center
P.O. Box 213
No. Bero, VT 05474-0213
802-372-5683
Fax: 802-372-6104

Franklin County Industrial Dev. Corp.
Small Business Development Center
P.O. Box 1099
St. Albans, VT 05478-1099
802-524-2194
Fax: 802-527-5258

Northeastern VT Dev. Assn.
Small Business Development Center
P.O. Box 630
St. Johnsbury, VT 05819
802-748-1014
Fax: 802-748-1223

Virginia
Lead Center:
Virginia Small Business Development Center
901 E. Byrd St., Suite 1800
Richmond, VA 23219

804-371-8253
Fax: 804-225-3384

VA Highland Community College
Small Business Development Center
P.O. Box 828
Abingdon, VA 24212
703-676-5615
Fax: 703-628-7576

George Mason University/Arlington Campus
Small Business Development Center
3401 N. Fairfax Dr.
Arlington, VA 22201
703-993-8128
Fax: 703-993-8130

Mt. Empire Community College
Southwest SBDC
Drawer 700, Route 23
Big Stone Gap, VA 24219
703-523-6529
Fax: 703-523-4130

New River Valley Small Business
Development Center
Donaldson Brown Center, Room 234
Virginia Tech
Blacksburg, VA 24061-0539
703-231-5278
Fax: 703-231-8850

Central Virginia Small Business
Development Center
918 Emmet St. N, Suite 200
Charlottesville, VA 22903
804-295-8198
Fax: 804-295-7066

Northern Virginia Small Business
Development Center
4260 Chainbridge Rd, Suite A-1
Fairfax, VA 22030
703-993-2131/2130
Fax: 703-993-2126

Longwood College
515 Main St
Small Business Development Center
Farmville, VA 23901
804-395-2086
Fax: 804-395-2359

Rappahannock Region Small Business
Development Center
1301 College Ave.
Seacobeck Hall
Fredericksburg, VA 22401
703-899-4076
Fax: 703-899-4373

James Madison University
Small Business Development Center
College of Business Building, Room 523
Harrisonburg, VA 22807
703-568-3227
Fax: 703-568-3299

Lynchburg Regional Small Business
Development Center
147 Mill Ridge Rd.
Lynchburg, VA 24502
804-582-6170
Fax: 804-582-6106

Small Business Development Center
Dr. William E.S. Flory
10311 Sudley Manor Dr.
Manassas, VA 22110
703-335-2500
Fax: 703-335-1700

Lord Fairfax Community College
Small Business Development Center
P.O. Box 47
Middletown, VA 22645
703-869-6649
Fax: 703-869-7881

Hampton Roads, Inc.
Small Business Development Center
P.O. Box 327
420 Bank St.
Norfolk, VA 23501
804-825-2957
Fax: 804-825-3552

Southwest Virginia Community College
Small Business Development Center
P.O. Box SVCC
Richlands, VA 24641
703-964-7345
Fax: 703-964-5788

Capital Area Small Business Development
Center
403 East Grace St.
Richmond, VA 23219
804-648-7838
Fax: 804-648-7849

The Blue Ridge Small Business
Development Center
310 First St., SW Mezzanine
Roanoke, VA 24011
703-983-0717
Fax: 703-983-0723

South Boston Small Business Development
Center
P.O. Box 1116
515 Broad St.
South Boston, VA 24592
804-575-0044
Fax: 804-572-4087

Loudoun County Small Business
Development Center
21515 Ridgetop Circle, Suite 200
Sterling, VA 22170
703-430-7222
Fax: 703-430-9562

Warsaw Small Business Development Center
P.O. Box 490
106 W. Richmond Rd
Warsaw, VA 22572
804-333-0286
Fax: 804-333-0187

Wytheville Community College
Small Business Development Center
1000 E. Main St.
Wytheville, VA 24382
703-223-4798 ext. 4798
Fax: 703-223-4850

Eastern Shore Office
P.O. Box 395
Belle Haven, VA 23306
804-442-7181

Mountain Empire Community College
Small Business Development Center
Drawer 700, Route 23 S.
Big Stone Gap, VA 24219

703-523-6529
Fax: 703-523-8139

Small Business Development Center
525 Butler Farm Rd., Suite 102
Hampton, VA 23666
804-622-6414

Washington
Lead Center:
Washington Small Business Development
Center
Washington State University
501 Johnson Tower
Pullman, WA 99164-4727
509-335-1576
Fax: 509-335-0949

Bellevue Community College
Small Business Development Center
3000 Landerholm Circle
Bellevue, WA 98007-6484
206-643-2888
Fax: 206-649-3113

Western Washington University
Small Business Development Center
College of Business and Economics
308 Park Hall
Bellingham, WA 98225-9073
360-650-3899
Fax: 360-650-4844

Centralia Community College
Small Business Development Center
600 West Locust St.
Centralia, WA 98531
360-736-9391
Fax: 360-753-3404

Big Bend Community College
Small Business Development Center
7662 Chanute St.
Building 1500
Moses Lake, WA 98837-3299
509-762-6289
Fax: 509-762-6329

Skagit Valley College
Small Business Development Center
2405 College Way

Mt. Vernon, WA 98273
360-428-1282
Fax: 360-336-6116

South Puget Sound Community College
Small Business Development Center
721 Columbia St. SW
Olympia, WA 98501
360-753-5616
Fax: 360-586-5493

South Seattle Community College
Small Business Development Center
6770 E. Marginal Way S
Seattle, WA 98106
206-764-5375
Fax: 206-764-5838

Washington State University at Seattle
Small Business Development Center
180 Nickerson, Suite 207
Seattle, WA 98109
206-464-5450
Fax: 206-464-6357

North Seattle Community College
Small Business Development Center
International Trade Institute
9600 College Way N.
Seattle, WA 98103-3599
206-527-3733
Fax: 206-527-3734

Community College of Spokane
Small Business Development Center
665 N. Riverpoint Blvd.
Spokane, WA 99202
509-358-2051
Fax: 509-358-2059

Washington State University at Tacoma
Small Business Development Center
950 Pacific Ave., Suite 300
Box 1933
Tacoma, WA 98401-1933
206-272-7232
Fax: 206-597-7305

Columbia River Economic Development
Council
Small Business Development Center
100 East Columbia Way

Vancouver, WA 98660-3156
360-693-2555
Fax: 360-694-9927

INSTITUTE of TECHNOLOGY

Yakima Valley Community College
Small Business Development Center
P.O. Box 1647
Yakima, WA 98907
509-454-3608
Fax: 509-454-4155

Columbia Basin College
Tri-Cities SBDC
901 N. Colorado
Kennewick, WA 99336
509-735-6222
Fax: 509-735-6609

Edmonds Community College
Small Business Development Center
20000 68th Ave. W
Lynwood, WA 98036
206-640-1435
Fax: 206-640-1532

Wenatchee Valley College
Small Business Development Center
P.O. Box 741
Okanogan, WA 98840
509-826-5107
Fax: 509-826-1812

Port of Walla Walla Small Business
Development Center
500 Tausick Way
Walla Walla, WA 99362
509-527-4681
Fax: 509-525-3101

Quest Small Business Development Center
327 East Penny Rd.
Industrial Bldg. #2, Suite D
Wenatchee, WA 98801
509-662-8016
Fax: 509-663-0455

West Virginia

Lead Center:
West Virginia Small Business Development
Center
West Virginia Development Office
950 Kanawha Blvd.
Charleston, WV 25301
304-558-2960
Fax: 304-558-0127

Fairmont State College
Small Business Development Center
Fairmont, WV 26554
304-367-4125
Fax: 304-366-4870

Marshall University
Small Business Development Center
1050 Fourth Ave.
Huntington, WV 25755-2126
304-696-6789
Fax: 304-696-6277

West Virginia Institute of Technology
Small Business Development Center
Room 102, Engineering Building
Montgomery, WV 25136
304-442-5501
Fax: 304-442-3307

West Virginia University
Small Business Development Center
P.O. Box 6025
Morgantown, WV 26506
304-293-5839
Fax: 304-293-7061

West Virginia University at Parkersburg
Small Business Development Center
Route 5, Box 167-A
Parkersburg, WV 26101
304-424-8277
Fax: 304-424-8315

Shepherd College
Small Business Development Center
Shepherdstown, WV 25443
304-876-5261
Fax: 304-876-5117

West Virginia Northern Community College
Small Business Development Center
College Square
Wheeling, WV 26003
304-233-5900, ext. 206
Fax: 304-232-9065

College of West Virginia Small Business
Development Center
P.O. Box AG
Bechkey, WV 25802
304-255-4022

Governor's Office of Community and
Industrial Development Small Business
Development Center
950 Kanawha Blvd. East
Charleston, WV 25301
304-558-2960
Fax: 304-558-0127

Elkins Satellite Small Business Development
Center
10 Eleventh St., Suite One
Elkins, WV 26241
304-637-7205
Fax: 304-637-4902

Wisconsin

Lead Center:
Wisconsin Small Business Development
Center
University of Wisconsin
432 N. Lake St., Room 423
Madison, WI 53706
608-263-7794
Fax: 608-262-3878

University of Wisconsin at Eau Claire
Small Business Development Center
P.O. Box 4004
Eau Claire, WI 54702-4004
715-836-5811
Fax: 715-836-5263

University of Wisconsin at Green Bay
Small Business Development Center
460 Wood Hall
Green Bay, WI 54301
414-465-2089
Fax: 414-465-2660

University of Wisconsin at LaCrosse
Small Business Development Center
School of Business
120 N. Hall
La Crosse, WI 54601
608-785-8782
Fax: 608-785-6919

University of Wisconsin at Madison
Small Business Development Center
975 University Ave., Room 3260
Madison, WI 53706
608-263-2221
Fax: 608-263-0818

University of Wisconsin at Milwaukee
Small Business Development Center
161 W. Wisconsin Ave., Suite 600
Milwaukee, WI 53203
414-227-3240

University of Wisconsin at Oshkosh
Small Business Development Center
157 Clow Faculty Bldg.
800 Algoma Blvd.
Oshkosh, WI 54901
414-424-1453
Fax: 414-424-7413

University of Wisconsin at Stevens Point
Small Business Development Center
Main Building, Lower Level
Stevens Point, WI 54481
715-346-2004
Fax: 715-346-4045

University of Wisconsin at Superior
Small Business Development Center
29 Sundquist Hall
Superior, WI 54880
715-394-8352
Fax: 715-394-8454

University of Wisconsin at Whitewater
Small Business Development Center
2000 Carlson Bldg
Whitewater, WI 53190
414-472-3217
Fax: 414-472-4863

University of WI at Parkside SBDC
284 Tallent Hall

Kenosha, WI 53141
414-595-2189
Fax: 414-595-2513

WI Innovation Service Center
Small Business Development Center
Univ. of WI at Whitewater
402 McCutchan Hall
Whitewater, WI 53190
414-472-1365
Fax: 414-472-1600

Wyoming
Lead Center:
Wyoming Small Business Development
Center
111 West 2nd St., Suite 416
Casper, WY 82601
800-348-5207
307-234-6683
Fax: 307-577-7014

Laramie County Community College
Small Business Development Center
1400 East College Dr.
Cheyenne, WY 82007-3298
307-632-6141

800-348-5208
Fax: 307-632-6061

University of Wyoming
Small Business Development Center
P.O. Box 3620
University Station
Laramie, WY 82071-3622
307-766-3050
800-348-5194
Fax: 307-766-3406

Northwest Community College
Small Business Development Center
John DeWitt Student Center
Powell, WY 82435
307-754-6067
800-348-5203
Fax: 307-754-6069

Wyoming Small Business Development
Center
P.O. Box 1168
Rock Springs, WY 82902
307-352-6894
800-348-5205
Fax: 307-352-6876

Get $100 to $25,000
To Start A Little Business

A recent survey showed that approximately
33% of the top 500 fastest growing small
businesses in the U.S. started with less than
$10,000. It doesn't take much money to start
a business in today's information age and
service economy. We're no longer in the
manufacturing age, when you needed a lot of
money to start a business because you
needed to buy an expensive plant and costly
equipment. Today, many businesses are
started with nothing more than a phone, a
desk, and business cards. Traditional
government money programs required
entrepreneurs to ask for at least $50,000 to
$100,000. Now the government has set up Microenterprise
Programs where you can ask for just a small amount of money to
make that big change in your life.

A Growing Unknown Resource

These programs are continually growing. They seem so successful
that policy makers are finding new ways to help them grow. But
this growth and success seems to be causing as many problems as
the opportunities they are creating. On one hand, the SBA
programs recently increased the number of banks that participate
in its microloan program from 100 to 200 and also added a
subcategory of lenders to include for profit and nonprofit
organizations. Grants under this program will increase from $45
million in 1995 to $98 million in 1997, and direct loans will
increase from $120 million to $250 million during the same

period. But, on the other hand, I read that programs like the one at the U.S. Department of Housing and Urban Development fell short of their quota by $1.5 billion because not enough people applied. This means that the poor bureaucrats administering the program couldn't give out all their money because not enough people applied. I even got a personal call from a local organization who had $50,000 of this money for someone to open up a bakery, and no one applied for it.

66% Chance of Being a Microloan Winner

Each year thousands of people will be getting microloans to start or expand their businesses. Although data is not available for every program, one of the major microloan lenders estimates that 66% of the people who apply for money, get it. Here are a few examples of recent recipients:

Up To $10,000 For Refugees

ORR/Division of Community Resettlement
370 L'Enfant Promenade, SW Sixth Floor
Washington, DC 20447
202-401-9246

Refugees can receive technical assistance, training, or loans of up to $10,000 through a program called the Micro-Enterprise Development Project. The program allows states and public or private, nonprofit organizations and institutions to apply to receive grants to develop and administer micro-enterprise programs consisting of small-scale financing ($10,000) available through microloans to refugees. It also includes funding for technical assistance and support to these refugee entrepreneurs. For information on organizations which were awarded grants, contact the office listed above.

* $5,000 to Street Smart, Inc., a street-hockey equipment distributor in Southeastern Pennsylvania

* $25,000 to Med-Ex Medical Express, a courier service that specializes in the health care field

* $15,000 to Jeannette Saunders and Pamela Marshall of Sacramento, CA to start P&J Word Processing Service

Your State Can Get You Money

Community Connections
Information Center
Office of Community Planning and Development
P.O. Box 7189
Gaithersburg, MD 20898-7189
800-998-9999

This is the second largest component of the Community Development Block Grant (CDBG) program and aids communities that do not qualify for assistance under the CDBG entitlement program. The grants assist communities in carrying out a wide range of community development activities directed toward neighborhood revitalization, economic development, and the provision of improved  community facilities and services. Funds can also be used to provide assistance to public and private organizations, agencies, and other entities (including nonprofits and for-profits to facilitate economic development in supporting micro-enterprise).

Funds can be used to establish credit (direct loans and loan guarantees, revolving loan funds, and more) for the stabilization and expansion of microenterprises; provide technical assistance, advice, and business support services to owners of micro-enterprises; and provide general support to owners of micro-enterprises and organizations developing micro-enterprises.

If you are an interested citizen, you should contact your local officials for more information. If your local government or state officials cannot answer your questions, you may wish to contact the HUD Field Office that services your area (contact your state information operator listed in the appendix for help). Be aware that the state administers the program and determines which local projects receive funding.

PUBLIC HOUSING ENTREPRENEURS

U.S. Department of Housing and Urban Development
Deputy Director of Resident Initiatives
451 Seventh Street, SW, Room 4112
Washington, DC 20410
202-619-8201

Call yourself a handyman and get money to fix up your neighborhood. Money is set aside to give to public housing residents to modernize existing public housing projects. The money can also be used to provide residents with on-the-job training in construction and contractor related trades. It's called the Comprehensive Grant Program, and is available to Public Housing Agencies of 250 housing units or more, which includes 897 public housing agencies nationwide. Contact your local Public Housing Authority for more information or you may contact the office listed above.

You can also contact: Community Connections, Information Center, Office of Community Planning and Development, P.O. Box 7189, Gaithersburg, MD 20898-7189; 800-998-9999.

STATE MICROLOAN PROGRAMS

In addition to the federal programs, many state governments are also putting their money into microloan opportunities. Here are a few microloan programs that are currently available at the state level:

- Iowa - Self Employment Loan Program ($5,000 for low income)

- Maine - Job Start Program ($10,000)

- New York - Micro Loan Program - NY Job Development

- North Dakota - Micro Business Loans

- Ohio - Ohio Mini-Loan Program

- South Carolina - Micro Enterprise Loan Program

- Texas - Rural Microenterprise Loan Program

New programs are being added all the time, so be sure to contact your state capital for the most current information. Contact your state information operator listed in the Appendix and ask for your state Office of Economic Development

Money To Start A Business In A Small Town

The **Intermediary Relending Program** (IRP) is a rural development program administered by the Rural Business-Cooperative Service (RBS). The purpose is to provide loans for the establishment of new businesses, expansion of existing

businesses, creation of new employment opportunities, saving of existing jobs, and funds to recipients for business facilities or community development projects in rural areas.

Loans are made to intermediaries who relend funds to recipients for business facilities or community development. You can borrow up to $150,000 with a maximum term of 30 years and an interest rate of one percent per annum.

For further information on these programs, contact your local Rural Development Office. Look in the blue pages of your telephone book under U.S. Department of Agriculture, contact your state information operator (listed in the Appendix), or contact the main office at Rural-Business-Cooperative Service, 1400 Independence Avenue, SW, Room 5050, South Building, Washington, DC 20250, 202-720-1019, {www.rurdev.usda.gov/rbs/oa/oadir.htm}.

SMALL TOWNS THAT OFFER YOU MONEY TO START A BUSINESS

Cities can get grants that can be used to lend you money to start a small business. The Entitlement Grants is the largest component of the Community Development Block Grant Program and provides annual grants to entitled cities (population 50,000) and counties (population 200,000) to develop viable urban

communities by providing decent housing and suitable living environments, and by expanding economic opportunities, principally for low and moderate income persons.

The program provides funds to carry out a wide range of community development activities directed toward neighborhood revitalization, economic development, improved community facilities and services, and micro-enterprise. Funds can be used to establish credit (direct loans and loan guarantees, revolving loan funds, and more) for the stabilization and expansion of micro-enterprise; provide technical assistance, advice, and business support services to owners of micro-enterprises; and provide general support to owners of micro-enterprises and organizations developing micro-enterprises.

To learn if your community received funds and the person to contact in your area for more information, contact your local U.S. Department of Housing and Urban Development Office listed in the blue pages of your telephone book and ask for the office in charge of Community Development Block Grants or contact: Information Office, Office of Community Planning and Development, P.O. Box 7189, Gaithersburg, MD 20898-7189, 800-998-9999, {www.hud.gov/whatwork.html}.

More Money For Small Town Entrepreneurs

The **Rural Business Enterprise Grant Program** (RBEG) is administered by the Rural Business-Cooperative Service (RBS), and provides grant funds to a local or regional intermediary which, in turn, lends funds in a flexible manner to local businesses. Funds are designed to facilitate the development of small and emerging private business, industry, and related employment.

Money can be used for the acquisition and development of land, and the construction of buildings, plants, equipment, access streets and roads, parking areas, utility and service extensions, refinancing, fees, technical assistance, startup operating cost, working capital, providing financial assistance to a third party, production of television programs to provide information to rural residents, and to create, expand, and operate rural distance learning networks. Grant applications are available from any USDA Rural Development State Office.

For further information on these programs, contact your local Rural Development Office. Look in the blue pages of your telephone book under U.S. Department of Agriculture, contact your state information operator (listed in the Appendix), or contact the main office at Rural-Business-Cooperative Service, 1400 Independence Avenue, SW, Room 5050, South Building, Washington, DC 20250, 202-720-1019, {www.rurdev.usda.gov/rbs/oa/oadir.htm}.

State Money and Help For Your Business

Who Can Use State Money?

All states require that funds be used solely by state residents. But that shouldn't limit you to exploring possibilities only in the state in which you currently reside. If you reside in Maine, but Massachusetts agrees to give you $100,000 to start your own business, it

would be worth your while to consider moving to Massachusetts. Shop around for the best deal.

Types Of State Money And Help Available

Each state has different kinds and amounts of money and assistance programs available, but these sources of financial and counseling help are constantly being changed. What may not be available this year may very well be available next year. Therefore, in the course of your exploration, you might want to check in with the people who operate the business "hotlines" to discover if anything new has been added to the states' offerings.

Described below are the major kinds of programs that are offered by most of the states.

Information

Hotlines or One-Stop Shops are available in many states through a toll-free number that hooks you up with someone who will either tell you what you need to know or refer you to someone who can. These hotlines are invaluable — offering information on everything from business permit regulations to obscure financing programs. Most states also offer some kind of booklet that tells you to how to start up a business in that state. Ask for it. It will probably be free.

Small Business Advocates operate in all fifty states and are part of a national organization (the National Association of State Small Business Advocates) devoted to helping small business people function efficiently with their state governments. They are a good source for help in cutting through bureaucratic red tape.

Funding Programs

Free Money can come in the form of grants, and works the same as free money from the federal government. You do not have to pay it back.

Loans from state governments work in the same way as those from the federal government — they are given directly to entrepreneurs. Loans are usually at interest rates below the rates charged at commercial institutions and are also set aside for those companies which have trouble getting a loan elsewhere. This makes them an ideal source for riskier kinds of ventures.

Loan Guarantees are similar to those offered by the federal government. For this program, the state government will go to the bank with you and co-sign your loan. This, too, is ideal for high-risk ventures that normally would not get a loan.

Interest Subsidies On Loans is a unique concept not used by the federal government. In this case, the state will subsidize the interest rate you are charged by a bank. For example, if the bank gives you a loan for $50,000 at 10 percent per year interest, your interest payments will be $5,000 per year. With an interest subsidy you might have to pay only $2,500 since the state will pay the other half. This is like getting the loan at 5 percent instead of 10 percent.

Industrial Revenue Bonds Or General Obligation Bonds are a type of financing that can be used to purchase only fixed assets, such as a factory or equipment. In the case of Industrial Revenue Bonds, the state will raise money from the general public to buy your equipment. Because the state acts as the middleman, the people who lend you the money do not have to pay federal taxes on the interest they charge you. As a result, you get the money cheaper because they get a tax break. If the state issues General Obligation Bonds to buy your equipment, the arrangement will be similar to that for an Industrial Revenue Bond except that the state promises to repay the loan if you cannot.

Matching Grants supplement and abet federal grant programs. These kinds of grants could make an under-capitalized project go forward. Awards usually hinge on the usefulness of the project to its surrounding locality.

Loans To Agricultural Businesses are offered in states with large rural farming populations. They are available solely to farmers and/or agribusiness entrepreneurs.

Loans To Exporters are available in some states as a kind of gap financing to cover the expenses involved in fulfilling a contract.

High Tech Loans

Energy Conservation Loans are made to small businesses to finance the installation of energy-saving equipment or devices.

Special Regional Loans are ear-marked for specific areas in a state that may have been hard hit economically or suffer from under-development. If you live in one of these regions, you may be eligible for special funds.

High Tech Loans help fledgling companies develop or introduce new products into the marketplace.

Loans To Inventors help the entrepreneur develop or market new products.

Local Government Loans are used for start-up and expansion of businesses within the designated locality.

Money For A Big Or Small Business

Childcare Facilities Loans help businesses establish on-site daycare facilities.

Loans To Women And/Or Minorities are available in almost every state from funds specifically reserved for economically disadvantaged groups.

Many federally funded programs are administered by state governments. Among them are the following programs:

The SBA 7(A) Guaranteed and ***Direct Loan*** program can guarantee up to 90 percent of a loan made through a private lender (up to $750,000), or make direct loans of up to $150,000.

The SBA 504 establishes Certified Development Companies whose debentures are guaranteed by the SBA. Equity participation of the borrower must be at least 10 percent, private financing 60 percent and CDC participation at a maximum of 40 percent, up to $750,000.

Small Business Innovative Research Grants (SBIR) award between $20,000 to $50,000 to entrepreneurs to support six months of research on a technical innovation. They are then eligible for up to $500,000 to develop the innovation.

 ***Small Business Investment Companies (SBIC)*** license, regulate and provide financial assistance in the form of equity financing, long-term loans, and management services.

Community Development Block Grants are available to cities and counties for the commercial rehabilitation of existing buildings or structures used for business, commercial, or industrial purposes. Grants of up to $500,000 can be made. Every $15,000 of grant funds invested must create at least one full-time job, and at least 51 percent of the jobs created must be for low and moderate income families.

Farmers Home Administration (FmHA) Emergency Disaster Loans are available in counties where natural disaster has substantially affected farming, ranching or aquaculture production.

Information USA, Inc.

FmHA Farm Loan Guarantees are made to family farmers and ranchers to enable them to obtain funds from private lenders. Funds must be used for farm ownership, improvements, and operating purposes.

FmHA Farm Operating Loans to meet operating expenses, finance recreational and nonagricultural enterprises, to add to family income, and to pay for mandated safety and pollution control changes are available at variable interest rates. Limits are $200,000 for an insured farm operating loan and $400,000 for a guaranteed loan.

FmHA Farm Ownership Loans can be used for a wide range of farm improvement projects. Limits are $200,000 for an insured loan and $300,000 for a guaranteed loan.

FmHA Soil And Water Loans must be used by individual farmers and ranchers to develop, conserve, and properly use their land and water resources and to help abate pollution. Interest rates are variable; each loan must be secured by real estate.

FmHA Youth Project Loans enable young people to borrow for income-producing projects sponsored by a school or 4H club.

Assistance Programs

Management Training is offered by many states in subjects ranging from bookkeeping to energy conservation.

Management Training

Business Consulting is offered on almost any subject. Small Business Development Centers are the best source for this kind of assistance.

Market Studies to help you sell your goods or services within or outside the state are offered by many states. They all also have State Data Centers which not only collect demographic and other information about markets within the state, but also have access to federal data which can pinpoint national markets. Many states also provide the services of graduate business students at local universities to do the legwork and analysis for you.

Business Site Selection is done by specialists in every state who will identify the best place to locate a business.

Licensing, Regulation, And Permits information is available from most states through "one-stop shop" centers by calling a toll-free number. There, you'll get help in finding your way through the confusion of registering a new business.

Employee Training Programs offer on-site training and continuing education opportunities.

Research And Development Assistance for entrepreneurs is a form of assistance that is rapidly increasing as more and more states try to attract high technology-related companies. Many states are even setting up clearing houses so that small businesses can have one place to turn to find expertise throughout a statewide university system.

Procurement Programs have been established in some states to help you sell products to state, federal, and local governments.

Export Assistance is offered to identify overseas markets. Some states even have overseas offices to drum up business prospects for you.

Assistance In Finding Funding is offered in every state, particularly through regional Small Business Development Centers. They will not only identify funding sources in the state and federal governments, but will also lead you through the complicated application process.

Special Help For Minorities And Women is available in almost every state to help boost the participation of women and minorities in small business ventures. They offer special funding programs and, often, one-on-one counseling to assure a start-up success.

Venture Capital Networking is achieved through computer databases that hook up entrepreneurs and venture capitalists. This service is usually free of charge. In fact, the demand for small business investment opportunities is so great that some states require the investor to pay to be listed.

Money For A Big Or Small Business

Inventors Associations have been established to encourage and assist inventors in developing and patenting their products.

Annual Governors' Conferences give small business people the chance to air their problems with representatives from state agencies and the legislature.

Small Business Development Centers (SBDCs), funded jointly by the federal and state governments, are usually associated with the state university system. SBDCs are a godsend to small business people. They will not only help you figure out if your business project is feasible, but also help you draw up a sensible business plan, apply for funding, and check in with you frequently once your business is up and running to make sure it stays that way.

Tourism programs are prominent in states whose revenues are heavily dependent on the tourist trade. They are specifically aimed at businesses in the tourist industries.

Small Business Institutes at local colleges use senior level business students as consultants to help develop business plans or plan expansions.

Technology Assistance Centers help high tech companies and entrepreneurs establish new businesses and plan business expansions.

On-Site Energy Audits are offered free of charge by many states to help control energy costs and improve energy efficiency for small businesses. Some states also conduct workshops to encourage energy conservation measures.

Minority Business Development Centers offer a wide range of services from initial counseling on how to start a business to more complex issues of planning and growth.

Business Information Centers (BICs) provide the latest in high-tech hardware, software, and telecommunications to help small businesses get started. BIC is a place where business owners and aspiring business owners can go to use hardware/software, hard copy books, and publications to plan their business, expand an existing business, or venture into new business areas. Also, on-site counseling is available.

Examples of Free Money From State Governments:

- Grants To North Dakota Women
- $100,000 to $300,000 From Massachusetts Venture Capital
- $25,000 To Upgrade Employees Skills (RI)
- $5,000 To Learn A New Technology (RI)
- $2,250 For Every New Job You Create
- $500,000 In Venture Capital From NY
- $150,000 For Tech Companies in MD
- $50,000 For Delaware Inventors
- $25,000 For Florida Tech Companies
- $40,000 To Recycle Tires (IN)
- $5,000 To Sell Overseas (IN)
- $30,000 To Start A Small Town Business (WI)
- $4,000 To Get The Technical Assistance You Need (MN)
- $15,000 For Entrepreneurs With Disabilities (IA
- $5,000 To Help You Write A Grant (KS)

State Economic Development Offices

Alabama
Alabama Development Office
401 Adams Avenue
Montgomery, AL 36104-4340
800-248-0033
334-242-0400
Fax: 334-242-0415
www.ado.state.al.us

Alaska
Alaska Department of Commerce
and Economic Development
P.O. Box 110800
Juneau, AK 98111
907-465-2017
800-478-LOAN
Fax: 907-465-3767
www.commerce.state.ak.us

Arizona
Department of Commerce
3800 N. Central, Suite 1650
Phoenix, AZ 85012
602-280-1480
800-542-5684
Fax: 620-280-1339
www.commerce.state.az.us/fr_abc.
shtml

Arkansas
Arkansas Economic Development
Commission
1 State Capitol Mall
Little Rock, AR 72201
501-682-1121
Fax: 501-682-7341
www.aedc.state.ar.us

California
California Trade and Commerce
Agency
801 K St., Suite 1700
Sacramento, CA 95814
916-322-1394
www.state.ca.us/s/business

Colorado
Office of Economic Development
1625 Broadway, Suite 1710
Denver, CO 80202
303-892-3840
Fax: 303-892-3848
TDD: 800-659-2656
www.state.co.us

Connecticut
Economic Resource Center
Connecticut Department of
Economic and Community
Development
805 Brooks St., Bldg. 4
Rocky Hill, CT 06067-3405
860-571-7136
800-392-2122
Fax: 860-571-7150
www.cerc.com

Delaware
Delaware Economic Development
Office
John S. Riley

99 Kings Highway
P.O. Box 1401
Dover, DE 19903
302-739-4271
Fax: 302-739-5749
www.state.de.us/dedo/index.htm

District of Columbia
Office of Economic Development
441 4th St., NW, Suite 1140
Washington, DC 20001
202-727-6365
www.dchomepage.net

Florida
Florida Economic Development
Council
502 East Jefferson Street
Tallahassee, FL 32301
805-222-3000
Fax: 850-222-3019

Enterprise Florida
390 N. Orange Ave., Suite 1300
Orlando, FL 32801
407-316-4600
Fax: 407-316-4599
www.floridabusiness.com

Georgia
Office of Economic Development
60 Executive Park South, NE
Suite 250
Atlanta, GA 30329-2231
404-679-4940
Fax: 800-736-1155
www.dca.state.ga.us

Hawaii
Department of Business,
Economic Development and
Tourism

P.O. Box 2359
Honolulu, HI 96804
No. 1 Capitol District Bldg.
250 S. Hotel Street
Honolulu, HI 96813
808-586-2593
Fax: 808-586-2589
www.hawaii.gov/dbedt/index.html

Commerce

Idaho
Idaho Department of Commerce
700 West State Street
P.O. Box 83720
Boise, ID 83720-0093
208-334-2470
Fax: 208-334-2631
www.idoc.state.id.us/pages/
businesspage.html

Illinois
Department of Commerce and
Community Affairs
620 E. Adams
Springfield, IL 62602
217-782-7500
Fax: 217-524-3701
www.commerce.state.il.us

100 West Randolph St.
Suite 3-400
Chicago, IL 60601
312-814-7179
Fax: 312-814-2370

Indiana
Indiana Department of Commerce
One North Capitol, Suite 700

Indianapolis, IN 46204
317-232-8888
800-463-8081
317-233-5123 Fax
www.ai.org/bdev/index.html

Iowa
Department of Economic
Development
200 East Grand Ave.
Des Moines, IA 50309-1827
515-242-4700
800-245-IOWA
Fax: 515-242-4809
TTY: 800-735-2942
www.state.ia.us/ided

Kansas
Department of Commerce and
Housing
700 SW Harrison St., Suite 1300
Topeka, KS 66603-3712
785-296-5298
Fax: 785-296-3490
TTY: 785-296-3487
www.kansascommerce.com

Kentucky
Kentucky Cabinet for Economic
Development
2300 Capital Plaza Tower
500 Mero Street
Frankfort, KY 40601
502-564-7670
800-626-2930
www.thinkkentucky.com

Louisiana
Department of Economic
Development
P.O. Box 94185
Baton Rouge, LA 70804

225-342-6000
225-342-5388
www.lded.state.la.us

Maine
Office of Business Development
Department of Economic and
Community Development
59 State House Station
Augusta, ME 04333
207-287-3153
Fax: 207-287-5701
TTY: 207-287-2656
www.econdevmaine.com

Maryland
Department of Business and
Economic Development
217 East Redwood St.
Baltimore, MD 21202
410-767-6300
800-811-0051
Fax: 410-333-6792
TDD/TTY: 410-333-6926
www.mdbusiness.state.md.us

Massachusetts
Massachusetts Office of Business
Development
10 Park Plaza, 3rd Floor
Boston, MA 02116
617-973-8600
800-5-CAPITAL
Fax: 617-973-8797
www.state.ma.us/mobd

Michigan
Michigan Jobs Commission
201 North Washington Square
Victor Office Center, 4th Floor
Lansing, MI 48913
517-373-9808

Fax: 517-335-0198
www.mjc.state.mi.us

Minnesota
Department of Trade and
Economic Development (MTED)
500 Metro Square Blvd.
121 7th Place East
St. Paul, MN 55101-2146
612-297-1291
800-657-3858
www.dted.state.mn.us

Mississippi
Department of Economic and
Community Development
P.O. Box 849
Jackson, MS 39205-0849
601-359-3040
800-340-3323
Fax: 601-359-4339
www.decd.state.ms.us

Missouri
Department of Economic
Development (DED)
Truman Building, Room 720
P.O. Box 118
Jefferson City, MO 65102-0118
573-751-4962
800-523-1434
Fax: 573-526-2416
www.ecodev.state.mo.us

Montana
Department of Commerce
1424 Ninth Ave.
P.O. Box 200505
Helena, MT 59620-0505
406-444-3814
800-221-8015 (in MT)
Fax: 406-444-1872
http://commerce.state.mt.us

Money For A Big Or Small Business

Nebraska
Department of Economic
Development
P.O. Box 94666
301 Centennial Mall South
Lincoln, NE 68509
402-471-3111
800-426-6505 (in NE)
Fax: 402-471-3365
TDD: 402-471-3441
www.ded.state.ne.us

Nevada
State of Nevada Commission on
Economic Development
5151 South Carson St.
Carson City, NV 89710
775-687-4325
800-336-1600
Fax: 775-687-4450
www.state.nv.us/businessop

555 E. Washington Ave.
Suite 5400
Las Vegas, NV 89101
702-486-2700
Fax: 702-486-2701

New Hampshire
State of New Hampshire
Department of Resources and
Economic Development
172 Pembroke Road
P.O. Box 1856
Concord, NH 03302-1856
603-271-2341
800-204-5000 (in NH)
Fax: 603-271-6784
www.ded.state.nh.us/obid

New Jersey
New Jersey Economic
Development Authority

P.O. Box 990
Trenton, NJ 08625-0990
609-292-1800
www.njeda.com

New Mexico
Economic Development Dept.
Joseph M. Montoya Bldg.
1100 St. Francis Drive
Santa Fe, NM 87505-4147
505-827-0170
800-374-3061
Fax: 505-827-0407
www.edd.state.nm.us

New York
Empire State Development
One Commerce Plaza
Albany, NY 12245
518-474-7756
800-STATE-NY
www.empire.state.ny.us

633 Third Ave.
New York, NY 10017
212-803-3100

North Carolina
Department of Commerce
Commerce Finance Center
301 N. Wilmington St.
P.O. Box 29571
Raleigh, NC 27626-0571
919-733-4977
Fax: 919-715-9265
www.commerce.state.nc.us/
commerce

North Dakota
Department of Economic
Development and Finance
1833 East Bismarck Expressway

Bismarck, ND 58504-6708
701-328-5300
Fax: 701-328-5320
TTY: 800-366-6888
www.growingnd.com

Ohio
Ohio Department of Development
P.O. Box 1001
Columbus, OH 43216-1001
614-466-5017
800-345-OHIO
Fax: 614-463-1540
www.odod.ohio.gov

Oklahoma
Department of Commerce
900 North Stiles
P.O. Box 26980
Oklahoma City, OK 73126-0980
405-815-6552
800-879-6552.
Fax: 405-815-5199
www.locateok.com
www.odoc.state.ok.us/index.html

Oregon
Economic Development Dept.
775 Summer St., NE
Salem, OR 97310
503-986-0260
Fax: 503-581-5115
www.econ.state.or.us/
javahome.htm

Pennsylvania
Department of Community and
Economic Development
433 Forum Building
Harrisburg, PA 17120
800-379-7448
www.dced.state.pa.us

Governor's Action Team
100 Pine Street, Suite 100
Harrisburg, PA 17101
717-787-8199
Fax: 717-772-5419
www.teampa.com

Rhode Island
Economic Development
Corporation
One West Exchange St.
Providence, RI 02903
401-222-2601
Fax: 401-222-2102
www.riedc.com

South Carolina
Department of Commerce
P.O. Box 927
Columbia, SC 29202
803-737-0400
877-751-1262
Fax: 803-737-0418
www.callsouthcarolina.com

South Dakota
Governor's Office of Economic
Development
711 East Wells Ave.
Pierre, SD 57501-3369
605-773-5032
800-872-6190
Fax: 605-773-3256
www.state.sd.us/goed

Money For A Big Or Small Business

Tennessee
Department of Economic and
Community Development
Rachel Jackson Bldg., 8th Floor
320 Sixth Avenue North
Nashville, TN 37243-0405
615-741-1888
Fax: 615-741-7306
www.state.tn.us

Texas
Dept. of Economic Development
P.O. Box 12728
Austin, TX 78711
512-936-0260
800-888-0511
www.tded.state.tx.us

Utah
Business and Economic
Development Division
324 South State St., Suite 500
Salt Lake City, UT 84111
801-538-8800
Fax: 801-538-8889
www.ce.ex.state.ut.us

Vermont
Department of Economic
Development
National Life Building, Drawer 20
Montpelier, VT 05620-0501
802-828-3221
800-341-2211
Fax: 802-828-3258
www.thinkvermont.com

Virginia
Economic Development
Partnership
P.O. Box 798
Richmond, VA 23206

804-371-8100
Fax: 804-371-8112
www2.yesvirginia.org/YesVA

Washington
Department of Community, Trade
and Economic Development
906 Columbia St. SW
P.O. Box 48300
Olympia, WA 98504-8300
800-237-1233
access.wa.gov

West Virginia
WV Development Office
1900 Kanawha Blvd., East
Charleston, WV 25305-0311
304-558-2234
800-982-3386
Fax: 304-558-0449
www.wvdo.org

Wisconsin
Department of Commerce
(COMMERCE)
201 W. Washington Avenue
Madison, WI 53707
Business Helpline:
 800-HELP-BUSiness
Fax Request Hotline:
 608-264-6154
Export Helpline:
 800-XPORT-WIsconsin
www.commerce.state.wi.us

Wyoming
Department of Commerce
2301 Central Ave.
Cheyenne, WY 82002
307-777-6303
Fax: 307-777-6005
http://commerce.state.wy.us

TECHNOLOGY ASSISTANCE

The Small Business Technology Transfer (STTR) Program is a highly competitive program that reserves a specific percentage of federal research and development funding for awarding to small business and nonprofit research institution partners.

Small business has long been where innovation and innovators thrive, and nonprofit research laboratories are instrumental in developing high-tech innovations. STTR combines the strengths of both entities by introducing entrepreneurial skills to hi-tech research efforts. There are specific requirements that must be met.

To learn more about how to apply and the various agencies involved, contact Office of Technology, U.S. Small Business Administration, 409 Third St., SW, Washington, DC 20416; 202-205-6450; {www.sba.gov/SBIR/ sbir.html}.

$50,000,000
To Start An Airline

The Airline Deregulation Act gave airlines almost total freedom to determine which markets to serve domestically and what fares to charge for that service. The Essential Air Service Program was put into place to guarantee that small communities that were served by certificated air carriers before deregulation maintain a minimal level of scheduled air service.

The Department of Transportation currently subsidizes commuter airlines to serve approximately 100 rural communities across the country that otherwise would not receive any scheduled air service.

For more information, contact Office of Aviation Analysis, Office of the Assistant Secretary, U.S. Department of Transportation, 400 7th St., SW, Washington, DC 20590; 202-366-1053; {http://ostpxweb.dot.gov/ aviation}.

$Money to Sell Overseas

The *Foreign Market Development Cooperator Program* is designed to develop, maintain, and expand long-term export markets for U.S. agricultural products. The program has fostered a trade promotion partnership between the U.S. Department of

$700,000 If Hurt By Imports

The Economic Development Administration of the U.S. Department of Commerce funds the *Trade Adjustment Assistance Program*. If your company is affected by import competition, you may file a petition for certification of impact. If your firm is certified, you may then apply for technical assistance in diagnosing your problems, and assessing your opportunities. Once approved, your firm can apply for technical assistance to implement the recovery strategy. The average grant is for over $700,000.

For more information, contact Economic Development Administration, U.S. Department of Commerce, 14th and Constitution Ave., NW, Room 7804, Washington, DC 20230; 202-482-5081; {www.doc.gov/eda}.

Agriculture (USDA) and U.S. agricultural producers and processors who are represented by nonprofit commodity or trade associations called cooperators.

The USDA and the cooperators pool their technical and financial resources to conduct market development activities outside the United States. Trade organizations compete for funds on the basis of the following allocation criteria: past export performance, past demand expansion performance, future demand expansion goals, and contribution levels. Projects include market research, trade servicing and more.

For more information, contact the Foreign Agriculture Service, Marketing Operations Staff, Stop Code 1042, U.S. Department of Agriculture, Washington, DC 20250; 202-720-4327; {www.fas.usda.gov}.

70,000 Businesses Get Uncle Sam's Venture Capital

The Small Business Investment Company (SBIC) programs are privately organized and privately managed investment firms that are licensed by the Small Business Administration. With their own capital and with funds borrowed at favorable rates through the federal government, SBICs provide venture capital to small independent businesses, both new and already established.

A major incentive for the SBICs to invest in small businesses is the chance to share in the success of the small business if it grows and prospers. Small businesses qualifying for assistance from the SBIC program are able to receive equity capital, long-term loans, and expert management assistance.

For more information on SBICs or for a Directory of Small Business Investment Companies, contact Investment Division, U.S. Small Business Administration, 409 Third St., SW, Washington, DC 20416; 202-205-6510; {www.sba.gov/INV}.

$200,000 For A Risky Business

Not-yet-possible technologies are the domain of the National Institute of Standards and Technology's **Advanced Technology Program (ATP).**

The ATP is a unique partnership between government and private industry to accelerate the development of high-risk technologies that promise significant commercial payoffs and widespread benefits for the economy. ATP projects focus on the technology needs of the U.S. industry. The ATP does not fund product development. It supports enabling technologies that are essential to the development of new products, processes, and services across diverse application areas. There are strict cost-sharing rules and peer-review competitions.

For more information on how to apply for funding, contact Advanced Technology Program, National Institute of Standards and Technology, A407 Administration Building, Gaithersburg, MD 20899; 800-ATP-FUND (287-3863); {www.atp.nist.gov}.

UNCONVENTIONAL LOAN PROGRAMS TO START A BUSINESS WHEN YOU HAVE NO MONEY

The following is a description of loan programs available to low and moderate income individuals, minorities, Native Americans, Hispanics, refugees, unemployed individuals, welfare recipients, youths, and low and moderate income individuals who don't qualify for credit through conventional methods.

Most of these programs allow individuals (depending on the situation) to roll closing costs and fees into the amount of the loan. So you actually go to the closing with NO money in your pocket.

The aim of these programs is to stimulate economic growth through small businesses or microenterprises. Helping individuals become self-sufficient is the main focus, and also to challenge conventional methods of providing credit. All of the programs hope to demonstrate that persons with limited incomes are responsible, will repay, and can become successful if given access to knowledge and resources.

Some programs are designed just for youths, (15-21 years old), to develop their own businesses, avoid drugs and crime, sharpen academic skills and form positive attitudes about themselves and their communities. This is accomplished by utilizing the leadership, communication, management and business skills they may have acquired through affiliation with the illegal drug trade and other street activities. Loan amounts can range from $50 to $2,000 with terms from six months to two years.

The following is a small sample of many success stories that we found:

Susanna Rodriquez started making ceramic figurines for children's parties. Susanna is a former teacher's assistant who presently works in the kitchen of her small apartment. Her creations fill every free corner. She was constantly looking for ways to expand her business. One day she was in a store where the owner sold similar products. As they were comparing notes, the owner mentioned ACCION New York. After four loans as a result of working with that organization, Susanna's monthly revenue from her ceramics business has increased from $350 a month to $800 a month. In time, she hopes to open her own store. She feels that if it were not for ACCION, she would not be at the advanced stage of business that she is enjoying now.

Jeff Hess of Virginia had fished and hunted with his father since the age of five. He earned his associates degree in business and was working in an assembly plant for a moderate hourly wage, but wanted more. At the age of 24, he didn't see opportunity coming to call on him because he had no money and no credit. He and his wife, Cherylanna, enrolled in the BusinessStart class at People, Inc. With this training, assistance in small business planning, and a small loan, Jeff and Cherylanna were able to buy a bait shop in Honaker and turn it into Bucks and Bass, a full service hunting and fishing store. Located in prime hunting and fishing country, Bucks and Bass has nearly doubled its sales in its first year alone. Both Jeff and Cherylanna have left their jobs and run Bucks and Bass full time.

Loan Programs

Alabama
SBA Microloan Program
Birmingham Business Resource
Center
110 12th Street North
Birmingham, AL 35203
205-250-6380
Fax: 205-250-6384
Email: bbrc@inlinenet.net

Arizona
Borrowers' Circle
Self-Employment Loan Fund, Inc.
201 N. Central Ave.
Suite CC10
Phoenix, AZ 85703
602-340-8834
Fax: 602-340-8953
TDD: 800-842-4681
Email: Self-Employment@
Juno.com

Small Business Loan
PEEP Microbusiness and Housing
Development Corporation
1100 East Hao Way, Suite 209
Tucson, AZ 85713
520-806-9513
Fax: 520-806-9515

Arkansas
*The Good Faith Fund (GFF) -
Peer Group Loan Program*
The Good Faith Fund (GFF)
2304 W. 29th Ave.
Pine Bluff, AR 71603
870-535-6233
Fax: 870-535-0741

Micro Loan
Good Faith Fund

2304 West 29th Street
Pinebluff, AR 71603
870-535-6233

California
*Micro Enterprise Assistance
Program of Orange County*
18011 Skypark Circle, Suite E
Irvine, CA 92614
949-252-1380

Self-Employment Loan Fund
Women's Economic Ventures of
Santa Barbara
1136 E. Montecito St.
Santa Barbara, CA 93103
805-965-6073
Fax: 805-962-9622

*Self-Employment
Microenterprise Development
(SEMED)*
Economic and Employment
Development Center (EEDC)
241 S. Figueroa St.
Los Angeles, CA 90012
213-617-3953

The West Company
The West Enterprise Center
367 N. State St., Suite 206
Ukiah, CA 95482
707-468-3553
Fax: 707-462-8945

Revolving Loan Fund
Tri-County Economic
Development Corporation
2540 Esplanade, Suite 7
Chico, CA 95973

530-893-8732
Fax: 530-893-0820
Email: tcedcloan@thegrid.net
http://tricountyedc.org

City of Long Beach
Microenterprise Loan
City of Long Beach Business
Assistance Division
200 Pine Avenue, Suite 400
Long Beach, CA 90802
562-570-3822
562-570-3800
www.ci.long-beach.ca.us/bdc

Micro-Loan Program
Oakland Business Development
Corporation
519 17th Street, Suite 100
Oakland, CA 94612
510-763-4297
Fax: 510-763-1273
Email: mike@obdc.com
www.obdc.com

ENTREPRENEURIAL RESOURCE CENTER

Entrepreneurial Resource Center
Loan
Entrepreneurial Resource Center
2555 Clovis Avenue
Clovis, CA 93612
559-650-5050

Micro Loan Fund
Start Up: An East Palo Alto
Micro-Business Initiative
1935 University Avenue

East Palo Alto, CA 94303
650-321-2193

The Los Angeles Community
Development Bank Micro Loan
Program
Community Financial Resource
Center
4060 S. Figueroa Street
Los Angeles, CA 90037
323-233-1900
Fax: 323-235-1686

Micro Loan Revolving Loan
Fund
Economic and Employment
Development Corporation
2411 Figueroa Street, Suite 240
Los Angeles, CA 90012
213-617-3953

Micro Loan Fund
Interfaith Service Bureau
2117 Cottage Way
Sacramento, CA 95828
916-568-5020

Women's Initiative Loan Fund
Women's Initiative For Self
Employment
450 Mission Street, Suite 402
San Francisco, CA 94105
415-247-9473

Small Business Micro-Lending
Program
Lenders for Community
Development
111 West St. John St., Suite 710
San Jose, CA 95113
408-297-9937
Fax: 408-297-4599

Peer Lending Circles
West Company
306 East Redwood Ave.
Suite 2
Ft. Bragg, CA 95437
707-964-7571

Colorado
Business Center for Women (BCW)
Mi Casa Resource Center for
Women
571 Galapago St.
Denver, CO 80204
303-573-1302
Fax: 303-595-0422

Project Success (PS)
Mi Casa Resource Center for
Women
571 Galapago St.
Denver, CO 80204
303-573-1302
Fax: 303-595-0422

Micro Loan
Credit for All, Inc.
2268 Birch Street
Denver, CO 80207
303-320-1955

Micro Loan
Colorado Capital Initiatives
1616 17th Street, Suite 371
Denver, CO 80202
303-628-5464

Small Business Loan
Colorado Enterprise Fund
1888 Sherman Street, Suite 530
Denver, CO 80203
303-860-0242

Email: microloans@
coloradoenterprisefund.org
www.coloradoenterprisefund.org

Community Enterprise Lending Initiative
Denver Small Business
Development Center
1445 Market Street
Denver, CO 80203
303-620-8076
Fax: 303-514-3200

El Valle Microloans
San Luis Valley Christian
Community Services
P.O. Box 984
309 San Juan Avenue
Alamosa, CO 81101
719-589-5192
Fax: 719-589-4330
Email: ccs@slvccs.org
www.slv.org/ccs

Connecticut
Hartford Economic Development Corporation Loan Programs
Hartford Economic Development
Corporation
15 Lewis St.
Hartford, CT 06103
860-527-1301
Fax: 860-727-9224

Trickle Up Grant
Action for Bridgeport Community
Development
955 Connecticut Ave.
Suite 1215
Bridgeport, CT 06607
203-382-5440
Fax: 203-382-5442

Delaware
Capital Works Team Success Loans
First State Community Loan Fund
and YWCA of New Castle County
100 West 10th Street, Suite 1005
Wilmington, DE 19801
302-652-6774
Fax: 302-656-1272
Email: fsclf@diamond.net.ude.edu

District of Columbia
Youth Microloan Fund
The Entrepreneurial Development
Institute
P.O. Box 65882
Washington, DC 20035-5882
202-882-8334

Micro Loan Fund
East of the River Community
Development Corporation
4800 Nannie Helen Burroughs
Washington, DC 20019
202-397-0685

Florida
SBA Microenterprise Loan Fund
Community Equity Investments,
Inc. (CEII)
302 North Barcelona Street
Pensacola, FL 32501
850-595-6234
888-605-2505
Fax: 850-595-6234
Email: ceii2234@aol.com
http://ceii.pensacola.com

Micro Loan
Florence Villa Community
Development Corporation
111 Avenue R NE

Winter Haven, FL 33881
941-299-3263
Fax: 941-299-8134

Working Capital Program
3000 Biscayne Blvd., Suite 101A
Miami, FL 33137
305-438-1407
Fax: 305-438-1411
www.workingcapital.org

Georgia
Working Capital Program
52 W. Alton St.
Atlanta, GA 30303
404-688-6884
Fax: 404-688-4009
www.workingcapital.org

Micro Loan Fund
Goodwill Industries of North
Georgia
2201 Glenwood Avenue
Atlanta, GA 30316
404-486-8400

Hawaii
Refugee Enterprise Development
Project
Immigrant Center
720 N. King St.
Honolulu, HI 96817
808-845-3918
Fax: 808-842-1962

RED Manini MicroLoan Fund
The Immigrant Center
720 North King Street
Honolulu, HI 96817
808-845-3918
Fax: 808-842-1962
Email: redmanini@hotmail.com

Idaho

JTPA Entrepreneurial Training
IDA-ORE Planning and
Development Association
10624 West Executive Dr.
Boise, ID 83704
208-322-7033
Fax: 208-322-3569

***Small Business Micro-Loan
Program***
Panhandle Area Council, Inc.
11100 Airport Drive
Hayden, ID 83835
208-772-0584

Illinois

Community Enterprising Project
Uptown Center Hull House
Association
4520 N. Beacon St.
Chicago, IL 60640
312-561-3500
Fax: 312-561-3507

***Peoria Area Micro Business
Development Program***
The Economic Development
Council for The Peoria Area, Inc.
124 S. West Adams St., Suite 300
Peoria, IL 61602
309-676-7500
Fax: 309-676-7534

Self-Employment Loan Fund
Chicago Association of
Neighborhood Development
Organizations
123 W. Madison St., Suite 1100
Chicago, IL 60602-4589
312-372-2636
Fax: 312-372-2637

***Self-Employment Training
Program***
Project NOW - Community
Action Committee
418 19th St., P.O. Box 3970
Rock Island, IL 61201
309-793-6388
Fax: 309-793-6352

WBDC Micro-Loan Program
Women's Business Development
Center
8 S. Michigan Ave., Suite 400
Chicago, IL 60603
312-853-3477
Fax: 312-853-0145

***Women's Economic Venture
Enterprise (WEVE)***
YWCA
229 16th St.
Rock Island, IL 61201
309-788-9793
Fax: 309-788-9825

***Women's Self-Employment
Project (WSEP)***
20 N. Clark St.
Chicago, IL 60602
312-606-8255
Fax: 312-606-9215

Self-Employment Loan Fund
Chicago Association of
Neighborhood Development
Organizations (CANDO)

123 West Madison, Suite 1100
Chicago, IL 60602-4589
312-939-7171

City of Rockford Microenterprise
Investment Match Program
City of Rockford
Illinois Community Development
Department
425 East State Street
Rockford, IL 61104
815-987-5610
Fax: 815-967-6933
www.ci.rockford.il.us

Special Initiative Funds
ACCION Chicago
3245 West 26th Street
Chicago, IL 60623
773-376-9004

Micro Loan Program for Small
Businesses
West Cook Community
Development
1127 S. Mannheim Rd., Ste. 1021
Westchester, IL 60559
708-450-0100
Fax: 708-450-0655

Indiana
Eastside Community Fund
Eastside Community Investments
(ECI)
26 N. Arsenal Ave.
Indianapolis, IN 46220
317-637-7300
Fax: 317-637-7581

Rural Business Assistance Grant
City of Madison Micro Loan
Program

P.O. Box 765
Versailles, IN 47042
812-689-5505

City of Madison Micro Loan
Program
SE Indiana Regional Planning
Commission
P.O. Box 765
Versailles, IN 47042
812-689-5505

Iowa
SBA Microloan Demonstration
Program
Siouxland Economic Development
Corporation
428 Insurance Centre
Sioux City, IA 51102
712-279-6286
Fax: 712-279-6920

Small Enterprise Development
Institute for Social and Economic
Development
1901 Broadway, Suite 313
Iowa City, IA 52240
319-338-2331
Fax: 319-338-5824

SBA Microloan Program
Siouxland Economic
Development Corporation (SEDC)
P.O. Box 447
Sioux City, IA 50102
712-279-6286

Kansas
SBA Micro-Loan
South Central Kansas Economic
Development District
209 East William

Suite 300
Wichita, KS 67202-4012
316-262-7033
www.sckedd.org

Kentucky
Bluegrass Microenterprise Program
Community Ventures Corporation
1450 N. Broadway
Lexington, KY 40505
606-231-0054

Community Loan Fund
Human/Economic Appalachian
Development Corp.
P.O. Box 504
Berea, KY 40403
606-986-8423
Fax: 606-986-1299

Micro-Enterprise Loan Fund
Kentucky Highlands Investment
Corporation
P.O. Box 1738
London, KY 40743
606-864-5175

SBA Micro Loan Program
Community Ventures Corporation
1458 North Broadway
Lexington, KY 40505
606-231-0054
Fax: 606-231-0261

Louisiana
Micro Loan Fund
Catholic Social Services
1220 Aycock Street
Houma, LA 70360
504-876-0490

Maine
Androscoggin Valley Council of Governments (AVCOG)
125 Manley Rd.
Auburn, ME 04210
207-783-9186
Fax: 207-783-5211

Aroostook County Action Program, Inc. - Fleet Bank Set-Aside
P.O. Box 1116
Presque Isle, ME 04769
207-764-3721
Fax: 207-768-3040

Auburn Community Development Block Grant (CDBG) Microloan
Lewiston/Auburn Economic
Growth Council
P.O. Box 1188
37 Park St.
Lewiston, ME 04240
207-784-0161
Fax: 207-786-4412

Enterprise Fund
Coastal Enterprises Inc. (CEI)
P.O. Box 268
Wiscasset, ME 04578
207-882-7552

Money For A Big Or Small Business

Entrepreneurs With Disabilities Loan Fund
Newmarket Tech
P.O. Box 724
Augusta, ME 04330
207-287-7370
Fax: 207-287-3038

Maine Centers for Women, Work and Community
46 University Dr.
Augusta, ME 04330
207-621-3440
Fax: 207-621-3429

Working Capital Program
Western Mountains Alliance
P.O. Box 29
Farmington, ME 04938
207-778-7274
Fax: 207-778-7247

SBA Microloan Program
Eastern Maine Development Corporation
One Cumberland Place
Suite 300
Bangor, ME 04401
207-942-6389
800-339-6389
www.emdc.org

Microloan Fund
Biddeford-Saco Area Economic Development Corporation
110 Main Street, Suite 1202
Saco, ME 04072
207-282-1748
Fax: 207-282-3149
Email: bsaedc@lamere.net
www.bsaedc.org

New Ventures Loan Fund
Maine Centers for Women, Work, and Community
Stoddart House UMA
46 University Drive
Augusta, ME 043303-9410
207-621-3440
Fax: 207-621-3429
Email: wkrose@maine.edu

NMDC Microloan Program
Northern Maine Development Commission
302 Main Street
P.O. Box 779
Caribou, ME 04736
207-498-8736
800-427-8736 (Maine only)
Fax: 207-493-3108

Commercial Lending Program
Perquis Community Action Program
P.O. Box 1162
Bangor, ME 04402
207-973-3500

Androscoggin Valley Micro Loan Program
Androscoggin Valley Council of Governments
125 Manley Road
Auburn, ME 04210
207-783-9186

Aroostook County Action Micro Loan Program
Aroostook County Action Program Inc.
P.O. Box 1166
Presque Isle, ME 04769
207-768-3033

Information USA, Inc.

Money For A Big Or Small Business

Maryland

Business Owners Startup Services (BOSS)
Council for Economic and Business Opportunities
800 N. Charles St., Suite 300
Baltimore, MD 21201
410-576-2326
Fax: 410-576-2498
www.cebo.com/

Women Entrepreneurs of Baltimore, Inc. (WEB)
1118 Light St., Suite 202
Baltimore, MD 21230
410-727-4921
Fax: 410-727-4989

Massachusetts

Hilltown Enterprise Fund
Hilltown Community Development Corporation
432 Main Rd. #A
Chesterfield, MA 01012
413-296-4536
Fax: 413-296-4020

Microenterprise Development Program
Brightwood Development Corp.
2345 Main St.
Springfield, MA 01107
413-734-2144
Fax: 413-746-3934

Microenterprise Training and Loan Program for Refugees
Jewish Vocational Service
105 Chauncy St., 6th Floor
Boston, MA 02111
617-451-8147
Fax: 617-451-9973

New Bedford Working Capital Network
Community Economic Development Center
166 William St.
New Bedford, MA 02740
508-999-9920
Fax: 508-990-0199

Hampton City Employment and Training Consortium
Springfield Business Development Fund (SBDF)
1176 Main St.
Springfield, MA 01103
413-781-6900

Hilltown Enterprise Fund
Hilltown Community Development Corporation
P.O. Box 17
Chesterfield, MA 01012
413-296-4536

Working Capital Program
Working Capital
99 Bishop Allen Drive
Cambridge, MA 02139
617-576-8620
Fax: 617-576-8623
Email: infor@workingcapital.org
www.workingcapital.org

Micro Loan
Twin Cities Community Development Corporation
195 Kimball Street
Fitchburg, MA 01420
978-342-9561

Small Business Loan Fund
Dorchester Bay Economic Development Corporation

Information USA, Inc.   391

594 Columbia Road, Suite 302
Dorchester, MA 02125
617-825-4200
Fax: 617-825-3522
Email: DBSBAP@aol.com

Cambodian American League Fund
Cambodian American League of
Lowell, Inc.
60 Middlesex Street
Lowell, MA 01852
978-454-3707

Greater Springfield Entrepreneurial Fund
Hampden County Employment
and Training Consortium
1176 Main Street
Springfield, MA 01103
413-781-6900, ext. 227

SEED

SEED Micro Loan Program
South Eastern Economic
Development Corporation
88 Broadway
Taunton, MA 02780
508-822-1020

Michigan
Wise Program
Ann Arbor Community
Development Corporation
2008 Hogback Rd., Suite 12
Ann Arbor, MI 48105
313-677-1400
Fax: 313-677-1465

Lansing Community Micro-Enterprise Fund
Lansing Community Micro-
Enterprise Fund
520 West Ionia
Lansing, MI 48933
517-485-4446
Fax: 517-485-4761

Project Invest
Northwest Michigan Council of
Governments
2194 Dendrinos Drive
P.O. Box 506
Traverse City, MI 49685-0506
231-929-5000
Fax: 231-929-5012
www.cog.mi.us

Minnesota
Arrowhead Microenterprise Program
Arrowhead Community Economic
Assistance Corporation
702 Third Ave. S.
Virginia, MN 55792-2775
218-749-2914
Fax: 218-749-2913

Business Development Services
Women Venture
2324 University Ave., Suite 200
St. Paul, MN 55114
651-646-3808
Fax: 651-641-7223

Emerging Entrepreneur Development Program
Northwest Minnesota Initiative
Fund
4225 Technology Dr.
Bemidji, MN 56601

218-759-2057
Fax: 218-759-2328

Northeast Entrepreneur Fund, Inc.
820 Ninth St., N., Suite 140
Virginia, MN 55792
218-749-4191
Fax: 218-741-4249

Revolving Loan Fund (RLF)
North Star Community
Development Corporation
604 Board of Trade Building
301 West First St.
Duluth, MN 55802
218-727-6690

Self-Employment Training Opportunities (SETO)
Women Venture
2324 University Ave., Suite 200
St. Paul, MN 55114
651-646-3808
Fax: 651-641-7223

Child Care Provider Loan
Arrowhead Community Economic
Assistance Corporation
8880 Main Street
P.O. Box 406
Mountain Iron, MN 55768-0406
218-735-8201
Fax: 218-735-8202
Email:aceac@rangenet.com

Micro Enterprise Loan Program
Neighborhood Development Ctr.
651 1/2 University Avenue
St. Paul, MN 55104
651-291-2480
Fax: 651-291-2597

Northeast Entrepreneur Fund
820 Ninth Street North
Virginia, MN 55792
218-749-4191
Fax: 218-749-5213

Revolving Loan Fund
North Star Community
Development Corporation
301 West First Street
Suite 604
Duluth, MN 55802
218-727-6690

Micro Loan
Phillips Community Development
Corporation
1014 East Franklin
Suite #1
Minneapolis, MN 55404
612-871-2435
Fax: 612-871-8131

Dayton Hudson Artists Loan Fund
Resources and Counseling for the
Arts
308 Prince Street, Suite 270
St. Paul, MN 55101
651-292-4381
Fax: 651-292-4315
TTY: 651-292-3218
www.rc4arts.org

Micro Loan Program
Northwest Minnesota Foundation
4225 Technology Drive, NW
Bemidji, NM 56601
218-759-2057
Fax: 218-759-2328
www.nwnf.org

SBA Loan
Women Venture
2324 University Avenue
St. Paul, MN 55114
651-646-3808

Mississippi
Small Farm Loan
Alcorn State University
Small Farm Development Center
1000 ASU Drive #1080
Alcorn State, MS 39096-7500
601-877-6449
Fax: 601-877-3931

SELF Loan Fund
Economic Alternatives
P.O. Box 5208
Holly Springs, MS 38634
601-252-1575

Missouri
Microloan Program
First Step Fund
1080 Washington, Suite 204
Kansas City, MO 64105
816-474-5111
Fax: 816-472-4207

SBA Microloan Program
Rural Missouri, Inc.
1014 Northeast Drive
Jefferson City, MO 65109
800-234-4971
Fax: 573-635-5636

Montana
*Action for Eastern Montana -
Microbusiness Loan*
2030 N. Merrill
Glendive, MT 59330-1309
406-377-3564

*Montana Microbusiness Finance
Program*
Montana Department of Commerce
1424 9th Ave.
Helena, MT 59620
406-444-3494
Fax: 406-444-2808

*Montana Women's Economic
Development Group (WEDGO)*
Women's Opportunity and
Resource Development
127 N. Higgins
Missoula, MT 59802
406-543-3550
Fax: 406-721-4584

*Opportunities, Inc. -
Microbusiness Finance Program*
Opportunities, Inc.
P.O. Box 2289
Great Falls, MT 59403
406-761-0310

Microbusiness Loan
District 7 Human Resources
Development Council
P.O. Box 2016
Billings, MT 59103
406-247-4710
Fax: 406-248-2943
Email: dist7hrdc@imt.net
www.imt.net/~dist7hrdc

Nebraska
*Rural Enterprise Assistance
Project*
Center for Rural Affairs
P.O. Box 406
Walthill, NE 68067
402-846-5428
Fax: 402-846-5420

Rural Business Enterprise Program
Central Nebraska Community
Services, Inc.
626 N Street
P.O. Box 509
Loup City, NE 68853
308-745-0780
Fax: 308-745-0824
Email; cncsbd@micrord.com

Northeast Nebraska Microloan Fund
Northeast Nebraska Economic
Development District
111 South 1st Street
Norfolk, NE 68701
402-379-1150
Fax: 402-378-9207
www.nenedd.org/mbu.htm

Small Enterprise Economic Development Loan (SEED)
Mid-Nebraska Community
Services, Inc.
16 West 11th Street
P.O. 2288
Kearney, NE 68848
308-865-5675

Lincoln Action Program Loan
Lincoln Action Program
2202 South 11th
Lincoln, NE 68502
402-471-4515

Micro Loan Program
New Community Development
Corporation
3147 Ames Avenue
Omaha, NE 68131
402-451-2939

Rural Enterprise Assistance Project (REAP)
Center for Rural Affairs
101 Tallman
P.O. Box 406
Walthill, NE 68067
402-846-5428
Fax: 402-846-5420

Microloan Funds

Micro Business Training and Development Project
Catholic Charities - Juan Diego
Center
5211 South 31st Street
Omaha, NE 68107
402-731-5413

Self Employment Loans Fund of Lincoln
Lincoln Partnership for Economic
Development
P.O. Box 83006
Lincoln, NE 68501-3006
402-436-2350
Fax: 402-436-2360
www.lped.com

Nevada
Nevada Microenterprise Initiative Microloan Funds
Nevada Microenterprise Initiative
116 East 7th Street, Suite 3
Carson City, NV 89701
702-841-1420
Fax: 702-841-2221

New Hampshire
Working Capital-Microenterprise Peer Lending
New Hampshire Community Loan Fund
7 Wall St.
Concord, NH 03301
603-224-6669
Fax: 603-225-7254

Working Capital
New Hampshire Community Loan Fund
7 Wall Street
Concord, NH 03301
603-224-6669
Fax: 603-225-7425

Citizens Bank Women Business Owners' Loan Fund
Women's Business Center
150 Greenleaf Avenue, Unit 8
Portsmouth, NH 03801
603-430-2892

Working Capital
Women's Rural Entrepreneurial Network (WREN)
2013 Main Street
P.O. Box 331
Bethlehem, NH 03574
603-869-9736
Fax: 603-869-9738
Email: WREN@connriver.net

New Jersey
Micro Loan
Trenton Business Assistance Corporation (TBAC)
36 Broad Street
Trenton, NJ 08608
609-396-8271

Fax: 609-396-8603
Email: tbacsba@earthlink.net
www.trentonj.com/tbac.html

New Mexico
Women's Economic Self-Sufficiency Team (WESST Corp.)
414 Silver SW
Albuquerque, NM 87102-3239
505-848-4760
Fax: 505-848-2368

Micro Loan Program
ACCION
#20 First Plaza NW, Suite 417
Albuquerque, NM 87102
505-243-8844

New York
Adirondack Entrepreneurial Center
Adirondack Economic Development Corporation
P.O. Box 747
Saranac Lake, NY 12983
518-891-5523
Fax: 518-891-9820

Entrepreneurship Training Program
Worker Ownership Resource Center, Inc.
400 E. Church St.
Elmira, NY 14901
607-737-5212
Fax: 607-734-6588

Micro-Enterprise Loan and Assistance Program
Church Avenue Merchants Block Association
885 Flatbush Ave., Suite 202

Brooklyn, NY 11211
718-287-0010
Fax: 718-287-2737

**Minority and Women Business
Development Center**
Urban League of Rochester, New
York, Inc.
215 Tremont St., Door #4
Rochester, NY 14608
212-803-2418

**Neighborhood Micro-Loan
Program**
Ridgewood Local Development
Corporation
59-09 Myrtle Ave.
Ridgewood, NY 11385
718-366-3806
Fax: 718-381-7080

**N.Y. State Department of
Economic Development
Entrepreneurial Assistance
Program**
Albany-Colonie Regional Chamber
of Commerce
1 Computer Dr. S.
Albany, NY 12205
518-458-9851
Fax: 518-458-1055

**Queens County Overall Economic
Development Corporation - NY
State Department of Economic
Development Entrepreneurial
Assistance Program**
Queens County Overall Economic
Development Corp.
120-55 Queens Blvd., Suite 309
Kew Gardens, NY 11424
718-263-0546
Fax: 718-263-0594

**Regional Economic Development
Assistance Corporation Mini Loan
Program**
New York City Economic
Development Corporation
110 William St.
New York, NY 10038
212-618-8900

Rural Opportunities

Rural Ventures Fund
Rural Opportunities, Inc.
400 East Ave.
Rochester, NY 14607
716-340-3387
Fax: 716-340-3337

WORC Loan Fund
Worker Ownership Resource
Center
One Franklin Square
Exchange Street
Geneva, NY 14456
315-789-5061
Fax: 315-789-0261
www.atworc.org

Manhattan Loan Fund
Manhattan Borough Development
Corporation
15 Park Row, Suite 510
New York, NY 10038
212-791-3660
Fax: 212-571-0873

Micro Loan Program
Project Enterprise
2303 7th Avenue

New York, NY 10030
212-690-2024

*ACCORD Business Development
Program*
ACCORD Corporation
50 West Main Street
Friendship, NY 14739
716-973-2322
Fax: 716-973-3014
Email: RVC_Fedz@eznet.net

Micro Loan Program
ACCION New York
235 Havemeyer Street
Brooklyn, NY 11211
718-599-5170
Email: accionnewyork@
compuserve.com
www.accion.org

Appleseed Trust
MicroCredit Group of Central
New York
222 Herald Place, 2nd Floor
Syracuse, NY 13202
315-424-9485
Fax: 315-424-7056

Trickle Up Program
Trickle Up
121 West 27th St., Suite 504
New York, NY 10001
212-362-7958

North Carolina
Child Care Providers
Self-Help
301 W. Main St.
Durham, NC 27701
800-476-7428
919-956-4400

Fax: 919-956-4600
www.self-help.org

Good Work
115 Market St. #211
Durham, NC 27702
919-682-8473
Fax: 919-687-7033

Microbusiness Development
WAMY Community Action, Inc.
P.O. Box 2688
Boone, NC 28607
828-264-2421
Fax: 828-264-0952

Mountain Microenterprise Fund
29 1/2 Page Ave.
Asheville, NC 28801
828-253-2834
Fax: 828-255-7953

*North Carolina Microenterprise
Loan Program (NCMLP)*
NC Rural Economic Development
Center, Inc.
4021 Carya Dr.
Raleigh, NC 27610
919-250-4314
Fax: 919-250-4325

*Northeastern Community
Development Corporation*
154 Highway 158 East
Camden, NC 27921
252-338-5466
Fax: 252-338-5639

*West Greenville CDC Micro Loan
Program*
West Greenville Community
Development Corporation

706 West 5th St.
P.O. Box 1605
Greenville, NC 27835-1605
252-752-9277

Micro Loan
Mountain Microenterprise Fund
(MMF)
29 1/2 Page Avenue
Asheville, NC 28801
888-389-3089
www.mtnmicro.org

Micro Loan
Good Work, Inc.
P.O. 25250
Durham, NC 27702
919-682-8473

Microenterprise Loan Program
North Carolina Rural Economic
Development Center
4021 Carya Drive
Raleigh, NC 27610
919-250-4314

**East Carolina Microenterprise
Loan Program**
315 Turner Street
Beaufort, NC 28516
252-504-2424
Fax: 252-504-2248

Ohio
Microenterprise Program
Lima-Allen Council for
Community Affairs
405 East Market St.
Lima, OH 45801
419-227-2586
Fax: 419-227-7626

**CAC Microenterprise Training
Program**
Community Action Committee
(CAC) of Pike County
941 Market St.
P.O. Box 799
Piketon, OH 45661
740-289-2371
Fax: 740-289-4291

**City of Cleveland Microloan
Program**
City of Cleveland Department of
Economic Development
601 Lakeside Ave., Room 210
Cleveland, OH 44114
216-664-2406
Fax: 216-664-3681

**Columbus/Franklin County
Microloan Program**
Columbus Countywide
Development Corp.
941 Chatham Lane, Suite 207
Columbus, OH 43221
614-645-6171
Fax: 614-645-8588

**Food Ventures Project and
Product Development Fund**
ACEnet
94 N. Columbus Rd.
Athens, OH 44701
740-592-3854
Fax: 740-593-5451

**HHWP Community Action
Commission**
Microenterprise Development
Program
HHWP Community Action
Commission

122 Jefferson St.
P.O. Box 179
Findlay, OH 45839
419-423-3755
Fax: 419-423-4115

*Neighborhood Economic
Development Loan Program
(NEDL)*
Office of Economic Development
City of Toledo
One Government Center
Suite 1850
Toledo, OH 43604
419-245-1426
Fax: 419-245-1462

Women Entrepreneurs, Inc.
P.O. Box 2662, C-OH45201
36 East 4th St., Suite 92
Cincinnati, OH 45201
513-684-0700
Fax: 513-684-0779

Micro Loan Fund
Neighborhood House, Inc
1000 Atchenson Street
Columbus, OH 43203
614-252-4544

Fax: 614-252-7919
Email: lboykin@beol.net

Appalachian Microloan Program
Enterprise Development
Corporation
9080 Hocking Hills Drive
The Plains, OH 45780
740-797-9646
800-822-6096
Fax: 740-797-9659

Child Care Loan
Lima/Allen Council on
Community Affairs (LACCA)
540 South Central
Lima, OH 45804
419-227-2586
Fax: 419-227-7626

MicroLoan Program
Hamilton County Development
Company, Inc.
1776 Mentor Avenue
Cincinnati, OH 45212
513-631-8292
Email: lawalden@hcdc.com

MicroLoan
Columbus Countywide
Development Corporation
941 Chatham Lane, Suite 300
Columbus, OH 43221-2416
614-645-6171
Fax: 614-645-85883
Email: ccdc@earthlink.net

Pike County Microloan
CAC of Pike County, Inc.
941 Market Street
Piketon, OH 45661
740-289-2371

Oregon

SBA Microloan Program
Cascades West Financial Services, Inc.
1400 Queen Avenue SE
P.O. Box 686
Albany, OR 97321
541-924-8480
Fax: 541-967-4651
Email: dsearle@cwcog.cog.or.us

Microenterprise Loan
O.U.R. Federal Credit Union
P.O. Box 11922
Eugene, OR 97440
541-485-1190

Micro Loan
Southern Oregon Women's Access
to Credit
33 North Central, Suite 209
Medford, OR 97501
541-779-3992

***Child Care Neighborhood
Network Loan Fund***
Rose Community Development
Corporation
7211 NE 62nd Avenue
Portland, OR 97206
503-788-0826

Pennsylvania

***Ben Franklin Enterprise Growth
Fund***
Ben Franklin Technology Center of
Southeastern Pennsylvania
1110 Penn Center
1835 Market St., Suite 1100
Philadelphia, PA 19103
215-972-0877
Fax: 215-972-5588

***Local Enterprise Assistance
Program (LEAP)***
Bloomsburg University College of
Business
243 Sutliff Hall
Bloomsburg, PA 17815
570-389-4591
Fax: 570-389-3892

Micro-Enterprise Development
Lutheran Children and Family
Service
45 Garrett Rd.
Upper Darby, PA 19082
610-734-3363
Fax: 610-734-3389

***Service for Self-Employment
Training and Support (ASSETS)***
Mennonite Economic Development
Associates
447 S. Prince St.
Lancaster, PA 17603
717-393-6089

Micro Loan
ASSETS
447 South Prince Street
Lancaster, PA 17603
717-393-6089
Fax: 717-290-7936

Micro Loan
Community Action Development
Corporation of the Lehigh Valley
605 Turner Street
Allentown, PA 18102
610-433-5703

Community Capital Works
Philadelphia Development
Partnership
1334 Walnut Street

Philadelphia, PA 19107
215-545-3100

Women's Opportunities Resource Program
Women's Opportunities Resource
1930 Chestnut Street, Suite 1600
Philadelphia, PA 19103
215-564-5500

Enterprise Growth Fund
Ben Franklin Technology Center
of Southeastern Pennsylvania
11 Penn Center
1835 Market St., Suite 1100
Philadelphia, PA 19103
215-972-6700
Fax: 215-972-5588

South Dakota
Revolving Loan Fund Program
Northeast South Dakota Economic
Corporation
414 Third Ave. East
Sisseton, SD 57262
605-698-7654
Fax: 605-698-3038

Tennessee
Community Microloan Program
Knoxville's Community
Development Corporation
Economic Ventures, Inc.
P.O. Box 3550
Knoxville, TN 37927-3550
423-594-8762
Fax: 423-594-8659

Micro Loan Program
Firestone Retirees CDC
659 N. Manassas St.
Room 106-107

Memphis, TN 38107
P.O. Box 80073
Memphis, TN 38108
901-454-9524

Texas
Micro Loan
ACCION El Paso
7744 North Loop Road, Suite A
El Paso, TX 79915
915-779-3727

Tyler Development Fund
Tyler Economic Development
Council, Inc.
P.O. Box 2004
Tyler, TX 75710
903-593-2004
Fax: 903-597-0699

MicroLoan Program
Corp. for Economic Development
of Harris County, Inc.
2223 West Loop South, Suite 400
Houston, TX 77027
713-840-8804
Fax: 713-840-8806

MicroLoan Program
Corporation for Economic
Development of Harris County,
Inc.
2223 West Loop South, Suite 400
Houston, TX 77027
713-840-8804
Fax: 713-840-8806

Utah
Utah Microenterprise Loan Fund
3595 South Main Street
Salt Lake City, UT 84115
801-269-8408

Vermont

Burlington Revolving Loan Fund
Community and Economic
Development Office
Room 32, City Hall
Burlington, VT 05461
802-865-7144
Fax: 802-865-7024

**Micro-Business Development
Program**
Central Vermont Community
Action Council, Inc.
195 US Route 302/Berlin
Barre, VT 05641
802-479-1053
Fax: 802-479-5353

Virginia

Eagle Staff Fund - Seed Grants
First Nations Development Institute
The Stores Building
1-1917 Main St.
Fredericksburg, VA 22408
540-371-5615

**Northern Virginia Microenterprise
Loan - SBA**
Ethiopian Community
Development Council, Inc.
1038 S. Highland St.
Arlington, VA 22206
703-685-0510

**Refugee Microenterprise Loan -
ORR**
Ethiopian Community
Development Council, Inc.
1038 S. Highland St.
Arlington, VA 22204
703-685-0510

Microloan Fund
Small Business Development
Center, Inc.
147 Mill Ridge Rd.
Lynchburg, VA 24502
804-582-6170

Business Loan Program
South Fairfax Regional Business
Partnership, Inc.
6911 Richmond Highway
Alexandria, VA 22306
703-768-1440
Fax: 703-768-0547

Micro Loan
VA Eastern Shore Economic
Empowerment and Housing Corp.
P.O. Box 814
Nassawadox, VA 23413
757-442-4509
Fax: 757-442-7530

New Enterprises Loan Fund
New Enterprises Fund
930 Cambria Street
Christiansburg, VA 24073
540-382-2002

**Northern Neck Enterprise
Program**
Northern Neck Planning District
Commission
153 Yankee Point Road
Lancaster, VA 22503
804-333-1900
www.nnpdc17.state.va.us

MicroLoan Program
Virginia Economic Development
Corporation
P.O. Box 1505

Charlottesville, VA 22902-1505
804-979-0114
Fax: 804-979-1597
Email: microloan.tjpd@state.va.us
www.avenue.org/Gov/TJPDC

Washington
African American Community Endowment Fund
Black Dollar Days Task Force
116-21st Ave.
Seattle, WA 98122
206-323-0534

Cascadia Revolving Fund
119 1st Ave. S., Suite 100
Seattle, WA 98104
206-447-9226
Fax: 206-682-4804

DownHome Washington Microloan Program
Snohomish County Private Industry Council
728 134th Street SW, Bldg. A, Suite 211
Everett, WA 98204
425-743-9669
425-353-2025
Fax: 425-742-1177
Email: snopic@gte.net

CASH Loan Program
Washington CASH- Community Alliance for Self-Help
410 Boston Street
Seattle, WA 98109
206-352-1945
Fax: 206-352-1899
Email: washcash@nwlink.com
www.washingtoncash.org

Micro Loan Program
Tri-Cities Enterprise Association
2000 Logston Boulevard
Richland, WA 99052
509-375-3268
www.owt.com/tea

SNAP Program

SNAP Program
Spokane Neighborhood Action Programs
212 South Wall
Spokane, WA 99201
509-456-7174
Email: lancaster@snapwa.org

Northwest Business Development Association
9 South Washington, Suite 215
Spokane, WA 99201
509-458-8555

West Virginia
Monroe Neighborhood Enterprise Center
Monroe County Community Services Council
P.O. Box 403
Union, WV 24883
304-772-3381
Fax: 304-772-4014

Lighthouse MicroLoan
Lightstone CDC
H 363 Box 73
Moyers, WV 26815
304-249-5200
Fax: 304-249-5310
www.lightstone.org

Wisconsin

ADVOCAP Business Development Loan Fund
ADVOCAP, Inc.
19 W. 1st St.
Fond du Lac, WI 54935
920-922-7760
Fax: 920-922-7214

Business Ownership and Operations
Juneau Business High School
6415 West Mount Vernon
Milwaukee, WI 53213
414-476-5480

Economic Development Project
West Cap
525 2nd St.
Glenwood City, WI 54013
715-265-4271
Fax: 715-265-7031

Self-Employment Project
CAP Services, Inc.
1725 W. River Dr.
Stevens Point, WI 54481
715-345-5200
Fax: 715-345-6508

Small Business Loan
Wisconsin Women's Business Initiative
2745 N. Dr. ML King Jr. Drive
Milwaukee, WI 53212
414-263-5450
www.wwbic.com
Email: info@wwbic.com

Job and Business Development Loan
Wisconsin Coulee Region Community Action Program
201 Melby Street
Westby, WI 54667
608-634-3104

Revolving Loan Fund
CAP Services
1725 West River Drive
Stevens Point, WI 54481
715-345-5200

West CAP Child Care Loan
West Central Wisconsin Community Action Agency, Inc. (West CAP)
119 West 6th Avenue
Menomonie, WI 54751
715-235-8525

Free Business Assistance Programs

A helping hand is just a phone call away for individuals who want to enter into a small business or microenterprise. If you fall into any of the following categories: low to moderate income, Native American, minorities, women, welfare recipients, or have little or no money, you may be eligible for a wide range of assistance.

 These programs are aimed to assist individuals toward self-sufficiency.

Imagine getting training, counseling, peer support and exchange, and mentoring for free to help you get the knowledge you need to start your own business. Learn how to prepare a business plan and get guidance from the best instructors in the country. One such program is NOVA, located in Arkansas. Their program has four major components: Group Training; Individual Sessions; Business Start-Up; and Networking and Mentoring.

Imagine youths able to receive effective business course training. One such program is Kidpreneur Enterprises, located in Michigan. This program is available to all youths who express an interest in owning and operating their own small business. Kidpreneur is designed to provide and instill concepts and experiences in the minds of youths.

Doors can open for entrepreneurs, like Adina Rosenthal, owner of Threadbearer, a fabric and accessory shop located on Capitol Hill. At a very young age, Adina knew she wanted to work with fabrics.

At age 17, she lost the use of her right arm when she was hit by a logging truck. After receiving her degree from the Fashion Institute of Design and Merchandising, she attempted to get work at various design companies only to be passed over time and time again. A friend suggested she join the Black Dollar Days' program for entrepreneurs. After completing their entrepreneurial program, Adina opened Threadbearer. She accredits her success to the assistance she received, and is still receiving, from the Black Dollar Days Task Force.

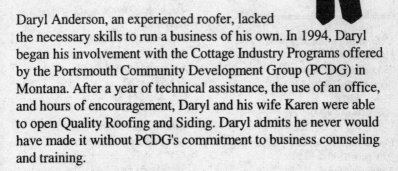

Daryl Anderson, an experienced roofer, lacked the necessary skills to run a business of his own. In 1994, Daryl began his involvement with the Cottage Industry Programs offered by the Portsmouth Community Development Group (PCDG) in Montana. After a year of technical assistance, the use of an office, and hours of encouragement, Daryl and his wife Karen were able to open Quality Roofing and Siding. Daryl admits he never would have made it without PCDG's commitment to business counseling and training.

The aim of these programs is to develop a participant's confidence and skills in understanding business enterprise and to further the development of viable business ideas.

Technical Assistance Programs

Arizona
Micro Industry Credit Rural Organization
P.P.E.P. Microbusiness and Housing Development Corp., Inc.
1100 E. Ajo Way, Suite 209
Tucson, AZ 85713

520-806-9513
Fax: 520-806-9515

Arkansas
New Opportunities for Venture Alternatives (NOVA)
Good Faith Fund (GFF)

2304 W. 29th Ave.
Pine Bluff, AR 71603
870-535-6233

California
Arcata Economic Development
Corporation
100 Ericson Court, Suite 100
Arcata, CA 95521
707-822-4616
Fax: 707-822-8982

```
BUSINESS
INCUBATOR
```

California Indian Manpower
Consortium
4153 Northgate Blvd.
Sacramento, CA 95834
916-920-0285
Fax: 916-641-6338

Center for Community Futures
P.O. Box 5309
Elmwood Station
Berkeley, CA 94705
510-339-3801
Fax: 510-339-3803

Micro Enterprise Assistance
Program of Orange County
18011 Skypark Circle, Suite E
Irvine, CA 92614
949-252-1380

Private Industry Council
2425 Bisso Lane, Suite 200
Concord, CA 94520
925-646-5377
Fax: 925-646-5299

Self-Employment Microenterprise
Development (SEMED)
Economic and Employment
Development Center (EEDC)
241 S. Figueroa St.
Los Angeles, CA 90012
213-617-3953

The West Company
The West Enterprise Center
367 North State St., Suite 206
Ukiah, CA 95482
707-468-3553
Fax: 707-462-8945

Training, Network and Business
Incubator
San Francisco Renaissance
275 5th St.
San Francisco, CA 94103
415-541-8580
Fax: 415-541-8589

Women's Economic Ventures of
Santa Barbara
1216 State St., Suite 610
Santa Barbara, CA 93101
805-965-6073
Fax: 805-962-9622

Colorado
Mi Casa Resource Center for
Women
571 Galapago St.
Denver, CO 80204
303-573-1302
Fax: 303-595-0422

Connecticut
Aid to Artisans, Inc.
14 Brick Walk Lane
Farmington, CT 06032

Money For A Big Or Small Business

860-677-1649
Fax: 860-676-2170

Entrepreneurial Center for Women
Hartford College for Women
50 Elizabeth St.
Hartford, CT 06105
860-768-5681
Fax: 860-768-5622

Hartford Economic Development Corporation
15 Lewis St.
Hartford, CT 06103
860-527-1301
Fax: 860-727-9224

District of Columbia
Accion International
Department of U.S. Operations
733 15th St. NW, Suite 700
Washington, DC 20005
202-393-5113
Fax: 202-393-5115

LEDC Microenterprise Loan Fund
Latino Economic Development
Corp., Inc.
2316 18th St., NW
Washington, DC 20009
202-588-5102
Fax: 202-588-5204

New Enterprise Training for Profits (NET/PRO)
Venture Concepts
325 Pennsylvania Ave., SE
Washington, DC 20003
202-543-1200
Fax: 202-543-0254

SCORE
National SCORE Office
409 3rd St., SW
Washington, DC 20024
800-634-0245

Youth Microloan Fund
The Entrepreneurial Development
Institute
P.O. Box 65882
Washington, DC 20035-5882
202-822-8334

Georgia
Entrepreneurial Training
Grasp Enterprises
55 Marietta, Suite 2000
Atlanta, GA 30303
404-659-5955
Fax: 404-880-9561

Hawaii
Pacific Business Center Program
University of Hawaii
BUS-AD 413
2404 Maile Way
Honolulu, HI 96822
808-956-6286

Refugee Enterprise Development Project
Immigrant Center
720 North King St.
Honolulu, HI 96817
808-845-3918
Fax: 808-842-1962

Illinois
Chicago Association of Neighborhood Development Organizations
123 W. Madison St., Suite 1100

Chicago, IL 60602
312-372-2636
Fax: 312-372-2637

Community Enterprising Project
Uptown Center Hull House
Association
4520 North Beacon St.
Chicago, IL 60640
312-561-3500
Fax: 312-561-3507

Peoria Area Micro Business
Development Program
The Economic Development
Council for The Peoria Area, Inc.
124 SW Adams St., Suite 300
Peoria, IL 61602
309-676-7500
Fax: 309-676-7534

Prison Small Business Project
Self-Employment Research Project
Roosevelt University
430 South Michigan Ave.
Chicago, IL 60605
312-341-3696

Women's Business Development
Center
8 South Michigan Ave., Suite 400
Chicago, IL 60603
312-853-3477
Fax: 312-853-0145

Women's Self-Employment
Project
20 N. Clark St.
Chicago, IL 60602
312-606-8255
Fax: 312-606-9215

Women's Economic Venture
Enterprise (WEVE)
YWCA
229 16th St.
Rock Island, IL 61201
309-788-9793
Fax: 309-788-9825

Indiana
Eastside Community Fund
Eastside Community Investments
(ECI)
26 North Arsenal Ave.
Indianapolis, IN 46220
317-637-7300
Fax: 317-637-7581

Indiana Small Business
Development Center Network
One North Capitol
Suite 1275
Indianapolis, IN 46204
317-264-6871
Fax: 317-264-2806

Iowa
Siouxland Economic Development
Corporation (SEDC)
428 Insurance Centre
Sioux City, IA 51102
712-279-6286
Fax: 712-279-6920

Small Enterprise Development
Institute for Social and Economic
Development
1901 Broadway
Suite 313
Iowa City, IA 52240
319-338-2331
Fax: 319-338-5824

Kentucky

Community Loan Fund
Human/Economic Appalachian
Development Corporation
P.O. Box 504
Berea, KY 40403
606-986-8423
Fax: 606-986-1299

**Community Ventures Corporation
Bluegrass Microenterprise
Program**
1450 North Broadway
Lexington, KY 40506
606-231-0054

Maine

**Androscoggin Valley Council of
Governments (AVCOG's)**
125 Manley Rd.
Auburn, ME 04210
207-783-9186
Fax: 207-783-5211

**Aroostook County Action
Programs, Inc.**
771 Main St.
Presque Isle, ME 04769
207-764-3721
Fax: 207-768-3040

Community Concepts Inc. (CCI)
P.O. Box 278
Market Square
South Paris, ME 04281
207-743-7716
Fax: 207-743-6513

Enterprise Development Fund
Coastal Enterprises, Inc.
P.O. Box 268, Water St.
Wiscasset, ME 04578

207-882-7552
Fax: 207-882-7308

**Greater Portland Economic
Development Council**
145 Middle St.
Portland, ME 04101
207-772-1109
Fax: 207-772-1179

Growth Council of Oxford Hills
150 Main St.
South Paris, ME 04281
207-743-8830
Fax: 207-743-5917

**Maine Centers for Women, Work
and Community**
46 University Dr.
Augusta, ME 04330
207-621-3440
Fax: 207-621-3429

New Ventures
Maine Centers for Women, Work,
and Community
Stoddard House
University of Maine
Augusta, ME 04330
207-621-3433
Fax: 207-621-3429

Service Corps of Retired Executives (SCORE)
66 Pearl St.
Portland, ME 04101
207-772-1147

University of Maine Cooperative Extension
5741 Libby Hall, Room 106
Orono, ME 04469-5741
207-581-3167
Fax: 207-581-1387

USM School of Applied Science/ Department of External Programs
University of Southern Maine
37 College Ave.
Graham, ME 04038
207-780-5439
Fax: 207-780-5129

Maryland
Business Owners Start-Up Services (BOSS)
Council of Economic and Business Opportunities
800 North Charles St., Suite 300
Baltimore, MD 21201
410-576-2326
Fax: 410-576-2498

Women Entrepreneurs of Baltimore, Inc.
1118 Light St., Suite 202
Baltimore, MD 21230
410-727-4921
Fax: 410-727-4989

Massachusetts
Berkshire Enterprises
University of Massachusetts
Donahue Institute

24 Depot St.
P.O. Box 2297
Pittsfield, MA 01201
413-448-2755
Fax: 413-448-2749

Brightwood Development Corporation
2345 Main St.
Springfield, MA 01107
413-734-2144
Fax: 413-746-3934

Hilltown Enterprise Fund
Hilltown Community Development Corporation
432 Main Rd. #A
Chesterfield, MA 01012
413-296-4536
Fax: 413-296-4020

Microenterprise Training and Loan Program for Refugees
Jewish Vocational Service
105 Chauncy St., 4th Floor
Boston, MA 02111
617-451-8147
Fax: 617-451-9973

Community Economic Development Center
166 William St.
New Bedford, MA 02740
508-979-4684
Fax: 508-990-0199

Small Business Development System (SBDS)
The Howells Group
SIS Management
930 Commonwealth Ave., South
Boston, MA 02215

717-264-6205
Fax: 717-731-6531

The Trusteeship Institute
15 Edwards Square
Northampton, MA 01060
413-259-1600

Michigan
Ann Arbor Community Development Corporation
2008 Hogback Rd., Suite 12
Ann Arbor, MI 48105
313-677-1400
Fax: 313-677-1465

Grand Rapids Opportunities for Women (GROW)
Center for Women
25 Sheldon Blvd. SE, Suite 210
Grand Rapids, MI 49503
616-458-3404

Kidpreneur Enterprises
Metropolitan Chamber of Commerce
400 N. Saginaw St., Suite 101A
Flint, MI 48502
810-235-5514
Fax: 810-235-4407

Northern Economic Initiatives Corporation
1009 West Ridge
Marquette, MI 49855
906-228-5571
Fax: 906-228-5572

Supportive Entrepreneurial Program
Community Action Agency of South Central Michigan

175 Main St.
Battle Creek, MI 49014
616-965-7766
Fax: 616-965-1152

Minnesota
American Institute of Small Business
7515 Wayzata Blvd., Suite 129
Minneapolis, MN 55426
612-545-7001
Fax: 612-545-7020

Arrowhead Community Economic Assistance Corporation
702 Third Ave. South
Virginia, MN 55792-2775
218-749-2914
Fax: 218-749-2913

Emerging Entrepreneur Development Program
Northwest Minnesota Initiative Fund
4225 Technology Dr.
Bemidji, MN 56601
208-759-2057
Fax: 208-759-2328

Northeast Entrepreneur Fund, Inc.
820 Ninth St., North, Suite 140
Virginia, MN 55792
218-749-4191
Fax: 218-741-4249

Self-Employment Investment Demonstration (SEID)
Minnesota Department of Human Services
444 Lafayette Rd.
St. Paul, MN 55155-3814

651-297-1316
Fax: 651-215-6388
www.dhs.state.mn.us/ecs/
program/seid.htm

*North Star Community
Development Corporation*
615 Board of Trade Building
301 West First St., Suite 604
Duluth, MN 55802
218-727-6690

Create Your Own Job

Missouri
Create Your Own Job
Missouri Western State College
4525 Downs Dr.
St. Joseph, MO 64507
816-271-5830

Montana
Action for Eastern Montana
2030 N. Merrill
Glendive, MT 59330-1309
406-377-3564

*Montana Women's Economic
Development Group (WEDGO)*
Women's Opportunity and
Resource Development
127 North Higgins
Missoula, MT 59802
406-543-3550
Fax: 406-721-4584

Opportunities, Inc.
905 1st Ave. North

Great Falls, MT 59403
406-761-0310

Nebraska
*Rural Enterprise Assistance
Project*
Center for Rural Affairs
P.O. Box 406
Walthill, NE 68067
402-846-5428
Fax: 402-846-5420

New Mexico
*Women's Economic Self-
Sufficiency Team (WESST Corp.)*
414 Silver SW
Albuquerque, NM 87102-3239
505-848-4760
Fax: 505-848-2368

New York
ACCION New York
235 Havemeyer St., 3rd Floor
Brooklyn, NY 11211
718-599-5170
Fax: 718-387-9686

*Microenterprise Loan and
Assistance Program*
Church Avenue Merchants Block
Association, Inc.
885 Flatbush Ave.
Brooklyn, NY 11226
718-287-0100
Fax: 718-287-2737

Ms. Foundation for Women
Ms. Foundation
120 Wall St., Floor 33
New York, NY 10005
212-742-2300
Fax: 212-742-1653

New York Department of
Economic Development
Local Development Corporation of
East New York
80 Jamaica Ave.
Brooklyn, NY 11207
718-385-6700
Fax: 718-385-7505

New York State Department of
Economic Development
Entrepreneurial Assistance Program
Queens County Overall Economic
Development Corp.
120-55 Queens Blvd. #309
Jamaica, NY 11424
718-263-0546
Fax: 718-263-0594

Rural Venture Fund
Rural Opportunities, Inc.
400 East Ave.
Rochester, NY 15607
716-340-3387
Fax: 716-340-3337

North Carolina
Rural Economic Development
Centers, Inc.
4021 Carya Dr.
Raleigh, NC 27610
919-250-4314
Fax: 919-250-4325

WAMY Community Action, Inc.
P.O. Box 2688
Boone, NC 28607
828-264-2421
Fax: 828-264-0952

Northeastern Community
Development Corporation
154 US Highway 158 East

Camden, NC 27921
252-338-5466
Fax: 252-338-5639

North Dakota
Center for Innovation and
Business Development
Box 8372, UND
Grand Forks, ND 58202
701-777-3132
Fax: 701-777-2339

Ohio
The Appalachian Center for
Economic Networks (ACEnet)
94 North Columbus Rd.
Athens, OH 45701
740-592-3854
Fax: 740-593-5451

The Chamber of Women's
Business Initiative Program
37 North High St.
Columbus, OH 43215
614-225-6910

Ventures in Business Ownership
Columbiana Career Center
9364 St. Rt. 45
Lisbon, OH 44432
330-424-9561, ext. 34
Fax: 330-424-9719
(Serving Columbiana, Mahoning,
Carroll counties and parts of
Pennsylvania and West Virginia)

Ehove Career Center
316 West Mason Rd.
Milan, OH 44846
419-499-4663
Fax: 419-499-4076
www.ehove-jvs.k12.oh.us

(Serving Huron, Erie and Ottawa counties)

Guernsey-Noble Career Center
57090 Vocational Rd.
Senecaville, OH 43780
740-685-2516
Fax: 740-685-2518
(Serving Guernsey, Noble, Muskingum and Perry counties)

Greene County Career Center
2960 West Enon Rd.
Xenia, OH 45385
937-426-6636
Fax: 937-372-8283
(Serving Montgomery, Greene, Clark and Miami counties)

Medina County Career Center
1101 West Liberty St.
Medina, OH 44256
330-725-8461
Fax: 330-725-3842
(Serving Medina county and surrounding area)

Penta County Vocational School
30095 Oregon Rd.
Perrysburg, OH 43551
419-666-1120
Fax: 419-666-6049
(Serving Northwest Ohio)

Polaris Career Center
7285 Old Oak Blvd.
Middleburg, OH 44130
440-891-7703
Fax: 440-826-4330
www.polaris.edu
(Serving Cuyahoga county)

Upper Valley Applied Technology Center
8811 Career Dr.
Piqua, OH 45356
937-778-8419
(Serving Miami, Shelby, Darke and portions of surrounding counties)

Women's Business Resource Program of Southeast Ohio
20 East Circle Dr., Suite 155
Athens, OH 45701
740-593-0474
Fax: 740-593-1795

Women Entrepreneurs, Inc.
36 East 4th St. #92
Cincinnati, OH 45202
513-684-0700
Fax: 513-684-0779

Women's Network Mentoring Program
Women's Network
526 S. Main St., Suite 221
Akron, OH 44311
330-379-9280
330-379-3454

Pennsylvania
A Service for Self-Employment Training and Support (ASSETS)
Mennonite Economic Development Associates

Money For A Big Or Small Business

447 S. Prince St.
Lancaster, PA 17603
717-393-6089

Micro-Enterprise Development
Lutheran Children and Family
Service
45 Garrett Rd.
Upper Darby, PA 19082
610-734-3363
Fax: 610-734-3389

Philadelphia Small Business Loan Fund
LaSalle University Small Business
Development Center
1900 West Olney Ave., Box 828
Philadelphia, PA 19141
215-951-1416
Fax: 215-951-1597

Rhode Island
Elmwood Neighborhood Housing Services, Inc. (N.H.S.)
9 Atlantic Ave.
Providence, RI 02907
401-461-4111

South Dakota
Northeast South Dakota Energy Conservation Corporation
NE South Dakota Energy
Conservation Corp.
414 Third Ave. East
Sisseton, SD 57262
605-698-7654

Vermont
Burlington Revolving Loan Fund
Community and Economic
Development Office
Room 32, City Hall

Burlington, VT 05461
802-865-7144

Micro-Business Development Program
Central Vermont Community
Action Council, Inc.
195 US Route 302/Berlin
Barre, VT 05641
802-479-1053
Fax: 802-479-5353

Virginia
Association of Farmworker Opportunity Programs
1611 N. Kent St., Suite 910
Arlington, VA 22209
703-528-4141
Fax: 703-528-4145

Oweesta Program
First Nations Development Institute
The Stores Bldg.
11917 Main St.
Falmouth, VA 22408
540-371-5615
Fax: 540-371-3505

United Community Ministries (UCM)
7511 Fordson Rd.
Alexandria, VA 22306
703-768-7106
Fax: 703-768-4788

Washington
Cascadia Revolving Fund
119 1st Ave. S., Suite 100
Seattle, WA 98104
206-447-9226
Fax: 206-682-4804

Money For A Big Or Small Business

*The Inner-City Entrepreneurial
Training Program (ICETP)*
Black Dollar Task Force
116-21st Ave.
Seattle, WA 98122
206-323-0534
Fax: 206-323-4701

West Virginia
Center for Economic Options
601 Delaware Ave.
Charleston, WV 25302
304-345-1298
Fax: 304-342-0641

*Monroe Neighborhood Enterprise
Center*
Monroe County Community
Services Council
P.O. Box 403
Union, WV 24883
304-772-3381
Fax: 304-772-4014

Wisconsin
Advocap, Inc.
19 W. 1st St.
Fond du Lac, WI 54935

920-922-7760
Fax: 920-922-7214

*Business Ownership and
Operations*
Juneau Business High School
6415 West Mount Vernon
Milwaukee, WI 53213
414-476-5480

Cap Services, Inc.
5499 Highway 10 East
Stevens Point, WI 54481
715-345-5200
Fax: 715-345-5206

Economic Development Project
West Cap
525 2nd St.
Glenwood City, WI 54013
715-265-4271
Fax: 715-265-7031

*Women's Business Initiative
Corporation*
2745 Dr. Martin Luther King Dr.
Milwaukee, WI 53212
414-372-2070
Fax: 414-263-5456

State Government Money Programs For Selling Overseas

Some state government economic development programs offer special help for those who need financial assistance in selling overseas. Contact your state Economic Development Office listed on page 370.

EXPORT-IMPORT BANK FINANCING (EXIMBANK)

The **Export-Import Bank** facilitates and aids in the financing of exports of United States goods and services. Its programs include short-term, medium-term, and long-term credits, small business support, financial guarantees, and insurance.

In addition, it sponsors conferences on small business exporting, maintains credit information on thousands of foreign firms, supports feasibility studies of overseas programs, and offers export and small business finance counseling.

To receive *Marketing News* Fact Sheets, or the *Eximbank Export Credit Insurance* booklet, or the Eximbank's *Program Selection Guide,* contact: Export-Import Bank, 811 Vermont Ave. NW, Washington, DC 20571, 202-566-4490, 1-800-424-5201; Fax: 202-566-7524; {www.exim.gov}.

Overseas Private Investment Corporation (OPIC)

This agency provides marketing, insurance, and financial assistance to American companies investing in 140 countries and 16 geographic regions. Its programs include direct loans, loan guarantees, and political risk insurance. OPIC also sponsors U.S. and international seminars for investment executives as well as conducts investment missions to developing countries. The Investor Services Division offers a computer service to assist investors in identifying investment opportunities worldwide. A modest fee is charged for this service and it is also available through the Lexis/Nexis computer network. OPIC has supported investments worth nearly $112 billion, generated $56 billion in U.S. exports, and helped to create 230,000 American jobs. Specific Info-Kits are available identifying basic economic, business, and political information for each of the countries covered. In addition, it operates:

Small Business Administration (SBA) Export Loans

This agency makes loans and loan guarantees to small business concerns as well as to small business investment companies, including those that sell overseas. It also offers technical assistance, counseling, training, management assistance, and information resources, including some excellent publications to small and minority businesses in export operations. Contact your local or regional SBA office listed in the blue pages of your telephone book under Small Business Administration, or Small Business Administration, Office of International Trade, 409 3rd St., SW, Washington, DC 20416, 202-205-6720; {www.sbaonline.sba.gov/oit/finance}.

* *Program Information Hotline*
Overseas Private Investment Corporation
1100 New York Ave., NW
Washington, DC 20527
202-336-8799 (Hotline)
202-336-8400 (General Information)
202-336-8636 (Public Affairs)
202-336-8680 (Press Information)
202-408-9859 (Fax)
Email: {info@opic.gov}
www.opic.gov

AGENCY FOR INTERNATIONAL DEVELOPMENT (AID)

The Agency for International Development was created in 1961 by John F. Kennedy. AID offers a variety of loan and financing guarantee programs for projects in developing countries that have a substantial developmental impact, or for the exportation of manufactured goods to AID-assisted developing countries. Some investment opportunities are region specific, which include the Association of Southeast Asian National, the Philippines, and Africa. For more information, contact the Office of Investment, Agency for International Development, 515 22nd St. NW, Room 301, Washington, DC 20523-0231; 703-875-1551; {www.info.usaid.gov}.

Grants to Train Local Personnel

The Trade and Development Agency has the authority to offer grants in support of short-listed companies on a transaction specific basis. These are usually in the form of grants to cover the cost of training local personnel by the company on the installation, operation, and maintenance of equipment specific to bid the proposal. The average grant awarded is $320,000. Contact: Trade and Development Agency, 1621 N. Kent St., Suite 200, Arlington, VA 22209; 703-875-4357; Fax: 703-875-4009.

Consortia of American Businesses in Eastern Europe (CABEE)

CABEE provides grant funds to trade organizations to defray the costs of opening, staffing, and operating U.S. consortia offices in Eastern Europe. The CABEE grant program initially began operations in Poland, the Czech Republic, Slovikia, and Hungary, targeting five industry sectors: agribusiness/agriculture, construction/ housing, energy, environment, and telecommunications. Contact: CABEE, Department of Commerce, 14th and Constitution Avenue, Room 1104, Washington, DC 20230, 202-482-5004; Fax: 202-482-1790; {www.ita.doc.gov/oetca}.

Consortia of American Businesses in the Newly Independent States (CABNIS)

This program was modeled after CABEE and stimulates U.S. business in the Newly Independent States (NIS) and assists the region in its move toward privatization. CABNIS is providing grant funds to nonprofit organizations to defray the costs of

opening, staffing, and operating U.S. consortia offices in the NIS.
Contact: CABNIS, Department of Commerce, 14th and
Constitution Ave., Washington, DC 20230, 202-482-5004;
{www.ita.doc.gov/export_admin/ brochure.html - info}. For
financing and a listing of grantees, contact {www.itaiep.doc.
gov/bisnis/finance/cabnis.htm}.

MONEY TO START A BUSINESS WHEN YOU'RE OUT OF WORK

There are literally hundreds of programs
around the country that provide training
and money to out-of-work and low-
income people who want to start their
own businesses. Most of these
organizations are nonprofit and obtain
money from a variety of sources,
including government grants. The target
population of many of these programs is
women.

The *Self-Employment Loan Fund* in
Phoenix, AZ, has helped over 350 people get training and money
to start their own businesses. For information, contact Self-
Employment Loan Fund, Inc., 201 North Central Ave., Suite
CC10, Phoenix, AZ 95073; 602-340-8834;
{www.onlinewbc.org/docs/wbcs/ AZPhoenix.html}.

Iowa has the *Self-Employment Loan Program*, which provides
low interest loans to people with low income or disabilities. For
more information, contact Iowa Department of Economic
Development, 200 E. Grand Ave., Des Moines, IA 50309; 800-
245-IOWA; {www.smart.state.ia.us/financial.htm#selp}.

Many of these programs offer business loans to people who are at or below the poverty level. These programs may be identified by contacting your state information operator listed in the Appendix and asking for your state Office of Economic Development or your state Office of Social Services.

The Aspen Institute keeps track of many of these organizations and sells a directory called *Directory of U.S. Microenterprise Development Programs* for $15.00. To order a copy, contact Aspen Institute, 1333 New Hampshire Ave., NW, Suite 1070, Washington, DC 20036; 202-736-5800.

Money For Entrepreneurs With Disabilities

Entrepreneurs with disabilities can apply for up to $50,000 from the Minority, Woman and Disabled Participation Loan Program in Illinois through the Department of Commerce and Community Affairs.

Iowa offers grants up to $15,000 through a program called Entrepreneurs with Disabilities from the Iowa Department of Economic Development. Iowa also offers low interest loans to those with disabilities through its Self-Employment Loan Program.

Connecticut has laws that make sure entrepreneurs with disabilities (and other minorities) get up to 25% of state government contracts through the Set-Aside Unit of the Department of Administrative Services.

Maryland even has venture capital set aside for the disabled in its Equity Participation Program of the Maryland Small Business Development Financing Authority.

The U.S. Small Business Administration used to have a special program for people with disabilities, but now includes them in its major loan program. See what your state has to offer by contacting your state information operator listed in the Appendix and asking for your state Office of Vocational Rehabilitation or your state Office of Economic Development.

Free Help In Starting a Business, Plus $800, If You Lose Your Job From A Dirty Company

Free entrepreneurial training is available if you lost your job because of a company's compliance with the Clean Air Act. The program was initiated from the Environmental Protection Agency's Clean Air Act, which amended the Department of Labor's Job Training Partnership Act (Title III). So it's the U.S. Department of Labor that runs the training program.

Are you confused yet?

There is also money in this program to get $800 to move to another city to look for a job. It may be hard to find at the state level, which get grants from the Feds to run the program. The state of Illinois runs it out of their Department of Commerce.

Contact your state information operator listed in the Appendix and ask for your state Department of Labor. You can also locate your state contact by contacting the Office of Worker Retraining and Adjustment Programs, Employment and Training

Administration, U.S. Department of Labor, Room N5426, 200 Constitution Ave., NW, Washington, DC 20210; 202-219-5577; {www.wdsc.org/layoff/title3.htm}.

When Your Business Fails: Get Free Money, Child Care and Training

The U.S. Department of Labor provides money to states under a program called *The Economic Dislocation and Worker Adjustment Assistance (EDWAA) Act*. Although the money is primarily meant for people who lose their jobs because of

layoffs, the money can also be used for people who are out of work because their small business failed or because they are a displaced homemaker as a result of a divorce.

Under this act, you can receive free courses and training for a new career, emergency financial aid, child care money, travel money for getting to work or training, and even relocation money if you have to move for a new job.

Contact your state Department of Labor and ask for the office that is designated as the state's Dislocated Worker Unit. The state information operator listed in the Appendix can help. If you have trouble contacting your local office, you may contact the Office of Worker Retraining and Adjustment Programs, Employment and Training Administration, U.S. Department of Labor, Room N-5426, 200 Constitution Ave., NW, Washington, DC 20210; 202-219-5577; {www.wdsc.org/layoff/title3.htm}.

FREE SEMINARS
On How to Sell Your Stuff Overseas

Kentucky offers free half-day seminars on how to sell and finance your products overseas. They may charge a fee if it's a full day program, but it's usually only $25 to cover the lunch.

They will bring in bankers and government money officials to show you how you can make deals and get them financed. The program is offered through the International Trade Office of the Department of Community Development.

Most states will offer training to help you generate business overseas whether you are a first time exporter/importer or an old pro. Contact your state Office of Economic Development and ask for the office that helps businesses sell overseas. The state information operator listed in the Appendix can help.

One Page Gets You A $150,000 Business Loan

A one-page form is all you have to fill out to apply for a loan of up to $150,000 for your business through the government's LOWDOC Loan Guarantee program. Contact your local office of the U.S. Small Business Administration to learn more about the steps necessary to apply for the loan.

Contact U.S. Small Business Administration, 409 Third St., SW, Washington, DC 20416; 800-8ASK-SBA; {www.sba.gov}. Here's what the application looks like.

Money For A Big Or Small Business

U.S. SMALL BUSINESS ADMINISTRATION
APPLICATION FOR LOWDOC LOAN

A. BORROWER
Please Print Legibly or Type (ALL BLANKS MUST BE COMPLETED, Use "N/A," If Blank is Not Applicable)

Business Name _____

Trade Name (if different) _____

Type: Proprietorship ☐ Partnership ☐ Corporation ☐ LLC ☐ Other ☐

Address _____

City _____ State _____ County _____ Zip _____

Mailing Address (if different from above) _____

City _____ State _____ County _____ Zip _____

Phone _____ IRS Tax ID # _____

Business Bank _____ Checking Balance $ _____

Nature of Business _____

Date Business Established _____

Date Current Ownership Established _____

Number of employees _____

Number of affiliate(s) employees _____

Total number of employees after Loan _____

Exporter? Yes ☐ No ☐   Franchise? Yes ☐ No ☐

Franchise Name _____

B. LOAN REQUEST

AMOUNT $ _____ Maturity _____ Purpose _____

Have you employed anyone to prepare this application? Yes ☐ No ☐   If Yes, how much was paid? _____   How much do you owe? $ _____

Name of Packager _____ Packager's Tax ID No. or Social Security No. _____

C. INDEBTEDNESS: Furnish information on ALL BUSINESS debts, contracts, notes and mortgages payable. Indicate by an (*) items to be paid by loan proceeds.

To Whom Payable	Orig. Amount	Orig. Date	Cur. Balance	Int. Rate	Maturity Date	Pmt. Amt.	Pmt. Frequency	Collateral	Status

D. PRINCIPALS: Submit all information in this section for each principal of the business. Use separate attachments for each principal.

D1 Full Name _____ Phone _____ Social Security Number _____ Title _____

Address _____ City _____ State _____ Zip _____

Date of Birth _____ Place of Birth (City, ST or Foreign Country) _____ U.S. Citizen? Yes ☐ No ☐ If No, Alien reg # _____

D2 Percentage Owned _____ % Veteran *: Non-Veteran ☐ Vietnam Era Veteran ☐ Other Veteran ☐   Gender *: Female ☐ Male ☐

Race*: African American ☐ Puerto Rican ☐ Native American ☐ Hispanic ☐ Asian/Pacific Islander ☐ Eskimo & Aleuts ☐ Caucasian ☐ Multi-Ethnic ☐

*This data is collected for statistical purposes only. It has no bearing on the credit decision. Disclosure is voluntary.

D3 PERSONAL FINANCIAL STATEMENT: Complete for all principals with 20% or more ownership.

Liquid Assets $ _____ Ownership in Business $ _____ Real Estate $ _____ Assets Other $ _____ Total Assets $ _____

Liabilities Real Estate $ _____ Liabilities Other $ _____ Total Liabilities $ _____ Net Worth (less value of business) $ _____

Annual Salary $ _____ Other Source of Repayment $ _____ Source _____ Residence: Own ☐ Rent ☐ Other ☐ Mflty Housing $ _____

D4 PREVIOUS SBA OR OTHER GOVERNMENT FINANCING: For all owners, principals, partners, and affiliates.

Borrower Name	Name of Agency	Loan No.	Date	Amount	Balance	Status

D5 ELIGIBILITY AND DISCLOSURES:

I.   Are you or your business involved in any pending lawsuits? Yes ☐ No ☐   If Yes, provide the details as Exhibit A.

II. Do you or your spouse or any member of your household, or anyone who owns, manages, or directs your business or their spouses or members of their households work for the Small Business Administration, Small Business Advisory Council, SCORE or ACE, any Federal Agency, or the participating lender? Yes ☐ No ☐ If Yes, please provide the name and address of the person and the office where employed. Label this Exhibit B.

III. Affiliates: Do you or the applicant business have any interest in any other business as owner, principal, partner or manager? Yes ☐ No ☐ If Yes, please provide details to Lender.

IV. Are you (a) presently under indictment, on parole or probation, Yes ☐ No ☐ or (b) have ever been charged with or arrested for any criminal offense other than a minor motor vehicle violation (including offenses which have been dismissed, discharged, or nolle prosequi) Yes ☐ No ☐ or (c) convicted, placed on pretrial diversion, or placed on any form of probation including adjudication withheld pending probation for any criminal offense other than a minor vehicle violation? Yes ☐ No ☐
If Yes to any "IV" question, Lender must submit application to local SBA Office for processing under the regular 7(a) program.

If you knowingly make a false statement or overvalue a security to obtain a guaranteed loan from SBA you can be fined up to $10,000 and/or imprisoned for not more than five years under 18 U.S.C. 1001; if submitted to a Federally insured institution, under 18 USC 1014 by imprisonment of not more than twenty years and/or a fine or not more than $1,000,000. I authorize the SBA's Office of Inspector General to request criminal record information about me from criminal justice agencies for the purpose of determining my eligibility for programs authorized by the Small Business Act, as amended.

V.   Principal Signature _____ Date _____

E. BORROWER SIGNATURE (Principal(s) should sign in Section "D," above)

I authorize SBA-Lender to make inquiries as necessary to verify the accuracy of the statements made and to determine my creditworthiness. I agree that if SBA approves this loan application I will not, for at least two years, hire as an employee or consultant anyone that was employed by the SBA during the one year period prior to the disbursement of the loan. And, I hereby certify that: (1) as consideration for any Management, Technical, and Business Development Assistance that may be provided, I waive all claims against SBA and its consultants, (2) all information contained in this document and any attachments is true and correct to the best of my knowledge, and
(3) I have received and read SBA Form 1261, STATEMENTS REQUIRED BY LAW AND EXECUTIVE ORDER _____ (Applicant initials)

Print Name _____ Date _____

Signature _____ Title _____

If Corporation. Attested By: _____

Signature of Corporate Secretary

SBA Form 4-L (3-98) Previous Editions are Obsolete   This form was electronically produced by Elite Federal Forms, Inc.

Lots of Loan Money,
Some At 0% Interest

The U.S. Small Business Administration runs the government's most popular loan program. Well, it's actually a loan guarantee program. This means that the government will tell a bank that they will pay back the loan if you can't.

About 70,000 loans a year are made through this program. But there are dozens, even hundreds, of other government loan and loan guarantee programs. The U.S. Department of Agriculture has direct loans and loan guarantees to entrepreneurs living in small towns. They even have programs that offer grants to nonprofit organizations, which in turn lend the money to small businesses.

And the states are loaded with loan programs for businesses. Maryland, for example, has about 10 loan programs at the state

Money To Buy Out The Boss

The government doesn't want your boss to move your company or close it down. So the government has set up state and local programs that help employees get the money they need to buy out the boss.

Wisconsin has a program called the *Employee Ownership Assistance Loan Program* that can be used to buy a company that has expressed the intent to downsize or close. Contact your state Office of Economic Development to investigate how you can buy out your boss. Your state information operator listed in the Appendix can help.

level and has 11 more business loan programs at the county level. It's not unusual for some of these loans to be low interest or even 0% interest. Contact your state information operator listed in the Appendix, ask for your state Office of Economic Development and go from there. And don't stop!

Sell Overseas at Government Expense

The U.S. Department of Agriculture's Foreign Market Development Cooperation Program grants over $3 million a year

to companies and cooperatives to sell their products overseas. Indiana's Trade Show Assistance Program offers grants up to $5,000 to attend a trade show in a foreign country.

Wisconsin also offers $5,000 to party overseas. I mean, to attend a trade show. Many states also offer special money programs to help finance your sales overseas through the Office of Economic Development.

The Export-Import Bank of the United States provides working capital to small businesses to finance their exports as well as Export Credit Insurance, Direct Loans and Loan Guarantees. Contact Export-Import Bank of the U.S., 811 Vermont Ave., NW, Washington, DC 20571; 800-565-EXIM; {www.exim.gov}.

430   *Information USA, Inc.*

The Overseas Private Investment Corporation (OPIC) also provides financing and insurance to small businesses to sell their goods and services overseas. Contact Investment Services Director, Program Development, Investment Development Department, 1100 New York Ave., NW, Washington, DC 20527; 202-336-8621; {www.opic.gov}.

Get Paid To Attend Entrepreneur Classes

If you lost your job and are eligible for unemployment, contact your local Unemployment Office and find out how you can collect your employment money while you are attending classes on how to set up your own business. You can't collect while you are starting a business, but you can collect while you are learning **how** to start a business.

This is very new and exciting program to help those who are unemployed develop their own jobs. Maryland, Delaware, California, New York, New Jersey, Oregon, Maine, and Pennsylvania run programs, and there are likely to be more. In 1998, the congress passed HR 4558 that extended this program and allowed all states to be eligible to provide similar programs.

Contact your state Unemployment Insurance office in your state capital and ask if they are participating in any self-employment programs.

Money To Start A Business In A High Unemployment Area

The Economic Development Administration makes grants to local communities with high unemployment, that in turn, make business loans to small entrepreneurs who can create jobs. This is done through the revolving loan fund of the Economic Adjustment Program. The Buffalo, New York area recently used this program to make loans to 182 companies targeting start-ups as well as minority and women-owned businesses.

Find out where in your area there may be revolving loan programs from your state Office of Economic Development, or contact the Economic Development Administration, U.S. Dept. of Commerce, 14th & Constitution Ave, Room 7800B, Washington, DC 20230; 202-482-5081; {www.doc.gov/eda}.

$75,000 Grant If Hurt By Imports

If your business suffers a loss due to imports, you may be eligible to receive up to $75,000 to pay for consultants to develop a new business plan to put you back on the road to success.

The program is called Trade Adjustment Assistance, and there are 12 regional offices around the country that help businesses apply for this help. These offices also help businesses with assistance and loans when they have been hurt by defense cutbacks.

Contact: Planning and Development Assistance Division, Economic Development Administration, Room H7315, Washington, DC 20230; 202-482-2127; Fax: 202-482-0466; {www.doc.gov/eda}.

Money If You Start A Business In A Certain Zip Code

Connecticut will give your business a grant of up to $2,250 per employee if your business is in certain enterprise zones. Plus, you pay only 50% in corporate taxes and only 20% in property taxes.

Locating your business in certain areas of Chicago will get you an exception of income taxes on money made from the area, low interest rate loans, and a big break on your sales and property

Save $2,000 On Preparing a Business Plan

Why spend thousands on attorneys, accountants, and management consultants when you are putting together your business idea? You can get some of the best help available to develop a business plan, marketing plan, financial plan, management plan, etc., for nothing or next to nothing by contacting your local Small Business Development Center.

Next to Social Security, this is probably one of the most valuable services Uncle Sam has ever offered. You can find your local office by contacting your state's main Small Business Development Center office listed on page 292.

taxes. The federal government has designated over 100 areas around the country as enterprise areas and offers special low interest loans, $3,000 tax credit for every employee you have, and an extra $20,000 tax deduction for capital investments, as well as a boat load of other services and money incentives.

Enterprise zones, also called empowerment zones, have been established in order to generate jobs and economic development in certain rural and urban areas around the country. Contact your state Office of Economic Development to identify the zones in your area; or contact U.S. Department of Housing and Urban Development, 451 7 St., SW, Washington, DC 20410; 202-708-1577; {www.hud.gov/ezeclist.html}.

Bureaucrats Will Fight the Government For You

You don't have to hire a hot shot "Washington Insider" at $200 an hour to fight a government regulation that you feel is unfair, or to fight an agency who is taking too long to pay a legitimate bill, or to suffer from a fine imposed by a government official that you feel is not justified. You can call *"BUREAUCRACY MAN"*. There are actually a number of government bureaucrats that will fight other bureaucrats for you:

★ The **Small Business Administration** has set up an office that will investigate complaints and help you get equitable settlements. They will even show you how to sue the government and get attorney's fees and costs. Contact Office of the National Ombudsman, U.S. Small Business Administration, 500 West Madison, Suite 1240, Chicago, IL 60661; 312-353-0880; Fax: 312-353-3426; 888-REG-FAIR; {www.sba.gov/regfair}.

★ Many **state capitals** have offices that will fight the state bureaucracy for you. The Michigan Jobs Commission has a service that will fight for you. Arizona has a Small Business Advocate that will help resolve issues with any government office, congress or state legislature. Contact your state Office of Economic Development, or your state governor's office.

★ The **IRS's Problem Resolution Center** has offices around the country that will fight the IRS for you after your efforts prove futile. They are listed in the blue pages of your telephone book under U.S. Department of the Treasury.

★ Your **elected official**, in both Washington and your state capital, is probably the only government office with a real motive to help you with a problem. They want your vote to keep their job. All the rest of the officials will keep their job whether they make you happy or not.

Free Help Selling Your Arts And Crafts

The Kentucky Craft Marketing Program can get your studio, shop or work listed in directories or on the web and can get you into fairs to sell your work. They also offer help to train you in other ways to market and sell your work.

Check with your state arts council located in your state capital for the kind of help you can get in your state. Illinois has a free *Art Fair Directory* showing you where you can display your work. Also, check into the American Folklife Center, Library of Congress, 101 Independence Ave., SE, Washington, DC 20540; 202-707-5510; {http://lcweb.loc.gov/folklife}.

$10,000
For Your 10-Year-Old Grandson To Start A Business

The U.S. Department of Agriculture (USDA) has a program that

loans money to kids between the ages of 10 and 21, who live in small towns, to start a business.

Nebraska runs entrepreneur camps for teenagers through their Center For Rural Affairs. The Pennsylvania Department of

Agriculture gives out loans to people starting at 18 years of age. Harris County in Texas has $10,000 to invest in youth entrepreneurs, and the City of Minneapolis has a program that trains youth in entrepreneuring by having them run a retail store that sells property confiscated by the police department.

For the USDA program, contact your local Farm Service, or the Farm Service Agency, Loan Marketing Division, Ag Box 0522, Washington, DC 20250; 202-720-1632; {www.fsa.usda.gov/}. For other local programs, a good place to start is your local County Cooperative Extension Service, listed under County Government in your phone book.

Get The Government To Pay Half Your Employees' Wages

If you hire some people who have had trouble getting a job, the IRS will give you back up to 35% of the first year's salary, and up to 50% of the second year's salary. You can get up to $2,400 back in tax credits for hiring someone from certain zip codes.

There are states, like Mississippi, that will give you up to $2,000 a year for five years in credits for new employees, or 50% back on any child care expenses you pay for your employees. There are many areas of the country where an employer can get back $2,400 just for creating A JOB for anyone.

Loans For Failures and Bad Credit Risks

That's what it sounds like when you investigate your local *Capital Access Program (CAP)*. Banks offering this program are more likely to lend to people who are less than credit worthy, because, if for some reason you can't pay back the bank, your state government will.

It's just another way for state government to encourage you to start and grow your business. New Hampshire, California, Virginia, Pennsylvania, Indiana and many more were offering the program the last time I checked. Contact your state Office of Economic Development to see if the program is offered in your state.

You wouldn't believe the types of tax credits available! There are even tax credits just for people in the wine business in Missouri. Contact your state Office of Economic Development to see what kind of credits are available to you.

Lots of Free Money
To Train Your Employees

Training is the business buzzword for the year 2000. Almost every state has money to help companies in their state train new or existing employees. Most of it is in the form of grant money

that you don't have to pay back.

States like Connecticut, Tennessee and Kentucky will give grants from $3,000 to $25,000 to train your employees. Indiana will go as high as $200,000 in grant money. Wisconsin will pay for 50% of your training costs. And in

Louisiana and Iowa, you can send your employees to the state's vocational schools and community colleges for free. Virginia even offers free video production so that you can produce your own training films.

Contact your state Office of Economic Development for information about training help for your company.

GET FREE LISTS OF YOUR CUSTOMERS

You can look in the Yellow Pages under mailing lists or marketing consultants and spend thousands of dollars for customer lists. Or, you can search the government and find many of the same lists for free or very low costs.

You can even find lists that the experts will tell you are not available. Did you know that in most states you can get lists of all the rich men over six feet tall that live in your zip code? Or all the overweight women who live within walking distance of your health spa?

The Division of Motor Vehicles makes drivers licenses and auto registration info available. It will cost, but it can be worth it.

You can also get a list of all the new businesses that open up in your area with the name, address, and phone number of the owners. When a business starts up, they have to register at the state Office of Corporation.

Or how about a list of physical trainers, sports agents, dry cleaners, lawyers, hearing aid dealers, day care centers, or insurance agents? All these people have to register with the state to get a license. Yea for public information!

Contact your State Information Operator listed in the Appendix to see where to go in your state for your mailing list needs.

60 Places For Women To Get Help To Start A Business

Sometimes you just need someone to show you the way. The Women's Demonstration Program has 60 sites across the country where women are trained and counseled in the skills necessary to launch their own businesses.

These sites get money from the government to offer financial, management, marketing, and technical assistance to current and potential women business owners.

Contact your local Small Business Administration office to find a site near you, or contact U.S. Small Business Administration, 409 3rd St., SW, Washington, DC 20416; 202-205-6673; 800-8-ASK-SBA; {www.sba.gov}.

HELP FOR WOMEN TO GET 5% OF GOVERNMENT CONTRACTS

The Federal Acquisition Streamlining Act of 1994 establishes a 5 percent government-wide goal for contract awards to small businesses owned by women. One way the Small Business Administration is helping to ensure that these new goals are achieved is through the Women-Owned Business Procurement Pilot Program.

Each of the following eleven federal agencies has designated a women-owned business advocate to act as a liaison. Each provides outreach, training, and marketing assistance to women-owned businesses. The Small Business Administration and the liaisons from each of the agencies meet regularly to assess the progress of the program, resolve problems, and develop new initiatives.

For more information on this program, you may contact your local Small Business Administration Office, or Office of Women's Business Ownership, U.S. Small Business Administration, 409 3rd St., SW, Washington, DC 20416; 202-205-6673; 800-8-ASK-SBA; {www.sba.gov}.

Procurement Pilot Program Contacts

Ms. Sharon Harris
U.S. Department of Agriculture
Office of Small and
Disadvantaged Business
Utilization
14th St. and Independence Ave.,
SW
Room 1323 South Bldg.
Washington, DC 202050
202-720-7117

Ms. Janet Koch
U.S. Department of Defense
Office of Small and
Disadvantaged Business
Utilization
Room 2A338
3061 Defense Pentagon
Washington, DC 20301
703-695-1536

Ms. Gloria Smith
U.S. Department of Energy
Office of Impact
1000 Independence Ave., SW
Washington, DC 20585
202-586-8383

Ms. Y. Angel Graves
U.S. Department of Health and
Human Services
Office of Small and
Disadvantaged Business
Utilization
Washington, DC 20201
202-690-6670

Mr. Joseph Piljay
U.S. Dept. of Housing and Urban
Development
Office of Small and
Disadvantaged Business
Utilization
Washington, DC 20582
202-708-1428

Mr. Joseph Bryan
U.S. Department of Justice
Office of Small and
Disadvantaged Business
Utilization
ARB Room 3235
Washington, DC 20530
202-616-0521

Ms. June Robinson
U.S. Department of Labor
Office of Small Business and
Minority Affairs
200 Constitution Ave., NW
Room C2318
Washington, DC 20210
202-219-9148

Ms. Margie Wilson
Environmental Protection Agency
Office of Small and
Disadvantaged Business
Utilization
401 M St., SW
Mail Code 1230C

Washington, DC 20460
703-305-7305

Ms. Elizabeth Ivey
General Services Administration
18th and F Sts.
Washington, DC 20405
202-501-4466

Ms. Rae Martel
National Aeronautics and Space
Administration
Headquarters
Washington, DC 20546
202-358-0640

Women Pre-Qualified Loans Cut Down On Banker Stress

Need help filling out your loan application package? The Women's Pre-Qualification Pilot Loan Program was developed to promote the Small Business Administration's business loan programs to current and prospective women small business owners. It also provides specialized support and assistance with the agency's loan application process.

This program uses nonprofit organizations as intermediaries to assist prospective women borrowers in developing a viable loan application package. The program focuses on the applicant's character, credit, experience, and reliability — not just her assets.

Eligible businesses must be at least 51 percent owned, operated, and managed by women. The loan guarantee is for $250,000 or less. The application can be submitted directly to the Small Business Administration for expedited consideration of a loan pre-qualification.

Currently, this program is available in 16 states. For more information on this program, you may contact your local Small Business Administration Office, or Office of Women's Business Ownership, U.S. Small Business Administration, 409 3rd St., SW, Washington, DC 20416; 202-205-6673; 800-8-ASK-SBA; {www.sba.gov}.

2,000 Productivity Specialists Offer Free Analysis

Lorrie Browing got help to find the best way to move her homemade beef jerky business out of her kitchen and into a real facility. A Texas wood products company turned their $35,000 loss in disposing of saw dust into a $15,000 profit by selling it as animal bedding for horse stable floors.

The U.S. Department of Commerce has established 70 not-for-profit centers that will analyze your program and help you determine the best way to solve your problem. The analysis is free, but there is a charge for follow up work.

These centers have been established to help small and medium size manufacturers increase their potential for success. They can help companies cope with a changing environment, decrease manufacturing costs, or discover ways to use new technology.

To identify your local center, contact Manufacturing Extension Partnership, National Institute of Standards and Technology, Gaithersburg, MD 20899; 800-637-4634; {www.mep.nist.gov}.

MONEY FOR WOMEN RUNNING A TAXI COMPANY OR THE AIRLINE CATERING BUSINESS

Actually, the money can be used by women in almost any kind of transportation related business. The U.S. Department of Transportation works hard at trying to help women succeed by helping them get contracts as well as offering short term working capital loans at prime interest rates while working on transportation related contracts.

In order to help spread the word about these and other opportunities, the U.S. Department of Transportation conducts trade fairs around the country. To learn more about these programs, contact National Information Clearinghouse, U.S. Department of Transportation, 400 7th St., SW, Room 9414, Washington, DC 20590; 800-532-1169; {http://osdbuweb. dot.gov}.

Short Term Lending Program Banks

Cathay Bank
777 North Broadway
Los Angeles, CA 90012
212-625-4709
States: AK, AZ, CA, CO, HI, ID,
MT, NV, OR, UT, WA, WY

Hamilton Bank, NA
8750 NW 87th Ave.
Miami, FL 33178
305-717-5726
States: AL, CT, DE, FL, GA, KY,

ME, MD, MA, MS, NH, NJ, NY,
NC PA, RI, SC, TN, VT, VA,
WV, Puerto Rico, US Virgin
Islands

NAB Bank
4928 North Broadway
Chicago, IL 60640
773-561-2300
States: AR, IA, IL, IN, KS, LA,
MI, MN, MO, ND, NE, NM, OH,
OK, SD, TX, WI

Free Marketing Help To Get A Government Contract

Need some help marketing your product or service to the government? The Procurement Assistance Offices are attuned to the federal procurement process, and can help you draw up a sensible business plan that will be successful. They can match the product or service you are selling with the appropriate agency, and then help you market your wares effectively.

Several programs even have online bid matching services. They can obtain specifications, get your name on solicitation mailing lists, and more. These Offices are located throughout the country. These offices are partially funded by the Department of Defense to assist businesses with Defense procurement.

To find the office nearest you, contact Small and Disadvantaged Business Utilization Office, Cameron Station, Room 4B110, Defense Logistics Agency, Alexandria, VA 22304; 703-767-1661; {www.dla.mil} then to the small business site.

Small Businesses Can Get Large Contracts

Every Federal government department has an Office of Small and Disadvantaged Business Utilization (OSDBU) that provides procurement assistance to small, minority, 8(a), and women-owned businesses. Their primary function is to ensure that small and disadvantaged businesses receive their fair share of U.S. Government contracts.

These offices are the contacts for their respective agencies and are excellent sources of information. Contact the federal government department directly, or for a listing of offices, contact U.S. Small Business Administration, 409 3rd St., SW, Washington, DC 20416; 202-205-6673; 800-8-ASK-SBA; {www.sba.gov}.

Free Help In Buying A Franchise

Franchises are big businesses in today's marketplace. But before you sign on the dotted line, learn the questions you need to ask and what the franchiser needs to tell you.

The Federal Trade Commission has several pamphlets that will help you learn your way through the franchise business. Some titles include: *Before You Buy*, *Your Legal Rights*, and *State Disclosure Requirements*. The FTC can also provide you with the Franchise Rule, as well as information on franchise fraud.

For your copies, contact Correspondence Branch, Federal Trade Commission, Washington, DC 20580; 202-326-2222; {www.ftc.gov}.

Appendix

Don't know who to call or where to turn for assistance? Try one of the offices listed below. Each listing should be able to either answer your question or direct you to an office near you.

The *Federal Information Center* can connect you with the appropriate federal government agency that handles your topic of interest. The *State Information Operator* can connect you to the correct state government office that can answer your question.

Federal Information Center
All locations
800-688-9889

State Information Offices

Alabama
334-242-8000
http://www.state.al.us

Alaska
907-465-2111
http://www.state.ak.us

Arizona
602-542-4900
http://www.state.az.us

Arkansas
501-682-3000
http://www.state.ar.us

California
916-322-9900
http://www.state.ca.us

Colorado
303-866-5000
http://www.state.co.us

Connecticut
860-240-0222
http://www.state.ct.us

Delaware
302-739-4000
http://www.state.de.us

District of Columbia
202-727-6161
http://www.ci.washington.
dc.us

Florida
850-488-1234
http://www.state.fl.us

Georgia
404-656-2000
http://www.state.ga.us

Hawaii
808-548-6222
http://www.state.hi.us

Idaho
208-334-2411
http://www.state.id.us

Illinois
217-782-2000
http://www.state.il.us

Indiana
317-232-1000
http://www.state.in.us

Iowa
515-281-5011
http://www.state.ia.us

Kansas
913-296-0111
http://www.state.ks.us

Kentucky
502-564-3130
http://www.state.ky.us

Louisiana
504-342-6600
http://www.state.la.us

Maine
207-582-9500
http://www.state.maine.us

Maryland
800-449-4347
http://www.state.md.us

Massachusetts
617-722-2000
http://www.state.ma.us

Michigan
517-373-1837
http://www.state.mi.us

Minnesota
612-296-6013
http://www.state.mn.us

Mississippi
601-359-1000
http://www.state.ms.us

Missouri
573-751-2000
http://www.state.mo.us

Appendix

Montana
406-444-2511
http://www.state.mt.us

Nebraska
402-471-2311
http://www.state.ne.us

Nevada
702-687-5000
http://www.state.nv.us

New Hampshire
603-271-1110
http://www.state.nh.us

New Jersey
609-292-2121
http://www.state.nj.us

New Mexico
505-827-4011
http://www.state.nm.us

New York
518-474-2121
http://www.state.ny.us

North Carolina
919-733-1110
http://www.state.nc.us

North Dakota
701-224-2000
http://www.state.nd.us

Ohio
614-466-2000
http://www.state.oh.us

Oklahoma
405-521-2011
http://www.state.ok.us

Oregon
503-378-3111
http://www.state.or.us

Pennsylvania
717-787-2121
http://www.state.pa.us

Rhode Island
401-222-2000
http://www.state.ri.us

South Carolina
803-734-1000
http://www.state.sc.us

South Dakota
605-773-3011
http://www.state.sd.us

Tennessee
615-741-3011
http://www.state.tn.us

Texas
512-463-4630
http://www.state.tx.us

Utah
801-538-3000
http://www.state.ut.us

Vermont
802-828-1110
http://www.state.vt.us

Virginia
804-786-0000
http://www.state.va.us

Washington
360-753-5000
http://www.state.wa.us

West Virginia
304-558-3456
http://www.state.wv.us

Wisconsin
608-266-2211
http://www.state.wi.us

Wyoming
307-777-7011
http://www.state.wy.us

Index

A

Accounting services, 256
Adult education
  clearinghouse, 166
Advanced Technology Program,
  380
Advocacy groups
  medical, 36-37
Agency for International
  Development (AID), 421
Aging, 61
Agriculture
  grants, 150
  study money, 197
Agriculture, U.S. Department of,
  21, 379
  volunteer programs, 260
Air courier services, 77
Airfare, reduced, 76
Air Force, U.S., 227
Airline Deregulation Act, 377
Alabama
  literacy programs, 166
  money for students, 144
  Small Business Development
    Centers, 292
  state procurement office, 283
  unconventional loan programs,
    383
Alaska
  literacy programs, 166
  money for students, 144
  Small Business Development
    Centers, 293
  state procurement office, 283
American Cancer Society, 58
American Council on Education
  GED information, 163
American Heart Association, 56
American Kidney Fund, 48
American Medical Association, 57

American Samoa
  literacy programs, 166
AmeriCorps, 152
Apprenticeship programs, 108
Architect grants, 186
Arizona
  business assistance programs,
    407
  literacy programs, 166
  money for students, 144
  Small Business Development
    Centers, 293
  state procurement office, 284
  unconventional loan programs,
    383
Arkansas
  business assistance programs,
    407
  literacy programs, 166
  money for students, 144
  Small Business Development
    Centers, 294
  state procurement office, 284
  unconventional loan programs,
    383
Army, Department of the, 227
Art critics grants, 187
Artists
  grants, state programs, 186
Arts
  festival grants, 187
  matching grants, 188
  money programs, 186
  organization grants, 188
Auctions, government, 67-69, 78
Auto Safety Hotline, 74

B

Behavioral sciences, 151
Breast cancer, 32-33

Index

Index

Florida
　literacy programs, 167
　money for students, 144
　Small Business Development
　　Centers, 300
　state procurement office, 284
　unconventional loan programs,
　　386
Flu shots, 37
Fogarty International Center, 202
Food
　grants to study, 150
Food and Nutrition Service
　free food for homeless, 248
　free food for nonprofits, 248
Food discounts, 25
Food stamps, 21
Foreclosed homes, 92
Foreign Agricultural Service, 230
Foreign languages, 148
　study, 153
Foreign Market Development
　Cooperator Program, 378, 430
Forest Service
　volunteer programs, 260
Forfeited property, 78
Foundation Center, 270
　nonprofit organization, 243
Foundations
　private, 269
Free clinics, 56
Free publications
　about home buying, 80, 86, 89
　aging, 62
　mammograms, 34
Freelancing
　benefits, 273
　demand, 272
　what you need, 274
　working for the government,
　　276
Fulbright-Hays, 199

G

General Services Administration
　real estate for nonprofits, 254
Georgia
　business assistance programs,
　　409
　literacy programs, 167
　money for students, 144
　Small Business Development
　　Centers, 301
　state procurement office, 284
　unconventional loan programs,
　　386
Glaucoma screenings, 60
Government contracts, 445
Government procurement
　Commerce Business Daily, 278
　congressional help, 279
　federal process, 278
　minority and labor surplus area
　　assistance, 281
　small business set-asides, 280
　veterans assistance, 280
　women-owned business
　　assistance, 280
Graduate degrees
　humanities, 151
　overseas research, 154
Graduate school
　criminal justice, 150
　mathematics, 149
　overseas study, 153
Grants
　air service, 377
　application procedures, 149
　Community Development
　　Block Grant Program, 357,
　　361
　dissertation, 151
　economic science, 151
　educational opportunity, 153
　engineering, 152

Index

K

Kansas
  literacy programs, 168
  money for students, 145
  Small Business Development Centers, 311
  state procurement office, 285
  unconventional loan programs, 388
Kentucky
  business assistance programs, 411
  literacy programs, 168
  money for students, 145
  Small Business Development Centers, 313
  state procurement office, 285
  unconventional loan programs, 389
Kidney disease
  funds for patients with, 48

L

Labor surplus areas, 281
Lead-based paint removal, 82
Librarian grants, 148
Library of Congress
  free books, 246
Library science, 155
Licensing, inventions, 231
Lions Clubs, 60
Literacy Volunteers of America, 165
Literary Agents of North America, 175
Literary Marketplace, 175
Loan guarantees, 85
Loan programs, 381
  state listings, 383
Loans. *See also* businesses, starting

direct from school, 154
health education assistance, 157
health professions students, 159
microenterprise, 355
National Health Service Corps, 162
nursing, 160
Perkins, 155
repayment program, 158
rural development program, 360
student, 154
Louisiana
  literacy programs, 168
  money for students, 145
  Small Business Development Centers, 314
  state procurement office, 285
  unconventional loan programs, 389
Lupus, 55

M

Mail Recovery Centers, 67-68
Mail, undeliverable, 67-68
Maine
  business assistance programs, 411
  literacy programs, 168
  money for students, 145
  Small Business Development Centers, 315
  state procurement office, 285
  unconventional loan programs, 389
Mammograms, 32-34
Marine Corps, 227
Marketing
  inventions, 231
Maryland
  business assistance programs, 412
  literacy programs, 168

Index

money for students, 145
Small Business Development
Centers, 315
state procurement office, 286
unconventional loan programs,
391
Massachusetts
business assistance programs,
412
literacy programs, 168
money for students, 145
Small Business Development
Centers, 316
state procurement office, 286
unconventional loan programs,
391
Mathematics
Defense Department grants,
150
graduate fellowships, 149
grants, 152
Meal delivery, 38
Medical care, free
clinics, 56
Medical services
clinical trials, 42-43
home equipment, 58
technology for the disabled, 40-
41
Medicare, 28
Social Security and, 28-29
videotapes, 39
Merchant Marines, 151
Michigan
business assistance programs,
413
literacy programs, 168
money for students, 145
Small Business Development
Centers, 317
state procurement office, 286
unconventional loan programs,
392
Microenterprise loans, 355

Microloans
state programs, 359
Micronesia
literacy programs, 167
Minnesota
business assistance programs,
413
literacy programs, 168
money for students, 145
Small Business Development
Centers, 319
state procurement office, 286
unconventional loan programs,
392
Minorities
energy majors, 153
energy-related conferences,
153
health professions education,
158
loan repayment programs, 161
set-asides, 280
Mississippi
literacy programs, 168
money for students, 145
Small Business Development
Centers, 321
state procurement office, 286
unconventional loan programs,
394
Missouri
business assistance programs,
414
literacy programs, 169
money for students, 146
Small Business Development
Centers, 323
state procurement office, 286
unconventional loan programs,
394
Mobile homes
buying/repair assistance, 87-88
Manufactured Housing and
Standards, 88

Montana
- business assistance programs, 414
- literacy programs, 169
- money for students, 146
- Small Business Development Centers, 325
- state procurement office, 286
- unconventional loan programs, 394

Mortgage payment assistance, 80
Music grants, 186

N

NAFTA, 123
National Association of Housing and Redevelopment Officials, 80
National Endowment for the Arts, 175
National Endowment for the Humanities, 151, 175, 211
- fellowships, 216
- media projects, 214
National Gallery Of Art
- art films and videos, 254
National Health Service Corps, 159
- loan repayment program, 158
National Institute for Literacy, 166
National Institute for Occupational Safety and Health, 159
National Institutes of Health (NIH), 42-43
- health research volunteers, 261
National Literacy hotline
- literacy resources, 164
National Park Service
- volunteer opportunities, 262
National Science Foundation
- international programs, 217
Native Americans
- government procurement assistance, 281

grants for college, 150
health professions scholarships, 157
Natural Resource Conservation Service, 247
Naval Recruiting Command, 227
Nebraska
- business assistance programs, 414
- literacy programs, 169
- money for students, 146
- Small Business Development Centers, 326
- state procurement office, 286
- unconventional loan programs, 394
Nevada
- literacy programs, 169
- money for students, 146
- Small Business Development Centers, 327
- state procurement office, 287
- unconventional loan programs, 395
New Hampshire
- literacy programs, 169
- money for students, 146
- Small Business Development Centers, 327
- state procurement office, 287
- unconventional loan programs, 396
New Jersey
- literacy programs, 169
- money for students, 146
- Small Business Development Centers, 328
- state procurement office, 287
- unconventional loan programs, 396
New Mexico
- business assistance programs, 414
- literacy programs, 169

Index

P

Palau
  literacy programs, 170
Pell Grant Program, 155
Pennsylvania
  business assistance programs, 416
  literacy programs, 170
  money for students, 146
  Small Business Development Centers, 340
  state procurement office, 288
  unconventional loan programs, 401
Pension Benefit Guaranty Corporation (PBGC), 70
Pension Search Directory, 70
Pensions, 70
Perkins loans, 155
Pharmaceutical Manufacturers Association
  hotline, 32
Ph.D studies
  humanities, 151
  overseas research, 154
Photography grants, 186
Physicians, locating, 57
Pilot Dogs, 30
Podiatric primary care, 158
Poetry grants, 186
Postal Service, U.S.
  free and cheap postage, 247
Prescription drugs
  free, 31
  indigent patient programs, 32
Presidential Management Intern Program, 157
Printmaking grants, 187
Procurement
  assistance offices, 279
  local help, 278
  state assistance, 283
Publishers, 175

Puerto Rico
  literacy programs, 170

R

Reading is Fundamental
  Smithsonian Institution, 165
Real estate, 78, 94
  state money, 95
Refugees
  business assistance, 358
Rent assistance, 82-83
Republic of the Marshall Islands
  literacy programs, 170
Respite care, 44
Rhode Island
  business assistance programs, 417
  literacy programs, 170
  money for students, 146
  Small Business Development Centers, 341
  state procurement office, 288
Robert C. Byrd Honors Scholarships, 156
Ronald E. McNair Post Baccalaureate Achievement, 156
Rural Business Enterprise Grant Program (RBEG), 362
Rural Business-Cooperative Service, 360
Rural development loans, 360
Rural Housing Service, 85-87
Russian studies, 151

S

Salvation Army, 26
Scholarships
  community service, 161
  exceptional need, 160
  health professions, 157, 162

Index

National Health Service Corps, 159
Native Americans, 157, 162
School-to-Work program, 172
Science
  grants, 152
  travel grants, 152
Section 8 Rental Assistance Program, 83
Self-employment. *See* entrepreneurs
Self esteem training, 101
Seminars
  overseas marketing, 427
Senior citizens
  federal job opportunities, 105
  volunteer opportunities, 264
Senior discounts
  banking, 27
  eyeglasses, 27
  tuition, 130
Senior services
  Eldercare Locator, 45
  transportation, 45
Service organizations, 58
SHARE, 25
Small Business Administration
  federal procurement, 278
  Selling to the Federal Government, 281
Small Business Development Centers, 290
  federal procurement, 278
  state listing, 292
Small Business Innovation Research Program, 236
Small Business Investment Company programs, 379
Small Business Technology Transfer Program, 377
Small businesses. *See* entrepreneurs
Smithsonian Institution
  curatorial-aides, 263

  museum tour guides, 262
Social sciences, 151
Social Security Administration, 22
Social Security
  Medicare premiums and, 28-29
  unclaimed checks, 72
South Carolina
  literacy programs, 170
  money for students, 147
  Small Business Development Centers, 341
  state procurement office, 288
South Dakota
  business assistance programs, 417
  literacy programs, 170
  money for students, 147
  Small Business Development Centers, 343
  state procurement office, 288
  unconventional loan programs, 402
Speakers
  for community groups, 263
Special education teaching grants, 154
State, U.S. Department of, 228
Storytelling grants, 186
Stroke
  victim's support, 56
Substance abuse treatment, 30-31
Summer jobs, 157
Supplemental Security Income (SSI), 21, 72

T

TAA-NAFTA Contacts, 124
Teachers
  overseas travel grants, 154
Technical Assistance Project, 40-41
Telemarketers. *See* telephone solicitors

Index

Telephone solicitors
Federal Communications
Commission's Consumer
Protection Act, 63
stopping, 63-64
Tennessee
literacy programs, 171
money for students, 147
Small Business Development
Centers, 343
state procurement office, 288
unconventional loan programs,
402
Texas
literacy programs, 171
money for students, 147
Small Business Development
Centers, 344
state procurement office, 288
unconventional loan programs,
402
Trade Adjustment Assistance
program, 122, 432
Trade Information Center, 230
Training
dentistry, 160
interpreters for the deaf, 156
nursing, 159
occupational safety, 159
podiatric primary care, 158
public health, 161
rehabilitation, 155
retired veterans, 152
rural health care, 159
Transplant assistance, 37
Transportation, U.S. Department
of, 378
Transportation assistance
airfare reduced, 76
for seniors, 47
for the disabled, 47
rides for seniors, 75

Transportation services
for seniors, 45
Travel grants
minority, 153
science students, 152
teachers, 154
Travel programs, 189

U

Unclaimed property, 65-66
Unemployment
due to Clean Air Act, 425
Economic Dislocation and
Worker Adjustment
Assistance Act, 426
entrepreneurial classes and, 431
Unemployment insurance, 22-23
University-Laboratory
Cooperative Program, 152
Upward Bound, 155
Urban Homesteading Act, 88-89
U.S. Information Agency
Arta America, 221
citizen exchange, 219
exchange program, 196
thematic programs, 191
Utah
literacy programs, 171
money for students, 147
Small Business Development
Centers, 347
state procurement office, 288
unconventional loan programs,
402
Utility bills
discounts, 23-24
energy-related repair
assistance, 18
gas and electric assistance, 19
telephone assistance, 20
Utility discounts
telephone, 20

464   *Information USA, Inc.*

Index

V

Venture capital, 379
Vermont
  business assistance programs,
    417
  literacy programs, 171
  money for students, 147
  Small Business Development
    Centers, 348
  state procurement office, 288
  unconventional loan programs,
    403
Veterans
  college grants, 152
  contracting, 280
  government procurement
    assistance, 280
  Post-Vietnam Era Veterans'
    Educational Assistance, 152
  retired, 152
  survivors and dependents
    educational assistance, 152
Veterans Affairs Administration,
  72
Vietnam veterans
  housing, 95
Virgin Islands
  literacy programs, 171
Virginia
  business assistance programs,
    417
  literacy programs, 171
  money for students, 147
  Small Business Development
    Centers, 349
  state procurement office, 289
  unconventional loan programs,
    403
Vision care, 59-60
  for low income families, 60
  for seniors, 59
Vocational rehabilitation
  grants, 152

Volunteering
  Fish and Wildlife Service, 260
  Forest Service, 260
  health care clinical research,
    261
  National Park Service, 262

W

Washington
  business assistance programs,
    417
  literacy programs, 171
  money for students, 147
  Small Business Development
    Centers, 351
  state procurement office, 289
  unconventional loan programs,
    404
West Virginia
  business assistance programs,
    418
  literacy programs, 171
  money for students, 147
  Small Business Development
    Centers, 352
  state procurement office, 289
  unconventional loan programs,
    404
Wheel chairs, 58
Widows
  job training, 100
Wisconsin
  business assistance programs,
    418
  literacy programs, 171
  money for students, 147
  Small Business Development
    Centers, 353
  state procurement office, 289
  unconventional loan programs,
    405
Women
  contracting help, 280